GW00836183

HOW TO BE A FAILURE
AND SUCCEED

HOW TO BE A FAILURE AND SUCCEED

Sir Ernest Hall

Book Guild Publishing
Sussex, England

First published in Great Britain in 2008 by
The Book Guild Ltd
Pavilion View
19 New Road
Brighton BN1 1UF

Copyright © Sir Ernest Hall 2008

The right of Sir Ernest Hall to be identified as the author of this
work has been asserted by him in accordance with the
Copyright, Designs and Patents Act 1988.

All rights reserved. No part of this publication may be
reproduced, transmitted, or stored in a retrieval system, in any form or by
any means, without permission in writing from the publisher, nor be
otherwise circulated in any form of binding or cover other than that in which
it is published and without a similar condition being imposed on the
subsequent purchaser.

Typesetting in Garamond by
Keyboard Services, Luton, Bedfordshire

Printed in Great Britain by
CPI Antony Rowe

A catalogue record for this book is available from
The British Library

ISBN 978 1 84624 163 5

Contents

Preface

This is the story of my life before it began.

It really began when I was 53 years old, in 1983. That was when I sold the majority of my shares in a highly successful property company I had built up over the previous 22 years. I gazed at the cheque in wonder when it arrived; for the first time in my life I knew what it was to have a substantial amount of money to my credit. Up to then, although my business appeared to have enjoyed untroubled prosperity, the reality had been a constant struggle to keep my creditors and the bank happy. I had always managed to do that, but it had been a wearing experience. The cheque was the ultimate antidote to many years of stress, uncertainty and insecurity.

However, my pleasure wasn't entirely complete. My first calling had been music – specifically, composing and playing the piano. From the moment I abandoned music to take up a job in the textiles industry in the 1950s, I always felt I had deserted a more important cause simply because I had been seduced by the prospect of a life made comfortable by financial success. In 1983 I started to make amends when, with my oldest son Jeremy, I bought Dean Clough Mills in Halifax. Together we turned an abandoned, semi-derelict, nineteenth-century manufacturing colossus – almost a mile long from end to end – into a thriving, dynamic, 'practical Utopia', combining enterprise and the arts. But most of that is for a second book.

Someone I once knew said he thought nature had got it wrong: we should be born old, and get younger. In my case, nature got it right. From my first moments of awareness in Bolton, a Lancashire cotton town, in the depressed 1930s, I was conscious of unemployment, poverty, illness and death – all the attributes of a miserable old age. Even though I was a child, I felt the anxieties of someone living in poverty at the end of their life, not the joys of someone at the beginning. I was full of fear:

of other children, of school, of authority, but most of all, of death. I have no happy childhood memories, only recollections of painful incidents which, no doubt, distort the reality of my childhood.

It's not difficult to understand why my life has seemed to be a journey from end to beginning. I was a sickly child, invariably too ill to enjoy Christmas, but as the years have passed my health has continually improved. My fears have been progressively eliminated and I have never felt healthier and more in control of my destiny than I do today.

Even the moments of success in my life never felt like a beginning; they seemed always to be stepping-stones *towards* a beginning. I never enjoyed the unswerving sense of vocation that an artist enjoys. I had passion for everything I was doing, but my passions were at times in conflict with one other. I never enjoyed the security of discovering myself. I longed to be many things at different points in my life, but without ever having the confident certainty that I knew what I was doing. Perhaps I was too easily influenced by people and events. I was successful, but never to such an extent in anything that it gave me the confidence that I had found my role in life. The different experiences which carried me to the beginning of my life were never organic developments. They were random events to which I responded with equal enthusiasm, without questioning whether they were carrying me in any logical direction.

And yet, I was aware from an early age that life wasn't something to be wandered through aimlessly. The sense that I had some kind of mission was first stimulated by my discovery of beautiful music. It happened one day when I was in primary school. Within months I started to play the piano, and soon believed that I was destined to be a famous musician. The lives of the great composers inspired me, and through them I began to imagine a life far removed from the world around me, a life devoted to the piano and music.

My love of music gave me ambition, purpose, and four wonderful years at the Royal Manchester College of Music (now the Royal Northern College of Music). It promised entry into a very different world from the industrial Bolton I saw every day around me, and in which my family lived and worked.

The fact that I didn't have access to a good piano at home, or any privacy in which to practise, never seemed like a reason for not playing well. I can't imagine how I managed to play as well as I did, but it never occurred to me to make excuses. I was too enthusiastic about playing to look for reasons why I couldn't do it.

My sights were set higher and higher, and for a while I continued to believe I was destined for a life of limitless possibilities. Starting at a comparatively low point seemed to give me an advantage. If my playing had been better when I first entered college, my progress might have seemed much slower. As it was, the improvement seemed to me to be astonishing, if not meteoric.

But the higher I climbed, the less certain I became about my future in music. At school my ability to play the piano gave me confidence, and it was easy to persuade myself that I was talented. At college I became progressively less sure. I struggled to overcome increasingly complex technical problems, and was unnerved by the prospect of competing against so many other talented pianists. I began to fear that my playing wasn't outstanding enough to ensure that I would stand head and shoulders above them. One event in particular powerfully influenced my decision to abandon the piano as a career – the arrival at the college of John Ogdon, now regarded by many as the most gifted British pianist of the 20th century. Even as a student, John's ability to play the piano was astonishing. There was nothing he couldn't do. I began to question whether I could ever hope to achieve as much.

The world of music is dominated by the concept of talent and genius, and in such a deadly competitive arena it's difficult to believe that ambition and commitment on their own count for a lot. The very few who rise to the top are easily persuaded that they're special by nature; the success they have in doing easily what most people find difficult reinforces this view. The rest are led to believe they don't stand a chance, and many will inevitably turn away from careers that once meant so much to them. This is what happened to me. My confidence declined so much that towards the end of my four years at the college I began to see a future not as an acclaimed performer but as a music teacher.

In the end I decided that a better alternative would be to abandon music as a career altogether, and get a job doing something else. I would reject a life of music before it had the chance to reject me.

At the time, it seemed like an acknowledgement of utter failure. With hindsight, it was probably the best decision of my entire life.

Without being aware of it, most of us are persuaded from the outset that we're powerless. We routinely hear the words 'clever', 'gifted', 'talented', 'exceptional' applied to other people. The implicit message is that we are without these qualities – and yet, when we're young we all dream of being successful. We sense our uniqueness, and feel it should be recognised by everyone else. It's this conviction that makes our early defeats so painful. It seems like a miscarriage of justice that we feel so special, and yet are unable to win every encounter. It's difficult for us to understand that our feeling of uniqueness is, in truth, shared by everyone else.

That shared quest for success is the spur to competition, and our experience of competition is the start of our rise or fall. The course of our lives can be determined, even dominated, by the degree of vulnerability and hurt we feel when threatened by other people's success. At school we soon discover whether we're on the winning or losing side of any subject. While we may long to succeed, if we feel we're losing, our only chance of preserving our sense of uniqueness may be to withdraw our commitment. But if we do that, we retreat into the sad security of being mediocre. Our sense of what is possible shrinks; our ambitions drop to the level at which we can find just enough confidence to achieve them. This process of self-destruction is a consequence of our fear of failure.

In order to overcome this fear, we need teachers or mentors who will persuade us that we can learn to do something very well even though we do it very badly at first. Ideally, we need to be taught by someone who found it impossible and discovered how to do it. A problem is that most teachers teach something they found easy to learn, and may therefore be the least qualified to inspire those who find it difficult. Under these circumstances it's hardly surprising that those who find it easy get better, and those who find it difficult abandon hope.

Another problem is that we need confidence to be the person we really are. Confidence is a fragile but necessary quality. When we lose it, we become less than ourselves. Our confidence grows if we seem to perform better than most people, and our ambition to succeed grows as we feel more confident. It's therefore difficult to fulfil an ambition if we're not confident.

A fortunate combination of circumstances led me to my first job in textiles. I never believed I could be happy doing anything but playing the piano, but during my national service I learnt to touch-type and found that I really enjoyed office work. Playing the piano was deeply satisfying, but also frustrating. I might work on a particular piece of music for a month, and still not be sure whether I was improving; it was impossible to demonstrate it clearly. Office work by contrast was pedestrian, but the evidence of the work was tangible. Immediately I ended national service, I had the opportunity of starting work in an office in a weaving mill in Bradford.

From the moment I walked into the mill, I was captivated by it. The sights and sounds of mill life had been so much a part of my childhood, but I had always been on the outside. Now I was on the inside, the memory of everything I'd heard from my family about life in the mill came flooding back, and I began to see them all in a new light. I had never realised before what extraordinary skill they had in their jobs as winders, warpers and weavers. I looked at them all with greater respect. I learnt to warp and wind, weave and inspect cloth, design, make out weaving and dyeing orders, and analyse fabrics. I was also fascinated by balance sheets and trading accounts.

In short, I fell in love with business. The enthusiasm which had motivated me to be a pianist now motivated me to be a businessman. The world of business became as romantic and intriguing as the world of music. A weaving shed in full production at night is a dramatic sight; the lights over the looms lend a theatrical quality that is absent during the day. I found myself dreaming of weaving sheds full of grand pianos.

I was intrigued by the differences between the worlds of music and business. In music, my confidence that I could scale great heights began to falter as I progressed. In business, no such obstacles presented themselves. The more success I achieved, the more certain I was that I could achieve even greater success. As a businessman, I felt for the first time that I was in control of my own life, and I never doubted that I'd made the right decision in moving from music to textiles – even though the UK textiles industry was starting its decline even as I joined it.

My success in business carried me further than I could ever have imagined. I enjoyed a lifestyle only the most successful pianists in the world could enjoy. I travelled all over the world in the course of my business career, staying in the best hotels and eating in the best restaurants – and yet, I could still enjoy playing the piano. In fact, in my heart I still longed to be a musician. Although business had become hugely important, I disliked describing myself as a businessman and still wanted to be regarded as a pianist and composer.

In the early days of my business career, music and textiles were undoubtedly in conflict, but in the 1970s the world of menswear was suddenly revolutionised by fashion. Following the Beatles and the 1960s fashion explosion, menswear retailing became a young man's world, and new shops emerged with a new image. I was lucky enough to catch the tide which transformed both my business and me. I supplied many of the hugely successful new fashion outlets with cloth, which at that time could still – just about – be made profitably in the UK. The young entrepreneurs who created this new business environment were keenly interested in the arts and ideas, and my background as a composer and pianist suddenly had unexpected relevance. As a consequence, alongside the extraordinary success I enjoyed in the fashion industry, I was able to revive my life as an artist.

This was no uneasy compromise. My success in business liberated the artist in me, and the artist in me became increasingly convinced that it should be possible to combine enterprise and the arts, to the lasting benefit of both. This led inevitably to the feeling that I needed to have a new career – which brings me back to the real beginning of my life, in 1983.

In the following pages I can only *try* to tell the story of my life. I have never kept notebooks or diaries, and too much time has passed for me to pretend that my recall of people, events and conversations can be wholly accurate. The favourite saying of someone I once knew applies here: 'It's all true, even though it may never have happened'. There are also gaps here and there that a fiction writer would be expected to fill, but some are very personal gaps and because my life isn't fiction, I have decided that filling them would serve no useful or happy purpose.

I have also changed the names of most of the key personalities in my narrative. They're all real people – or were, as most of them are no longer alive – but I felt uncomfortable about using their real names when they can only be shown here as products of my imperfect memory. None the less, I'm confident that this memoir is more truthful and accurate in essence than any attempt at slavishly sticking to the facts could ever be.

In the end, success has triumphed over failure in my life for reasons which can never be entirely clear to me. I have attempted to reconstruct the journey which carried me from the abyss of failure to the success I dreamt of as an adolescent, in the hope that it will encourage others to make the same journey. It will also, I hope, help to illustrate one of the most important lessons I have learned from life: that *knowing how to transform failure into success is more important that knowing how to succeed.*

1

Born in Bolton

I am afraid. Fear assails me from every quarter. It seizes hold of me and paralyses me. Its presence is constant and no happiness can overcome it; it makes my surroundings ugly. The most frightening room is the bedroom. Dad says that people die in bed, so when he has flu he sleeps in the armchair downstairs.

Mam wheels me in the pram to the park. One day she meets a strange woman who stares at me. Her eyes are black and cold and I feel afraid. She speaks to Mam and I can tell Mam is afraid too. Later, she tells Nanny that the woman said I won't live to be two. When I have whooping cough I'm so ill that Mam and Dad think I'll die. Dad carries me to a chemical works because someone tells him that if he holds me over a vat of chemicals, the fumes will cure me. On the way we meet someone who works there who says, 'Eh, don't do that! A child died last week when it was taken there.'

Dad is frightened of dying. His mam died of TB when he was five and her three sisters all died as well. He nearly died a few times himself. He has an ugly, shiny red scar round his neck. When I ask what it is, he tells me, 'I had some infected glands they had to cut out.' I shiver at the thought. As we walk past the mill dam just round the corner, there are some boys fishing. The water looks cold and black, like that strange woman's eyes. Dad warns, 'Be careful, water's dangerous. It draws you like a magnet. I was standing on the edge of a mill dam once and I could feel myself being pulled toward the water. I couldn't stop it. I jumped in but I couldn't swim. My head went under and I would have drowned, but someone passing by jumped in and pulled me out.'

Death is always lurking in dark corners, like a spider ready to pounce. It sits silently waiting for the right moment and gets you in different ways. If you're holding a metal knife during a storm and lightning strikes, you'll be electrocuted. If you eat berries off a tree you'll be poisoned.

1

When you walk on the sands at Blackpool, if you stand on a jellyfish it'll sting you fatally. Auntie Phoebe is having a baby and when it's born, it's dead. Everyone whispers about it.

I go with Mam and Dad to see one of their friends, who is very ill. Before we go they tell me that when he was a boy he took away some red lanterns from a hole in the road and they gave him ten strokes of the birch on his back. They tell me that they rubbed salt into the wounds on his back. I decide never to do anything like it.

Their house is about half an hour's walk away. The man's bed is in the front room. I've never seen anyone look so ill. His wife tells Mam that when he's sick it looks like coffee grains. A week later, he's dead.

The brick terrace where we live faces a giant multi-storey cotton mill in which many of our family work. The electric lights in the windows of the mill light up the street on winter nights. The steam from the boilerhouse and the smoke from the great chimney are constantly rising into the grey sky. The smells of oil, cotton and smoke combine with the noise of clattering clogs, particularly when the mill lads and lasses are leaving at the end of the day. They're the urban equivalent of the smell of mown grass and the noise of rooks. They are in their own way just as evocative.

Nanny and Big Dad and ten of Mam's brothers and sisters live next door but one. Nanny's word is law to her children and together they form an alliance against Big Dad. She confides in them, 'He's a miserable bugger. Don't upset him, you know what he's like.'

When Big Dad comes home from the pub at night they can hear his peg leg on the pavement outside. 'Hey, be quiet, that miserable sod's here.' Yet they're all so frightened of him that the instant he enters the house you can't hear a sound.

Mam likes to live near Nanny, and she does everything Nanny says.

'Lizzie, you'll have to stay with Mrs Jenkins for a few nights. She's just lost her husband and we can't leave her on her own.'

'But Mam, I've got a husband and baby to look after.'

'It doesn't matter, you'll have to do it whether you like it or not. Oh, and do the bread and butter for tea.'

'Is there only jam and bread for tea?'

Nanny stiffens and lets fly at Ste. 'Don't let me hear you bloody complaining about that again! Just remember there are thousands with nothing to eat. You're bloody lucky to have jam and bread.'

Harry butts in. 'I've been to a Labour Party meeting with Ken Horrocks, and the man said if we vote Labour everyone will be better off.' Nanny looks at Harry with fury.

'The only buggers who'll be better off are those who run the Labour Party. Folk who vote Labour are idle buggers who want something for nothing. They're jealous of everybody who's better off. I wouldn't trust those sods as far as I could throw 'em. You can trust the Tories because they're gentlemen. You don't want the Labour Party to give you anything, you want to earn it. Our Lizzie were proud to be earning a wage when she were eleven. She were such a little 'un. I cried when she started in t'mill. When t'horse and cart ran over her foot I thought she'd never walk again, but everything turns out better than you think in the end. And remember, however badly off you think you are, there's always somebody worse off.'

Nanny pours herself a cup of tea from the teapot on the hob. 'Oh Mam, that tea's poison, it's been stewing for an hour.'

'That's how I like it. And don't forget, any of you, how well off you are. If I hear any of you moaning I'll clatter yer lughole. All you'll ever need is each other. When our Ste were four and dying of pneumonia, the doctor said he'd die without a lumbar puncture. I said, "He'll not die in hospital, if he's going to die anywhere it'll be at home." We rocked him night and day for four months and look at him now.'

Uncle Ste likes to perch on top of the door between the two rooms like a goblin. He tells me you can't say ninety-nine if you have pneumonia. When I'm in bed I say ninety-nine and am relieved I haven't got pneumonia.

I love going to Nanny's and being with so many people; it feels very safe. There's always a peg rug being made. Dolly is cutting rags into strips and May is sewing them into the sacking. Peg rugs look dark and miserable, but everyone seems proud of them. Nanny has a big, long-handled black pan on the hob, full of potatoes and water, a slice of carrot and onion and a few small pieces of meat. She calls it taty ash.

'Our Florrie's a real comedian. Go on Florrie, do *Burlington Bertie*.' Florrie puts on a pair of George's trousers and gets Big Dad's walking stick. She struts up and down in the confined space, singing 'I'm Burlington Bertie, I rise at ten thirty' with enormous confidence. 'I'm sure our Florrie could be as famous as Gracie Fields.'

'Course she could. I bet she will be.'

Big Dad always sits in the armchair at the end of the day. He has a big belt with a big metal buckle round his trousers. I look at him with

3

fear because I have heard how Big Dad used the buckle end of the belt on the older boys, Harry and George. But by now he's getting soft. Everyone wonders how he could have changed so much. His head is small and covered in grey bristle, but his grey moustache is bushy and thick. He takes his peg leg off, and I watch as he slides a cream woollen footless sock off the stump. He moans gently with pain. The end of the thigh is all funny. It's covered in red veins. Everyone says that the pain is the nerve ends of his leg, which are still alive. 'Emm, go get me jug of beer.' I go with Nanny to Hubbersty's corner shop and watch them pull a hand-pump and fill the jug with frothing beer. Big Dad lets me have a taste, but it's bitter and horrible. Big Dad spits a lot into a sawdust-filled spittoon at the side of his armchair.

There's always a fire burning in the black-leaded range. A cord runs from one end of the mantelpiece to the other for drying clothes. Sometimes socks and underwear are put in the oven at the side of the fire to dry. One or two pans are always on the hob, as well as a large copper kettle, blackened with the smoke and heat.

On the wall is a photograph of a group of soldiers, Big Dad among them, and a picture of the royal family. When his daughter Maud's husband Harry Howarth drops by, they reminisce about the war. I sit listening and they don't notice I'm there. Harry says, 'That day, I was driving a horse and cart, I'll never forget. When the bloody shell exploded I couldn't remember anything when I came to but I was lying on a gravestone. I must have been blown straight into a churchyard I didn't even know was there.' He chuckles at the memory. Big Dad has his own story.

'One day I noticed a man walking so slowly, he was holding us up. I was going to swear at him when I noticed his face was half shot away with shrapnel and he was blind. I got back to the headquarters pillbox and didn't recognise it. It had been hit by shell after shell and the entrance was just a pile of bodies. They were all pals of mine who'd run for cover and been killed.

'The whole bloody thing was a farce. We'd hammer hell out of them with shellfire and advance twenty yards, and the next day they'd hammer hell out of us and we'd retreat twenty yards.

'Shells, shells and more bloody shells. I can't remember the explosion that took my leg off. Shrapnel wiped out a lot of my pals. I was lucky it left me alive. When the night came all I could hear was moaning and groaning all around. I did my own share. A lot of them crawled into shell-holes like rats, hiding from the machine-guns, but the holes were

4

full of water and it was still draining into them, so the level was rising. A lot must have drowned or died during the night because it was quiet next morning. I was lying in no man's land for two days and nights before someone found me. When I got to the hospital my leg was gangrenous and they thought I was a goner. They put screens round the bed and I knew that meant they thought I was on the way out. "Take those bloody curtains away, no bloody German's going to kill me".'

As I listen to their stories, I can't imagine having the physical courage to behave like them. I'm terrified at the thought that it might happen to me and expose me as a coward. I'm not brave in any way. I'm timid and nervous. I'm even frightened of most of the children I meet. I'm scared of going to bed and being left alone. My fear makes me feel ill. The more I listen to stories of corpses decaying, horses dying painfully in the deep mud, clouds of yellow chlorine gas suffocating everyone who breathes it, the more I think that only the hero can survive. The stories of their heroism frighten me but inspire growing admiration for heroes and a longing to prove myself a hero one day.

In the backyard of our house is a wash place with a corrugated iron roof. Under the roof is a big iron mangle, dolly tub and clothes line. When the clothes line isn't being used for drying clothes, sparrows fly on and off it. There are no trees for the sparrows, just gutters, stone flag walls and clothes lines. Next to the wash place is a small hen pen. I love to sit with the hens clucking round me, eating the hen food. It's warm and has a pleasant taste.

It's Monday, and Monday is wash day. I watch Mam with the dolly peg in her hand, plunging and turning the clothes in the tub. It makes a sucking, swishing noise. The dolly tub is full of clothes and Mam is working quickly. It's chilly, and I'm warming my hands on the corrugated side of the tub, which is full of hot, soapy water. Mam is squeezing the clothes from the dolly tub and putting them through the big wooden rollers of the mangle. As she turns the handle, soapy water splatters noisily on to the stone flags. She mangles the clothes twice, then pegs them out on the line. The handle of the mangle makes a clinking noise, and the cog wheels at the end, continually turning and interlocking, fascinate me. I watch mesmerised as they revolve, then can resist it no longer. I put a finger into the cog wheels. It's the third finger of my right hand, and the top joint is nearly severed. I scream with fright and pain. Mam scoops me up in a woollen shawl and runs to Nanny's, two doors away. 'Mam, quick, I need our May or Phoebe or Florrie to go with me to the hospital.' She frantically and tearfully explains what happened.

'Yer careless bitch!' Nanny is angry. Fortunately, Florrie is home from the mill and together they run to the hospital. Only desperation overcomes their fear of the hospital.

As we enter the strange, pungent building I'm overcome with a new fear, which intensifies the pain in my finger. I scream as we wait in the casualty room. The smell scares me. A blue-uniformed matron appears, fierce-looking, with no hint of a smile. 'Stop that crying!' she orders. No one has ever spoken to me like that before, and I'm too frightened to cry. The finger end is barely attached, but it's stitched and a bandage wrapped round it. 'It's a miracle he didn't lose his finger,' Mam says. 'If you put your trust in the Lord he does look after you.'

All my aunts want to read me books. I soon learn the stories, and can follow the words with my finger before I know properly what they mean. 'Look, he can read!' They're all excited because they think I can read. I feel very proud, as I don't know anyone else my age who's learning to read.

My favourite stories are about fairies. The magical world they live in is remote from the harsh world I see around me. It's a world of secret doorways and concealed staircases, of coloured lanterns, enchanted houses, flowers, birds, butterflies. It's alive with busy, cheerful, brightly dressed pixies and elves and gnomes. The sky is always blue, the sun is always shining, the birds are always singing. It's a happy world in which my imagination roams endlessly, and once I enter it I never want to leave. This is the world I want to live in. The books that give me access to it are my most precious possessions and they give me comfort when I'm near them.

Sometimes I imagine I'm in this world when I play the mouth organ, because some of the fairy stories are about magic pipers. I love to play all the tunes I hear on the mouth organ. Big Dad looks at me with pride.

'I'm going to write to Larry Adler and tell him I've a grandson who's only three who can play any tune on the mouth organ.'

I lie on the black horse-hair sofa in Nanny's. The horse-hair is hard, shiny and prickly, and on the sofa is a pile of magazines. One has a photograph of Jessie Matthews in a swimsuit. I feel a strange but powerful excitement that makes me feel guilty, and I pretend I'm not looking at it. I feel safe surrounded by everyone; I close my eyes when it's bedtime and desperately want to stay. 'Just look at him, he's pretending to be asleep.' They all laugh good-naturedly. Mam and Dad take me home and put me in bed. I feel terror as I imagine goblins and evil spirits waiting under the bed to get me when I'm on my own. I can hear their rustling as I lie looking at the ceiling. I know they're staying out of sight so they can scare me before pouncing on me. I imagine their horrible grins as they plot when to emerge from the shadows. Mam and Dad are kind and patient but I know they will leave me as soon as they can. I sweat with fear and have only nightmarish thoughts as I try to go to sleep. If I make a sound by moving, my imaginings will become real. I am hot; I see smoke rising from my forehead. The evil spirits under my bed are lighting a fire. It is dark, with terror stalking relentlessly.

My first visit to the cinema comes into my mind. I was carried in a shawl by Mam. I see a girl cowering under a table and I feel her terror. A man is looking for her and I can tell that he wants to hurt her. He looks everywhere and I know he'll find her. I'm sweating with dread and afraid even to wipe the beads of perspiration creeping slowly down the side of my face. The man lifts the cloth covering the table, and the girl lets out a bloodcurdling scream. It's more frightening than anything I can imagine.

I can still smell the kippers cooking when Mam gets back to Nanny's with me in her arms after the pictures.

Every other Saturday dinner-time there is a constant stream of men walking down our street to see the football match at Burnden Park. They all wear cloth caps and scarves, and some have clogs.

At the bottom of the street is St Bartholomew's School. Everyone tells me how lucky I am to go there. Mam went to the Ragged School in St Helens. That doesn't stop me feeling very afraid of the other children, despite being brought up in a family with countless cousins.

One day we put some small black seeds in some earth in a small tin and add water. When we look at it two days later, it's all bright green.

Being afraid of school often makes me feel ill in the mornings, and Mam and Dad always let me stay at home. But my school book is marked V. Good, because my writing is neat and I'm a good reader.

One morning the normal routine of school life is disturbed when we're all led in procession to the nearby church. We've never been before, and we're taken not to a religious service but to stand in a large circle in the middle of the church and listen to the vicar. He's telling us about the history of the church. Although it isn't particularly old, it has been built in a style intended to make it look so. The vicar points to some Gothic script in a stained glass window and asks if anyone can tell him what it says. I look at the strange letters, desperate to decipher them. With a flash of excitement I realise what it says. No one else has shown any sign of answering, so I put up my hand and when the vicar catches my eye blurt out, 'St Bartholomew's!' As this is the name of the school it should have been obvious, but the vicar is none the less surprised and impressed, particularly as I'm one of the youngest children there. He comments favourably to the nearest teacher. A feeling of pleasure and pride overwhelms me. Success is sweet, and I am never to forget that moment of pleasure. A gold star, a look of approval, a moment of even unimportant achievement can nurture our feeling of self-worth for a lifetime.

The moment we get back to school, my moment of success fades as several older boys gather round me.

'What did you have to say that for?'

'We knew the answer.'

'Don't think you're so clever.'

'You stupid little sod, showing off.'

'You're a bloody idiot.'

The malevolence comes thick and fast. My earlier pleasure in being recognised as special is replaced by fear as I am threatened. Finally, one boy lunges forward and kicks me in the stomach.

The world gradually sharpens around me as I recover consciousness. I realise with some surprise that I'm inside the school building and must have been carried from the playground where I had fallen. I've been put on a chair by a teacher who is smoothing ointment on to my forehead. The memory of the kick in the stomach and the surrounding circle of baying children comes back to me.

I feel more guilt than resentment at being attacked in this way. I always feel responsible for every situation. Because the incident might have been my fault, I can't help but detect resentment from the teacher as he bandages my head.

I'm not only unusually nervous but also, it seems, prone to accidents, so it comes as no great surprise to Mam when I return home swathed in bandages. There is no fuss or concern about how it happened. Mam thinks every bang and bruise is an inevitable part of growing up. Even if she is responsible in some way for an accident, she still regards it as the inevitable hand of fate. She never feels guilt, or agonises over her role. Life is unfair and harsh and life itself is responsible for events. Everything is a consequence of fate and destiny, or, if it's a fortunate outcome, providence.

Dad works in Swan Lane Mill, a short distance from my school. The brick is redder and shinier, and its architecture more ornate, than all the other mills in that part of Bolton. Dad started in the mill when he was eleven years old. He worked for half the day and went to school for the other half until he was thirteen, when he went full time in the mill. One day I'm taken to the mill because Dad has forgotten his dinner. After we've climbed up several floors, Mam opens the sliding door of the mule room where Dad works as a mule spinner. I feel overwhelmed by the sudden heat. The mule frame glides mesmerisingly backwards and forwards, its many parallel lengths of white cotton seeming to extend and then shrink, all the while remaining taut. Dad looks so thin, dressed in a ragged pair of trousers which stop short of his ankles and bare feet. The trousers are tied round the waist with string, and he is naked from the waist up. His emaciated body glistens with sweat as he slips in and out of this moving iron frame, his fingers effortlessly repairing the inevitable, unpredictable breaks in the yarn. He comes over to speak to Mam for a few minutes and get his dinner box, but the machine never stops and he must very quickly return to his work. Mam and I walk out of the mill and back home.

In the middle of one morning I'm at home because I feel sick. Dad walks into the room, looking ashen.

'I've been sacked.'

There is both bewilderment and anger in his voice.

'Whatever for?'

'The foreman said I spilt oil on some cones.'

I feel afraid as I look at his face and wonder what he means; I imagine he's been attacked.

'We'll manage on the dole till you get another job.'

'I've already been to the labour and there aren't any jobs.'

'George or Harry might get you a job where they work.'

'Perhaps we can get a shop. I thought I could make lemon cheese and sell it on the market.'

Now Dad is on the dole I go out with him a lot. He likes to go to the herbal stall in Bolton market and have a drink of dandelion and burdock or sarsaparilla. I look in shop windows.

'I can't have any toys, can I, 'cause we've no money?'

Dad and I are in the little backyard, standing next to the iron mangle. It's very cold and we have no coats on. We're shivering. I feel worried. I know something's happening but don't know what. A woman who arrived earlier comes to the back door and says, 'You can come in now'. I go in and discover that I have a baby brother. I can't begin to understand where he's come from but I feel so excited. I look at him and feel very proud. Mam lets me lie next to him on the bed for a few minutes.

Dad still hasn't got a job and he hasn't made any lemon cheese.

It's Bank Holiday, and we walk into the middle of Bolton and catch the tram to Moss Bank Park. I sit on my own at the front of the tram, pretending I'm not with Mam and Dad and my little brother.

'Eh, look at him, he doesn't want to be with us.' Dad laughs but I feel guilty, particularly because he's not taken offence. When we arrive at the terminus I love to sit looking through the end window of the tram as we turn. The tram is full, and everyone gets off to start walking into the country or into Moss Bank Park.

A particularly big house with a large garden next to the terminus attracts everyone's attention when they get off the tram. We all look into the garden, and I'm not sure what everyone is looking at. I look at the house and wonder how anyone can be rich enough to live in it. It's so remote an experience that I don't feel jealous. As we walk up the hill towards the moors, the houses and gardens are gradually left behind and it's just green fields. The smell is different from normal, and I breathe it in with pleasure. I listen to birds singing more tunefully than I'm used to. As we continue I see some enormous stone pillars and iron gates. A sign tells us it is Open To The Public, so we walk along the drive to a large, beautiful stone house. I know the stone is old because it's all worn; I guess that the windows are old because they're all in small diamond panes and each window is a different size. The great arched doorway has a massive wooden door covered with iron bolts. As I look at it, I feel as if I've seen it all before.

We walk into the house and I'm entranced by the wooden pillars and planks and white walls, the flag floors and the wonderful furniture in gleaming dark wood. The main room is dominated on one side by a huge stone fireplace, on the other by diamond-pane windows with coloured glass pictures. Mam, Dad and David have walked on and I'm on my own. I touch the wood of the walls and furniture and the stone of the fireplace. The light in the room is magical, as it's filtered by the glass in the windows. I look up and see that there is no ceiling. The great wooden supports for the roof criss-cross over my head, and I try to fix this picture of so much beauty in my brain. This is paradise. This is a house for angels. I breathe in and the stillness is deafening. I stand transfixed, convinced I'm in a world where no clock can advance. This is eternity, but even so I feel I'm looking into my own future.

2

An Unforgettable Day

I look forward to going to Nanny's every day after school, sitting on the prickly black sofa looking at the magazines, listening to everyone talking. It feels so safe to be in a room with so many people. The fire burns in the grate, socks hang over the string running from side to side of the range, and the black copper kettle is on the hob, steam coming out of its spout. Uncle Harry is speaking. He is very small but makes up for it with a look of great determination whenever he speaks. He looks at Mam and Dad. He has his own shop now, and also works at night in a woodworking business. Uncle Ste said he works so hard that one early morning he fell asleep on his bike on the way home after the night shift. I wonder how anyone can possibly work that hard. He is worried about Dad not having a job.

'There's a cookshop in Farnworth on Glyn Street. They do dinners for the millworkers and I'm sure you could make a go of it. They only want forty-five pounds for it.'

'Where could I get forty-five pounds?'

'There's a money-lender near the Town Hall. He lends without security and you'll have to pay a high interest rate, probably fifty per cent. But if you take a chance you'll do it, I'm sure.'

'Well, I'm sure we could make a go of it.' But Dad looks much less sure than he sounds.

Auntie Dolly's nursing my baby brother, who is crying.

Big Dad is in his chair, listening and fingering the gold fob on his watch chain, which hangs from two pockets in his waistcoat. His leg stump is raised on a stool, his walking stick propped at the side of his chair. He says, 'Our Mary's a good worker,' as if he wants to persuade Dad to do it.

Nanny can't stay to listen to everything because she's serving in the shop, which sells the bread and barm cakes Big Dad bakes. On the front

13

of the shop is the word TUROG in big gold letters. It seems very important.

'The cookshop must be just round the corner from our Lily,' Dad says. Immediately they're all off on a tangent.

'Your poor Lily,' Mam says as she comes back into the room.

'It were terrible,' Dad continues. 'You don't know what that girl went through with her step-sister. She never had a mother. I were only nine when me Mam died of TB, and our Lily and Jim and Albert were not much more than babies.'

'Your Dad had no right to get married to that woman after your mother died. She came from America with her daughter and from the beginning she resented all of you. She made your lives a misery.' Big Dad speaks his own indignant mind. 'She had too much of her own way. She's a domineering woman and your Dad never stood up to her.'

'But it were pitiful how that girl of hers treated your Lily. She were a cruel devil. She used to pinch Lily all night in bed and then hit her if she complained.' Mam looks angry as she speaks. 'She were black and blue.' Nanny comes into the room just as Mam's speaking. 'That woman needed a bloody good hiding if anybody did, and as for her daughter she should be locked up.'

I listen, feeling pity but without understanding why no one could stop this horrible girl from hurting Auntie Lily.

The next day I go with Mam and Dad to see the cookshop. I feel a shiver of excitement as I walk into the front room. It has tables and wooden seats with backs and is different from anything I've seen. But I also feel scared. It smells funny, and I'm frightened of changing school.

We go to see Auntie Lily round the corner. She looks very ill. Her house smells horrible. Her voice is the saddest I've ever heard. Her cheeks are hollow and her face is yellow. She has two babies who cry all the time. Her husband is a big man.

We move into the cookshop, and Mam and Dad work very hard. We're too far away from Nanny's for any of Mam's sisters to help, and my baby brother cries all the time.

My new school is round the corner from the cookshop and is a lot bigger than St Bartholomew's. It's much fuller of older children, and much noisier and rougher at playtime. I hate going out at playtime and want to stay in the classroom, but the teachers won't let me.

'You can't stay in here. Get outside with all the other children.'

I walk outside slowly, terrified of the big boys. One boy is in the corridor, leaning against the wall. As I pass him he turns and follows me into the playground. As soon as we're outside he grabs my shoulder and squeezes it as hard as he can.

'What you talking to the teacher for?'

'I wasn't.'

'You were.'

'I wanted to stay in the classroom because I don't feel well.'

'Teacher's pet, are you?'

'No.' He keeps squeezing my shoulder and suddenly I feel a short punch in my back. It's so hard that I lose my balance and nearly fall on the ground. He punches me against the wall.

'I'll get you every playtime. I'll be looking for you. If you tell teacher I'll kill you.' He leers and I feel the fear spread through me. When the bell goes I climb the stone steps to the classroom and go to my desk, still trembling with fear.

Auntie Emma comes once a week to take David for a walk in the pram, but most of the time he's on his own. One day he's crawling on the floor in the yard and a pair of stepladders falls on him. Instead of being killed outright, when Mam finds him he's sitting smiling, encased by the treads of the ladders.

'Just look what a miracle,' she says. Dad comes out and together they grin.

Opposite the cookshop is a baker's shop. One day Dad asks me to go for some iced buns. I cross the road and get them. When I get back, Dad looks at them and the change.

'You've got the wrong ones. You should have got the stale ones, they're two a penny.'

As I cross the road for the second time I hear a shout, and out of the corner of my eye I see a silver bumper. In an instant I'm lying in the road hysterically calling, 'Dad, Dad, Dad!' I keep calling his name even when Mam comes flying out of the cookshop. They take me to the hospital and I stay for a few days. The man who was driving the car comes to see me and brings me a basket of fruit as if to say sorry. I feel I'm being spoiled.

* * *

15

'Why don't you want to go to school?' Dad keeps asking me but I don't want to say. I feel ashamed of my fear.

'Is anybody bullying you?' Dad has guessed what's wrong without my saying. Dad tells me to manouvre the boy close to the school railings at break time next day. Sure enough, next morning the boy begins to pick on me and I walk over to the school railings as Dad had told me. Dad is on the other side of the road, but in no time at all he's grabbing hold of the boy through the railings. He shakes him violently and says, 'If you touch my lad again I'll break your bloody neck.' I see the fear in the boy's face as he realises Dad is serious. I'm suddenly transformed from easy victim into someone to be avoided on pain of retribution. He walks away, hardly daring to look in my direction. It's the end of my bullying.

I like drawing, and one day the teacher says, 'One boy's work is so outstanding that I'm putting him into the next class.' I'm sure he's talking about me. I can't believe it when he points to another boy whose drawing I think isn't as good as mine. I experience my first feelings of real anger.

Every Saturday I go to the cinema with friends and we see a cowboy serial which ends just as the hero is going to be killed. I can't wait to see how he manages to escape every week.

Next door to the cookshop is a sweetshop. The shelves are polished wood, and all the jars of sweets are side by side. Mrs Parker serves in the shop and she's very old. My favourite is sherbet, which she puts in a small paper bag. I lick my finger and put it in the bag and then suck it. I love the sharp sweetness as it melts in my mouth.

Dad has started baking pasties and pies and they open on Saturday nights. They're working all the time but it's too tiring for Mam. They decide to move to a baker's shop which is for sale. The cookshop is doing much better than when they started and they can afford to buy the baker's shop with the money they get. The shop is just off the main Blackburn Road, very near the town centre. It feels exciting to live near enough to walk there.

It's easy to assume that poverty is a great leveller, but a casual walk round the area we now live in reveals sharp differences. Houses with dirty milk-bottles on the step are next door to houses proudly superior with their clean milk-bottles. The flags and stone steps of some houses are stained and unwashed, while others sparkle with white donkey stone. Net curtains hanging in one front room might be full of holes and dirty, but in other houses clean and neat. Some parents are protective and caring of their offspring, while other children are pitifully neglected.

Some are indifferent to morals, law and self-discipline; others are intent on preserving, under difficult conditions, a sense of pride and personal responsibility. We are definitely in the latter category.

The baker's shop may be closer to the centre of town but we're now on the opposite side of Bolton. As none of the family lives nearby, it's a district I don't know. The street consists of two rows of terrace houses with three pubs and a few shops mixed in. At the top of the street is a foundry which emits dense, acrid brown smoke accompanied by great spurts of flame which become more obvious and dramatic at night. There are two fish-and-chip shops, but ours is the only baker's shop. It's no bigger than the rest of the terrace houses but the front parlour has been converted into a shop with a plate glass window, and at the back of the living-room the small lean-to kitchen has been enlarged to make a bakehouse. The backyard is very small, with only a few feet between back door and outside lavatory. Dad often gets me to tear up newspaper into squares which we thread on to a piece of string. This is the only lavatory paper we ever use. In some of the other backyards in the street people keep ferrets, guinea pigs or rabbits in cages, but our backyard is too small for anything except a short clothes-line. Having a shop at the front and a bakehouse at the back means that there is no natural light in the living-room. A single gas mantle suspended from the ceiling provides the only light when we first move in.

The district is a fascinating jumble of streets, back-streets, yards, ginnels, factories, mills, chapels, churches, schools, shops and waste land. For anyone living in a better-off district it must be impossible to imagine how anyone can enjoy living here, let alone flourish. But for me, the mixture of squalour, adventure, excitement and pathos becomes fuel for my dreams and a spur to my ambitions.

The closeness of the houses in the street means that secrets are few, and often no attempt is made to hide family arguments. Fighting sometimes breaks out in the street between members of the same family, in full view of the neighbours.

Nightmarish images seem an inevitable consequence of everyday life. No one can afford funeral parlours to hide away bodies. Every front room has to do its turn of duty as a funeral parlour. In a small terrace house the smell can be overpowering, as funerals are usually held four or five days after death. The front parlour becomes public property during this period, as it is considered unthinkable not to allow anyone in, even children, to view the open coffin. I'm too scared to go and look at a dead body. But one day Jimmy Higgins comes for me.

'Come on quick, there's a man been run over by a tram!' I follow him, not knowing what to expect. As we walk along St George's Street I can see the tram and a crowd of people. As we get nearer I feel my stomach begin to churn with fear. I then see an inert bundle of dark clothes under the steel wheels of the tram. I feel physically sick and turn away.

By contrast, the town mortuary at the top end of Haydock Street and just along from the foundry is inaccessible to the public. Only imagination can probe its dark secrets. In the evenings we climb on to the window sills. The glass is blacked out, but we feel a sense of daring that we're so near to what we imagine are untold numbers of corpses.

About a hundred yards from the mortuary is my new school, St George's. Its back entrance faces the slum district we live in, and the grand, but unused, front entrance faces St George's Street, which leads directly to the town hall, passing on its way St George's Church, a couple of rows of seedy looking shops, a funeral director's and one or two terraced houses.

The more usual entrance to the school is on a narrow cobbled side street leading to the playground. There, adjacent to the street wall, is a foul-smelling urinal for the boys, open to the sky. On the opposite side of the narrow street is a small sweetshop which sells all our favourite boiled sweets, as well as sticks of liquorice and arrowroot.

Every Friday morning we walk from school to the church for a service. While sharing a name, the two buildings could hardly be more different in character. The school is a mock-Gothic stone building which has lost all its sense of grandeur and importance and now looks dirty and depressing, as if to match the area it serves. By contrast, the church is a handsome, redbrick Georgian-style building with a square tower, which relates much more to the grander architecture of the town centre. On top of the tower, the flag of St George flutters in the wind.

The standard of the school is as poor as the area, and the attitude of the teachers indicates that they have little pleasure in working there. They are authoritarian, strict, and rarely smile. My timid and nervous nature makes me a natural conformist. The idea of breaking rules terrifies me, and as a consequence I'm only punished once – caned, for bumping into Miss Heys. She is small, formidable, sharply-spoken and middle-aged. Her grey hair is combed into a bun, she wears metal-rimmed spectacles on a severe face, and always carries a cane. I'm walking along a corridor past the classrooms during the milk break when a boy who is being chased knocks into the back of me with such force that I'm propelled into Miss Heys as she walks towards me. I'm dumbfounded that she regards me as the guilty party. I try to explain what happened but she won't listen, and fiercely demands that I put my hand out for the cane. I've never been caned before and am taken aback by the astonishing force as the cane comes down swiftly three times. I've been let off lightly, as twenty strokes is not uncommon. But the pain is sharp and my eyes fill with tears. The palm of my right hand stays bright red for the rest of the day, but the strong sense of injustice stays a lot longer.

Nevertheless, it is in this intimidating and unpromising environment that I experience something that changes my life. I go to school without any premonition that it will be an unforgettable day.

During the morning, someone we don't know comes into the classroom. He sets up a wind-up gramophone and pulls some records out of a case. 'I don't know whether any of you ever listen to music, but I've brought some special music to play for you today.' I don't know why, but I feel I must pay attention to what he's saying. 'This is music that can tell a story. As you listen, you can imagine what's happening. It's called programme music. The story is set in an imaginary castle. Music begins to play in the great ballroom and ghostly dancers emerge from the shadows. Gradually, more and more dancers join the dance. As the music reaches its climax, the dancers are swirling in delight to the haunting melody. Then, one by one, they begin to leave until finally the ballroom is empty again and the music comes to an end.'

I'm agog to listen to music that can bring to life such an exciting spectacle. He puts on the record, the music begins, and I listen.

I have never heard anything so intoxicatingly beautiful in my life. This is not music as I know it, but some divine sound that affects me in a way I have never, ever experienced. It's so wonderful, the vision before me is so inspiring, that the whole world changes in the time it takes for the record to finish. What I had thought was reality is simply an ugly cover for a much more beautiful world lying hidden beneath. In a dingy, depressing schoolroom, the language of music reveals a fairytale castle more real to me than the school. Shabby teachers are replaced by romantic men and women, handsome and beautiful, dancing with such elegance and verve that the boredom of school is banished. I surrender to this world as I listen, captivated by its mystery. From now on this is my new reality: a universe revealed by the miraculous alchemy of music. This sudden, profound and important discovery makes me realise that life will never be the same again. I leave school that day knowing that music and my life are now inextricably entwined.

No one else I know has experienced what has happened to me in the classroom. It's like finding a hidden treasure of priceless jewels too important to disclose to anyone else until the consequences have been very carefully considered. When I get home, I say nothing about the revelation I have had, because I know that without experiencing it, it will be impossible to understand. It's too precious to expose to Mam and Dad, who would laugh at me.

Weekdays in the shop are frenetic, particularly at dinner-time when the mill workers crowd into the shop for pies. The coke oven never seems to get hot enough. Dad lights it at six in the morning but it usually sulks and the fire refuses to take hold and brighten up. The result is that as more trays of bread, cakes and pies go in, the colder it gets. At twelve o'clock the shop is full of mill workers anxious to get their meat and potato pies for dinner, and Mam will curse the oven and Dad because nothing is ready. He is red and flustered, opening the oven doors to look too frequently and slowing down the baking of the pies even more. Often Mam will start getting the pies out of the tins before they're properly cooked, just to serve the customers. She puts a knife round the inside of the tins to loosen the half-cooked pastry, which collapses when the pies are pulled out. Inside the pies is thin gravy which runs out into the paper bags. Only weekends bring respite from this stressful daily crisis.

Although the shop is open all day on Saturdays, the mills close at lunch-time and the workers are in no rush to get their dinners. They can go home and cook their own, but usually fish and chips and steak puddings are the favourite on a Saturday.

From the moment Saturday starts, the thought of no school for two days and no panic for pies makes it the best day of the week. Even the oven, no longer under pressure, seems more good humoured, and when it finally goes cold in the afternoon there is a wonderful feeling of tranquillity. The house is tidied and dusted, and a weekly visit to the cinema makes it a day of delights. The relentless ping of the shop bell becomes less frequent and eventually stops.

Sunday, with no baking and no shop open, ought to be the best day but it isn't. The silence and calm are oppressively unreal, and the slums seem dirtier and smellier when no one is working. The quiet is as depressing as a funeral service, and the void is filled by visiting, or being visited by, relatives. This is a ritual that must be respected. Dad sulks in his chair when relatives arrive because he thinks Mam is too close to her brothers and sisters and he's jealous. He usually has a sick headache on Sunday, so his scowling, resentful look can always be blamed on that.

One Sunday we visit Auntie Florrie and Uncle Jim, who live near Moses Gate, just a mile or two from the town centre, on the edge of scruffy country. Although there is more green near their house than Haydock Street enjoys, it doesn't seem much of an improvement.

Uncle Jim has an allotment with a shed a short way from the house, but he grows nothing and keeps a fierce dog chained up in the shed. It seems very cruel to lock a dog up in a shed without windows, particularly as there appears to be no reason for it.

On this particular day I'm playing on my own in the house because my three cousins are younger than me. In the parlour is an upright piano which no one plays; the lid is open, and on the music stand is a Smallwood Tutor, the most popular tutor of the day. Almost without being aware of what I'm doing, I open the tutor and begin to read.

The first thing I notice is a drawing of the black and white piano keys and a line connecting these keys to black notes on or between lines. It seems simple. Of course, there is a fundamental problem: the notes for the left hand are different from the notes for the right hand, and it's difficult at first to remember which is which. Clearly they have to be different, otherwise both hands would be playing the same keys, which would be physically impossible. And the notes for the left hand need to go down the piano and the notes for the right hand up the piano if there is to be any effective use of the hands and the keys. My fascination with music notation begins, and by the end of Sunday I have identified the notes for *The Bluebells of Scotland* in a very simple form. When I play it through for Mam and Dad they're so impressed that a week later they buy an upright piano for one pound ten shillings, but it isn't a bargain. As we discover later, it's impossible to tune because it has a broken spine.

When the piano arrives at Haydock Street I feel very excited and desperately want to learn how to play it. In our family everyone turns to a relative for help, whether it's decorating the house, moving, or, in my case, learning to play the piano. Only one member of the family can play, and this is Auntie May's husband, Uncle Harold. He is my first teacher. I go for my first lesson and play for him. I've already been practising the few simple pieces in the Smallwood Tutor and I decide to play the first piece I learned at Auntie Florrie's. I'm very proud that I've been able to learn to play without a teacher, but when I finish he says nothing complimentary. Instead he asks:

'Can you sing tonic sol-fa?'

'I don't know.' I don't even know what he means. I stand looking at him, unsure what to say or do.

'You must know the scale do, re, mi, fa, so, la, te, do.' He sings the letters. 'That's easy enough, isn't it?'

'I think so.' I'm not sure what's coming next.

'Well, you know the tune you've just played for me that you learnt on your own, *The Bluebells of Scotland*? Sing it in tonic sol-fa.'

I stand bewildered, wondering how to do it. After an awkward silence, Uncle Harold begins to sing: 'So, do, te, la, so, la, te, do, mi, mi, fa, re, do.' I'm amazed he can do it so easily. 'Can't you do that?' he asks me, with surprised amusement. It seems impossibly difficult. He continues to demonstrate his skill with other tunes and I'm baffled. Why can he do it but I can't? He makes no effort to help me and I feel a deep sense of inadequacy and frustration. He has a gift I don't have and he seems to gloat over it. It also seems that his facility with tonic sol-fa helps him to play any new melody on the piano without trial and error. When I try, I can only find the right notes in the tune after finding a lot of wrong ones. He hears a melody and can immediately sing it in tonic sol-fa, so that he knows exactly where the notes are on the piano. I long to do the same thing, but soon abandon hope. It's on this unpromising foundation that I begin my piano lessons with Uncle Harold.

I begin to play simple pieces week by week, and my inability to do tonic sol-fa means that I cling to the music even more. I loved reading it on the first day at Auntie Florrie's, and can soon read the music fluently. I make quick progress in playing because I love it so much, but I'm only given trivial music to play. I've started listening to more and more wonderful music on the radio, and I mention it to Uncle Harold, but he makes it clear that he has no interest in it. He delights in playing the popular tunes of the day, and he listens to nothing else. His natural gifts have not led him on to discover great music. He has no sense of the miraculous beyond his ability to do what few people are able to do: play melodies and harmonies on the piano without music.

My inability to do this is one of my earliest experiences of failure. I want to be a musician because I love music so passionately, yet I feel

I've been denied a gift. What makes it worse is that this gift has been given to someone to whom music is clearly nothing more than entertainment. I can feel and experience the most wonderful world of sound, and yet I have a deficiency in understanding the technique of analysing the sound. But this doesn't make me determined to overcome the problem. My reaction instead is to gloss over, to ignore, to conceal, to decide that this skill is irrelevant, to convince myself that only my passion for music matters. I don't recognise that this self-delusion is a kind of systemic poison. Untreated, it will forever haunt me with a sense of personal inadequacy and ultimately, with every other moment of failure adding to it, might be enough to persuade me that however passionate I might be, perhaps I'm not capable of being a musician.

But failure or not, for now my love of music is too powerful for me to consider abandoning my dream of being a musician.

3

A Passion to Play

The day has not assumed any significance in my mind, and certainly not in Mam and Dad's. I wake up in the morning with a sick feeling and decide that it's enough of an excuse for staying in bed. Mam and Dad always seem content to encourage self-indulgence if it means staying away from school. They would never insist on me going even on a normal day, let alone today. But the day clearly has significance in one person's mind: my headmaster, Pop Rawlinson.

Perhaps his subsequent promotion to the headship of the much larger Holy Trinity depends on having at least one St George's pupil pass the eleven-plus. I'm dimly aware that I've become his star pupil, not least because he has selected me to be St George in a play for St George's Day. His voice, so different from the usual shop customers, pushes its way through the early morning air. One remark stands out:

'He won't get another chance'.

I'm deeply embarrassed that Pop Rawlinson has come to the house to make sure I take the eleven-plus. It's his importance, not that of the examination, that persuades Mam to get me out of bed.

I have to go to Clarence Street School, only a short walk away, to take the exam. The school is larger, and the unfamiliar room with its symmetrically arranged desks is intimidating. It becomes gradually clearer as I sit there that this really is an important day, and the early morning feeling of sickness is soon forgotten. Many of the questions seem to consist of baffling riddles. I have no way of knowing whether I've done well or badly, and once it's all over I soon forget both the exam and the occasion.

Several weeks later, I'm reading the Bolton Evening News, the only daily paper we take. I rarely do more than glance at it, so it's by sheer accident that I find a list of eleven-plus results which includes my name. I've got a place at Bolton Municipal Secondary School. The surge of

25

excitement I feel makes me realise that it matters more than I would ever have admitted, even to myself.

By chance that evening, Dad and I go to the Theatre Royal for a variety show. My favourite turns are the magicians. Tonight, beautiful iridescent metallic spheres glide smoothly around and above the magician without any obvious mechanics, defying gravity. The combination of magic in the theatre, and the knowledge that I too have been elevated by some mysterious process, makes my evening. As we return home I feel excited about my success. But my pleasure and happiness are not shared by Mam and Dad. They display no parental pride in any of my achievements. When I'm St George in the school play, it seems every other parent is in the audience but mine. They express no interest in being there, and no interest in knowing what it was like when I get home.

I'm sure Mam and Dad would be just as happy if I had no interest in the piano at all. But it's their lack of interest that reinforces my passion to play. They never try to influence me positively in what I'm doing. Instead, their opposition develops in me a powerful awareness that my future depends on me and not them. My interests develop because they're mine and I discover them, not because they're thrust under my nose. Their lack of interest in the music I find so wonderful only increases its importance to me. I become fiercely protective of my own interests, and my determination to do what I want grows. I increasingly want to find ways to demonstrate that I'm not the same as other members of the family.

This inevitably opens up a divide. Their culture is one of sharing everything. They have no aspirations to go one better; they have the security of being banded together as one. No one in the family attempts to be different or superior. Their strength lies in their unquestioning acceptance of who they are. They believe a grammar school is not a stepping-stone to a better life but a stepping-stone to being different, to ceasing to be one of the family, to despising the family's values. Any sign of adopting a 'posh' interest, habit or accent is considered a betrayal: a rejection of the unifying bond on which everyone's survival depends. Clothes, houses and furniture must show no sign that the owner might long to be part of a different world. The world in which they live is good enough. They have a contentment which satisfies them, but all it does is stimulate my interest in a different lifestyle.

The world of great houses becomes real in my imagination through my mother's stories of my great-grandmother working in a large house.

I dream of gardens with wide paths, a pony and cart, a governess, and the privilege of being a child in such a house. I imagine myself elegantly dressed, cosseted and protected, with parents on whom the world looks with respect. This world is not middle-class but upper-class, remote and seemingly inaccessible. But paradoxically, it's a world with which Mam and her sisters and brothers are desperate to claim a connection. Despite having had the same conversation time after time, they can't resist indulging in it whenever the opportunity arises.

'Me Dad was a proper gentleman. His father lived near Cirencester and he took up with one of the servants. They wouldn't accept her in the family so he left home. He said, "If she's not good enough for you, I don't want any of your money." It was a big house where they lived; I think it was called The Beeches. Our Harry spent days in Liverpool looking through the newspapers because someone said they'd seen an advert saying, "If Henry Digby Mann will contact such-and-such a solicitor he will hear something to his advantage". That was the family name, Henry Digby, and Dad gave it to our Harry when he was born.'

The words change but the gist is always the same, and whenever Uncle Harry is present he confirms that despite finding nothing in Liverpool, he knows that there is a crock of gold waiting for him somewhere. There can be no question about it: the family has come from toffs. Though the only remnant of their ancestry is the name, they never tire of reminiscing about their imagined origins. Even when the sisters marry, they cling tenaciously to their ancestors in a way that makes the families of all the husbands an irrelevance. As there are many more girls than boys in the family, one might have expected that marriage would have weakened the legend of aristocratic origins, but instead it has turned the family into a powerful matriarchy, with each son-in-law surrendering any claim on behalf of his own family and accepting that his wife's family is the more important.

Yet this obsession with a glorious, if illusory, family history does nothing to encourage special care and attention to ensure that their children can enjoy a future that befits their past. The rigour and hardship of their own lives reinforces a view that everyone should have to endure the same thing. Instead of believing that education is the way for children to enjoy a better life, there is resentment that it may provide the way to an easier life.

Mam and Dad never come out and say it, but I'm sure it's the reason for their opposition to my going to grammar school.

I begin to notice resentful looks and comments after the announcement in the paper, particularly from Mam. She disapproves of my pleasure in passing the eleven-plus, as if it's a weakness in my character. She has a powerful sense of what she wants and I know that something exceptional will have to happen if she is going to be persuaded to let me go. No argument can make any impression on her once her mind is made up. But, ironically, it's her deep sense of social inferiority that overcomes her opposition.

Visits by school inspectors are a frequent occurrence in and around Haydock Street, but visits by teachers are a rarity. Pop Rawlinson's second visit takes everyone by surprise. I'm in the back street when my two younger brothers rush up, gasping with wide-eyed and hurried earnestness: 'Guess who's outside – Pop Rawlinson!'

The news is too dreadful to wait for any response from me, so they run off. My heart pounds with fear. As I enter the small living-room I can see Mam doing her best to tidy up, but a few hours' work can't be achieved in seconds. She's always embarrassed by visits from people she thinks come from a better class.

'I just don't know what'll happen next,' Mam mutters with a bad-tempered shrug of the shoulders.

'It's not my fault, is it?' I try to be defiant but feel guilty that it is indeed my fault.

'You must have told him you wanted to go.' Mam guesses that the visit relates to the vexed question of my place at the grammar school.

'I didn't. You and me dad both said I could if I passed.' I'm not sure they did, but I feel that as I've passed I deserve to go.

'He'll be too stuck up if he goes there,' Mam says, turning to Dad.

'I don't want him to go anyway,' Dad retorts.

'Leaving school at sixteen. You could be earning money then. I was proud to work for my mother and take home a wage for her.'

'But I might be able to earn more money if I go to a grammar school.'

'You know what Grandma said about the boys in the house she worked at. They both got stuck up. No time for their own parents. That's what education does for you. It turns you against your own parents. You're ashamed of them. You mix with posh people and talk with a posh accent and don't want to know your own parents.'

She remembers Pop Rawlinson still standing waiting in the shop, and goes to invite him in.

He is an immensely tall man with a smallish head, and he stoops as he comes through the small shop, stepping over vegetable boxes to get into the living-room. He's ill at ease and sits on the edge of an upright chair. David and Jack reappear at the door, standing awestruck at the sight of my dreaded teacher. The tales of his severity, temper and harshness are legendary, though I've never personally suffered at his hands. As the whole family face him, he speaks.

'I understand you don't want Ernest to take up his place at the grammar school.'

'Well, that's his mother.' Dad smiles innocently and shrugs his shoulders, as if to say 'It's no good talking to me'. As soon as Pop Rawlinson understands who needs convincing, he turns and looks directly at Mam.

'Why don't you want him to go?'

'I don't believe in so much education. It gives them ideas. They get too big for their own parents. I've seen it happen. In any case, I think they're better off working.' Mam speaks with determination, and what she lacks in height she makes up for in spirit.

'Well, I'd strongly advise you to let him go. He won't get another chance. I think there would come a time when you'd regret stopping him.'

Mam has spoken her mind and can't think of anything else to say. She is vulnerable to strong men and Pop Rawlinson is very strong by any standard. She wavers as he gives her his strict teacher's stare.

'I would advise you to let him go.' He repeats himself, but this time as if addressing an obstinate pupil.

'It's up to you.' Dad speaks again, putting all the weight of the decision on to Mam.

'Well, I don't know.' It's Mam's first moment of hesitation. She seems to be losing confidence. It's enough to convince Pop Rawlinson that the matter is now settled.

'Good, I'm glad. I'm sure you won't regret it. By the way,' he turns towards me, 'here's something for you.' He hands me a shilling piece and leaves the room. I'm nonplussed by such a remarkable and unexpected gesture, which seems to make the decision irreversible. Mam is distinctly bad-tempered at being overruled. She knows what her sisters will say when she tells them she's changed her mind and I'm going to the posh school after all, but the matter has been settled and a reversal is never considered.

My lessons with Uncle Harold are arranged without any proper agreement

29

about cost or regularity. As a member of the family he accepts the responsibility of helping a relative, but I sense a subtle hostility. I know that there is a growing gulf between us because of my passion for great music and his own taste for popular tunes. The music I study while I am his pupil reflects his taste, not mine. There is nothing inspiring about any of the music he gives me to play, but there is still the pleasure of playing intricate hand and finger movements, which is quite distinct from the pleasure of listening to the intoxicating sound of beautiful music.

For whatever reason, Uncle Harold seems to find more and more excuses for cancelling my lessons and eventually they stop. If I'm to continue to learn, I need a new teacher.

Mr Marsh has a rather large Victorian house on the last residential road before the centre of Bolton really begins. It's a seedy row but grand in style, certainly incomparably better than any of the smaller terraced houses round where I live. Before I become one of his pupils I have passed Mr Marsh's house several times and noticed the always highly-polished brass plate on the wall. It displays his name with a lot of letters behind it and a list of seven musical instruments, including piano, which he teaches. This impresses Mam and Dad and is proof positive that he has all the necessary credentials. They have no doubt that he is a good teacher.

My music lessons with Mr Marsh are neither inspiring nor important enough for me to concern myself too much as I walk there each week. After my experience with Uncle Harold I've already decided that my love of music and the piano can't be shared with anyone else. However inadequate my playing, I'm driven by something that can't be discouraged. My passion to play makes the role and opinion of my teacher seem irrelevant. My progress doesn't depend on anyone else because I have my own inner drive. Mam and Dad play no part in either encouraging me to practise or taking any interest in my progress. They take my self-motivation for granted. I know that some of their more ambitious, better-off acquaintances are desperate to see their children play the piano. They buy bikes, train sets and cinematographs in the hope that they will practise. After a few weeks the practice stops and it's a constant battle of wills between parents and child.

Mam and Dad never have any concern about my practising. They arrange a teacher who is both affordable and convenient, and that's that.

I always arrive in good time for my lesson and I'm shown into a small waiting room for a few minutes. In a pile of magazines on the table, I discover a book with nude photographs of women. Photographs of nudes are unknown at home, and so are all the more irresistible. On each visit I pick the book up and quickly look through it, terrified in case I'm discovered. The silence of the room and the surroundings combine to make this book particularly incongruous and dangerous. Several times I hastily close it, thinking I hear approaching footsteps. Finally, Mr Marsh appears, dressed in an old-fashioned tweed suit and stiff wing collar. Despite what I think is his great age, his face always has a shiny, clean, healthy appearance and his narrow, quick eyes dart behind a pair of steel-rimmed spectacles.

The routine is always the same.

'Come in.' He leads the way into the front room, which contains all seven instruments he teaches.

'Now, let me hear your study.'

It's a soulless and impersonal business operation. He meticulously fills thirty minutes in order to complete his bargain without involving himself in friendliness, enthusiasm or encouragement. I sense that few of his pupils have ever shown any great enthusiasm for playing, and as his working life is coming to an end it's not something that concerns him now. The only time he ever becomes personal or enthusiastic is when he reminisces about his own career in music.

'I conducted a touring opera company for many years. We did a large repertoire but I didn't have the right connections to get further.' He narrows his cold eyes as he speaks. 'That's what you need: influence. It doesn't matter what you do, if you haven't got influence you'll get nowhere.'

My confidence in my future momentarily reduces. But I'm still in that state of innocence when the future is an unmarked canvas, and despite old Marsh's gloomy foreboding I'm not at all concerned about my lack of influence. I feel sure that whatever the problems I face in the future, I can overcome them.

'Yes, I could have risen to the top of the tree. I composed as well, you know.' He says this with a hint of challenge, as if he imagines I doubt him, even though I'm trying to show interest and convey utter acceptance of everything he says.

'I conducted without score – *without score*, what do you think of that, eh? I could play all the instruments. I used to know every singing part. If any singer forgot, I could prompt them every time. But I lacked influence, and that's what matters.' It's a personal, bitter diatribe which he quite obviously indulges in whenever he senses a receptive ear; when he can make clear his prowess and explain why he is now a second-rate music teacher in a seedy area of Bolton.

'Carry on with your piece.' He struts about the room as I play, coming back to correct or admonish frequently.

'Better, better.' He turns and looks at me severely. 'If you want to be a musician you must keep working hard at it. You can't play about in the streets like other boys.' It's the first time words approximating to encouragement and advice are spoken, and because of this the effect is like a blinding flash of lightning. What would, under other circumstances, have been a trite comment seems prophetic and inspired. It suggests that I am different. That I am a musician. I have never dared think of myself as a musician. Suddenly I feel elevated to some privileged position. I have increasingly come to revere those extraordinary people whose lives in music mean so much to me. It has never occurred to me that I could join their ranks, but Mr Marsh has now suggested it and I seize the idea eagerly.

Now I feel the need to sustain, protect and develop my career as a musician. As I walk home, ambition fills my whole being, and from that moment I'm increasingly carried along by thoughts of a career sustained by inspiration and passion. Yet as I near home, I'm afraid I'll lose this feeling of triumph and wellbeing. So I keep walking in the direction of the moors, which lie just outside the town.

Over the past year I've discovered the joy of walking and breathing the fresh air of the moorland and dreaming of a beautiful future. The smell of grass and heather cleanses my mind, allowing the inspiration of beautiful music to overwhelm me. The shackles of parents, brothers and relatives are cast off, and I feel the power of dreams carrying me toward the future.

4

It Was Wrote

I'm very apprehensive on my first day as I walk from Haydock Street, past St George's and the town hall, to my new school. I have no anxious protective parents guiding me to the school and making sure I arrive on time. I'm on my own.

Bolton Municipal Secondary School is an imposing redbrick building ornamented with florid whirls around the large windows and doors. The scale is remote from domestic architecture and the overall effect is intimidating. The tiled internal surfaces and wooden floor lend menace to the noise of walking feet. Any raised voice echoes, any note of anger is amplified. The smell is a pungent mix of disinfectant, floor polish and chemicals from the laboratory, combined with a depressing odour of sweaty clothes. It's not a building to feel comfortable or relaxed in. St George's had been intimidating but I had had the security of feeling special. At my new school I know no one before I arrive. The excitement of passing the eleven-plus has long since gone, particularly after I hear rumours of frightening initiation ceremonies.

From the moment I start, I feel an outsider. Most of my classmates have come from schools which have closer contact with the grammar school, so they're better prepared. The maths teacher assumes everybody in the class has covered the work done by those schools. How can I tell him I haven't?

At St George's I felt I was ahead of the rest of the class. Here, I begin to realise I'm behind. I had left St George's with a feeling of triumph, believing that I would continue in the same way in my new school. Instead, I soon begin to feel mediocre. At best I get middling results in every subject. I feel my confidence ebbing away. No teacher offers hope or encouragement, no teacher suggests that the poor results can be reversed. All the teachers behave as if my results are only what they expect. No one suggests I'm capable of doing better.

33

It's not difficult to understand why confidence is lowered and self-belief damaged when teachers clearly regard others as superior. The brightness of pupils who are elevated and favoured creates deep shade in which the remainder wither.

But I don't wither. My consuming interest in music and piano playing, fortunately unrelated to schoolwork, elevates me above the abyss of failure. The inspiration and dreams of a life in music give me immunity against my continuing mediocre performance in school. The apparent impossibility of enjoying a successful school career lends added importance to my musical career. I have no competition from any fellow pupils because no one else shares my passion for music.

My inability to do well in most school subjects reduces my commitment to and interest in them. The boredom I experience in doing the work is in sharp contrast to the intoxicating love I have for music. The forces which discourage and reduce my interest in conventional school subjects give me an enormous boost in music.

Mam and Dad's continuing resentment of grammar school education becomes less and less of a problem as my own commitment to it declines. They feel no threat from my devotion to the piano. They assume I'm talented because I do it without any need to be pushed by them. Their belief that it is talent also means that they attach as little importance to my music teacher as I do.

Their total conviction that I know what I'm doing despite my youth and inexperience could have damaged my development, but it didn't. Their unworldliness is a protection against cynicism, against knowing everything and spoiling my delight in discovery. I can dream of doing things which educated parents might ridicule. Their innocence makes me vulnerable, but it also has great benefits.

My own future seems to be unfolding in such a dynamic way that I feel I have little control over its direction. I'm being drawn forward continually by the sound of beautiful music and my passion to play the piano. School work has no relevance to my destiny. None of the classroom subjects contribute to it in any way. My consistently mediocre marks are an indication that school is peripheral to my life, though I make a half-hearted effort to do the work. Mam and Dad bitterly resent my doing homework; they're still working hard and book work offends their sense of right and wrong. One evening that resentment is expressed in a decision to make me share the drudgery. A full bucket of potatoes is needed for each day's meat and potato pies, and it takes Dad a good hour's peeling every night.

'You can peel the potatoes for us.'

It's spoken in a way that implies I've done too little. I'm not used to being forced to do things and can't suppress hot tears. I sit in the corner of the room, pick up the potato peeler and start on the first of many evenings of spud-bashing. I can understand why they feel as they do, but I hate their crude resentment.

Ever since the magic moment of revelation in St George's, music has become the centre of my life. I listen to it and play it continuously. I tune in to every radio programme I think will be interesting. In all kinds of ways I'm adding to the stock of pieces I love. There is a simple musical quiz on a radio programme called *Monday Night At Eight*. The tunes are played on a piano, mostly light music or popular classics, which I delight in guessing. One tune strikes me as familiar and exciting, and I try desperately to remember what it is. To my surprise, the answer means nothing to me. It's the march from Tchaikovsky's Sixth Symphony, which I don't know. I long to hear it played by an orchestra, so I scour the Radio Times looking for a performance. After a week or two I find one, an evening concert.

I tune in and listen while everyone around me gets on with their normal business. My brothers play, Dad and Mam grumble that I've taken over the radio. The symphony starts and I wait; it's a long wait but I never relax my attention for a moment, and then I hear it. It's wonderful. The simple tune had thrilled me on the piano, but orchestrated by Tchaikovsky it's sensational. I'm overwhelmed by excitement and decide that Tchaikovsky is one of my favourite composers.

Discovering harmonious sequences and melodies and orchestral sounds is a continuous, almost feverish delight. I feel the prickles up and down my spine as I listen to Tchaikovsky. I'm enchanted by the *Nutcracker Suite* and feel my emotions stirred by the Fifth Symphony. I imagine playing the heroic opening of the First Piano Concerto. My growing ambition is nourished by my passion to be a part of such a beautiful world.

Every time I hear a pianist I'm spellbound by the sound of the piano, so much better in quality than my own piano. But as I play, my inner ear makes good my instrument's deficiencies. As I play the chords and passages I've heard on the radio and on records, the mentally adjusted sound I make is deeply satisfying to me.

Each new piece I hear, I want to play. If I think it exceptional and I can afford it, I order the music at the Co-op's music department, and when it arrives I'm always fascinated to see on paper what I've been transported by in sound. Sometimes I can't easily connect the two. I listen to a record of Eileen Joyce playing Lizst's *Gnomenreigen.* Her playing is always remarkably clear and liquid and this piece is, it seems to me, miraculously played. When the music arrives I look at it with bewilderment. It's some strange edition in which no more than two bars per line are printed. The grace notes are so big and clumsy that it's difficult to imagine it transformed into the gossamer miracle of rapid sound I've heard.

I've also discovered Rachmaninov's piano music. I borrow the Second Piano Concerto from the library and gaze in wonder at passages which seem incredibly difficult. Rachmaninov represents the goal I want to reach: the virtuoso pianist and the romantic composer.

One day I go into Co-op to ask if they have any Rachmaninov records. The assistant comes back with just one: the final movement of the First Piano Concerto, with Rachmaninov playing. It's unknown to me but I buy it on impulse. It's the most exciting piano music I've ever heard, and it's difficult even to imagine playing it. The breathtaking speed of the piano entry of the last movement defies belief.

As my enthusiasm for Rachmaninov increases, I'm determined that my life will be devoted to music. My friends at school all take it for granted that I'm destined to be a pianist and composer. I sometimes take in manuscripts of my latest compositions. As none of them can read music they're more impressed than they might otherwise be, but their approval reinforces in me a sense of destiny about my future.

Some suggest that I give a talk to the school music society. I've never realised there is one, because I'm so uninvolved with school activities, but I agree and choose Rachmaninov as the subject. One of the boys takes a great deal of trouble designing a poster advertising the talk. As the day draws near, I begin to sense that it's a more important occasion than I've anticipated. I enter a crowded lecture room with only my one record of the last movement of the First Concerto. I'm sure most people in the audience will know the Second Piano Concerto, which is very popular. I've compiled some facts about Rachmaninov, which I use to try to convey the excitement I feel when I listen to him playing. I quote him:

"'I have chased three hares in my life – playing, composing and conducting – and I don't think I caught one of them". What an inspiration to everyone, to be so pessimistic about one's life and yet to achieve so much,' I comment, and then prepare to play my record. 'I want to be sure you realise that Rachmaninov wrote more than the Second Piano Concerto. This is the final movement of the First, played by Rachmaninov himself.'

I put on the record and float on a magic carpet into a realm where I share Rachmaninov's experience. I feel a sense of achievement about giving the lecture, as well as a small sense of pride, but I don't anticipate the consequence.

A few weeks later I leave school as usual but I'm particularly anxious to get home. Over the past months I've been seized by a growing urge to compose music. I've bought manuscript paper and have begun to write. I pluck sounds and rhythms out of the air around me. I crystallise them as quickly as I can on manuscript, and although the written version of my dreams is always a little disappointing, I'm unable to stop. I carry on ignoring the real sounds of my life, living only in this private world of sound during my periods of creation. I'm not consciously a composer, I'm simply obeying an instinctive urge to dream and write. Each time, the writing falls short of the dream but there's no loss of excitement about doing it. I leave the manuscript on the music stand of the piano, so I can re-enact my private dreams and either question them or simply enjoy them.

As I return home, Dad glances at me. Greetings are seldom spoken in our house. 'Mr Marsh called today. He's putting up the price of his lessons.' There's a hint of bad temper. Dad has been waiting for me to come home to get this off his chest. But he seems more upset than I expect him to be.

'He saw your music on the piano. He said you're wasting your time. He's written music and never got anywhere with it. He said you need influence to get anywhere. Just writing music is a waste of time. He said so.'

I understand immediately that he's been upset by the rubbishing of my composing, because he has somehow shared my delight in it. I've seen his look of quiet pleasure more than once as I've feverishly written. Now Mr Marsh has ruined it for him, and he's taking it out on me. I feel my happiness in composing turn sour and become a lead weight in my stomach. I go upstairs to the bedroom I share with my brothers, and lie on the bed. Stupid Marsh with his smug, small, scrawny face and scrawny neck and wing collar. I look up at the ceiling and my eyes scan

37

the familiar cracks. I look out through my bedroom window and over the rooftops to the distant mill chimneys as I struggle to recover from the assault on my dreams. I want to cry, but I can't. I lie until my emotions are more under control, by which time it's dusk. As I go downstairs, no look suggests I've been missed. The problems of everyday living leave no time to consider the bruised feelings of children.

After the usual bread-and-jam tea, I sit at the piano practising. Each week I set myself a target of memorising a piece of complex contrapuntal music. I also divide up my time carefully so I can work on the different technical deficiencies in my playing. Constant repetition of the same exercises never bores me. On some days I have the exciting feeling that I've made a breakthrough and my technique is better than ever. That's enough to ensure that I never tire of practising. For everyone else in the house, the sounds I make must be monotonous but no one ever complains. I'm sure that my playing sometimes does get on Mam and Dad's nerves, but they tolerate it with stoicism.

The improvement in my piano playing and my growing reputation results in invitations to play at small concerts in all sorts of places. At this stage in my career, being asked to play is considered sufficient honour in itself and no one ever suggests paying anything. None the less, I never doubt that one day my piano playing will bring me great financial success. It will also, I'm sure, provide something more: a way of life other than a working lifetime in a mill or a shop.

All my many relations started work in the mill like Mam and Dad. They all loved their work in the mill, but what they wanted more than anything was to feel in control of their own lives. Work in the mill was constantly threatened by unemployment, so several of them came to realise that owning a shop might give them the security they wanted. After suffering through the depression years, feeling themselves tossed whichever way the unpredictable swell took them, they had the illusion that they were on dry land. It was hard work, but it gave them a feeling of pride. They could believe they had succeeded.

But my life is different. I've been inspired by music and, without the slightest idea how, I'm convinced I'll find another way to live and be proud. Somehow, the secret of this wonderful way of life will reveal itself. My conviction is not shaken by words of warning from the family's frequent visitors.

'You'll have to play dance music. You can't make a living playing that stuff. What will you do when you have a family? You'll be glad to do anything.' Of course I disagree passionately. They're saying that in the

38

end I'll be forced to become one of them, and abandon my dream of a life in music. But this constant hammering of what people have to do for money forges in me a steely determination to die rather than capitulate to the sordid demands of materialism.

Increasingly, my piano playing and school work are so much in conflict that it's always a pleasure when the end of term draws nigh and I know I can concentrate on my piano without any distractions. It's therefore with a particularly happy heart that I troop into the assembly hall for the headmaster's end of term speech before the long summer holiday.

The hall is packed with the six hundred-odd boys and girls. We all sit on the floor looking towards the headmaster, Mr Grundy. A feeling of happiness and optimism fills the air. Even the weather is agreeable: the sun shines on a serious, hard-working school with every pressure applied to the pursuit of facts in order to ensure that the maximum numbers acquit themselves well in the School Certificate exams. Even the teachers are relaxed, and we all breathe more easily. In just another couple of days, several weeks of holiday will start.

Only one small price has to be paid. We have to listen to Mr Grundy's admonishments for whatever shortcomings he has observed during the term. His hard, spectacled face stares malevolently at us.

'Some of you have worked hard, some of you haven't.' He half shuts his eyes, menacingly. 'But there are other things apart from your learning. There's manners. *Manners.*' His glare roves slowly round his audience. 'How to behave. You want to know how to carry on when you're mixing with people who know better. You have to learn a few basic facts. What to do, what not to do.' His voice is rising.

'I saw a boy eating an orange in the street.' He displays an expression of loathing and disgust. 'What would it look like if everyone ate an orange in the street? You have to forget some of your crude northern habits. Eating fish and chips out of paper! Can you imagine everyone eating fish and chips out of paper? The disgusting smell, the mess, the paper on the floor.'

As he speaks he jams his right hand in his trouser pocket and starts groping wildly around. This habit is so well known that even before the harangue starts all 1,200-odd eyes are riveted to this spot, waiting for the performance to start. There is of course a fearful tendency to laugh, and anyone who can't suppress it sets off everyone round them. More insides of mouths are bitten raw during the headmaster's talk than at any other time of the year.

The diatribe against the uncouth manners of his poor northern pupils continues with much repetition of the same points for a long time. The longer he goes on, the less impact his words have. Suddenly he regains our attention by switching subject. 'Now I want to mention another matter. During the term, one of the boys gave a talk. A very interesting talk on Rachmaninov.' Every boy and girl nearby looks at me. I shuffle uneasily and begin to blush, fear spreading through every fibre of my body, knowing I'm not going to like what will come next. 'In the course of this talk he said, "It was wrote..." *It – was – wrote...*' He relishes repeating this example of appalling grammar, slowly and deliberately. He tries to make it sound as bad to us as it does to him.

The knowledge that every pupil in the school knows it's me as surely as if I'd been charged by name, overwhelms me with shame. I close my ears to Mr Grundy's continuing lecture on the importance of speaking grammatically at all times. The blood pounds in my head and I sit sweating, distraught, waiting for the end of my public torture.

Once the school assembly is dismissed, I harden myself as well as I'm able against the barrage of taunts and jeers from my fellow pupils. I can think of nothing clever to say or do. I walk on, red with shame and anger, out of the school into the fresh air and back to my piano.

5

Shabby Magic

As I practise the piano that evening, I imagine returning to the school as a world-famous pianist. All the public humiliation I've experienced will be transformed into hushed respect as I sit at the piano and prepare to play the *Waldstein Sonata* in the school hall. Mr Grundy will sit astounded by my playing and crushed by the beauty of the music. My curse of social inferiority will be lifted.

The differences between me and the other pupils are painfully obvious. They all have bathrooms, school blazers, coloured pencils for geography, a school cap and football boots. They have parents who take an interest in their work at school. They have parents who are respected by the teachers. But in the end, I'll gain their respect and admiration through music. I'll show them all that I have a special place in the world.

As I play my piano and dream, I'm interrupted by Dad, who is sitting reading the evening paper. 'There's an advert here for artistes to join a concert party. Why don't you try it? You've got to turn up next Wednesday evening at eight at the Mechanics' Institute. You've got to start somewhere. Those big bands in America were all started by somebody who started at the bottom.'

I'm apprehensive and not at all convinced it's what I want. Even though I have so little experience, the advert doesn't suggest it's a rung on any ladder I want to climb. Instinct tells me it's probably seedy and third-rate. In the end, ambition overcomes my scruples and persuades me that there might be something to be gained and nothing to be lost by at least turning up.

Shortly after seven-thirty I wend my way towards the town centre. I've not been inside the Mechanics' Institute but know where it is. As I enter, I feel acutely uneasy. I'm not sure what to expect and feel nervous when I see so many contenders already inside the room. There is a platform and an upright piano; a young woman is singing a popular song.

The acts which follow are all people trying to be someone else. No one is confident enough to be themselves; they all want to be Bing Crosby or George Formby. When someone signals that I'm next to go, I feel embarrassed to be so different. A serious pianist seems incongruous in such company, but I choose a popular piece I think will appeal called *The Rustle of Spring*.

My performance isn't particularly good, but immediately I come off the platform I'm approached by the organiser. He's a smallish, swaggering man with protruding features; he has light hair with curious frontal waves which stand up a good three inches from his scalp, and on his nose I notice the largest blackheads I've ever seen.

'My name's Eddy Walsh. How do you do?' He shakes hands over-emphatically. 'I like a bit of class. Give me your address and I'll be in touch with you.' I inwardly wince at his comment about class, but I'm not used to mixing with anyone from the world of entertainment and am naive enough to be impressed by his apparent experience of show business.

Among the performers I notice a few young ladies who are dressed and made up in a more alluring way than any women I've ever seen. I leave feeling a mixture of curiosity, excitement and deflation. As I walk home I know it will be difficult to talk about it to Mam and Dad. Experience has taught me that their interest always manages to reduce my own enthusiasm, often because they're interested for what I think is the wrong reason. I decide that it's best to say as little as possible.

When I arrive home I get my comment in first as I put my music back on top of the piano. 'Not much use I don't think.' Double negatives are more comfortable, and I use them at home frequently. Speaking grammatically seems pretentious.

'Why? Didn't you play?' Dad asks.

I sit at the piano without looking round, open my music and prepare to play.

''Course I did.'

I play immediately I've spoken, as a way of bringing the conversation to an abrupt end. Dad tries to interrupt but I continue to play and ignore him. He soon gives up.

* * *

42

To my surprise, one evening two weeks later, Eddy Walsh turns up at home. He seems ordinary now as he comes into the living-room. He looks and sounds like someone who has fallen under the spell of show business and is trying to impress everyone in the same way he's been impressed. He's star struck. Mam and Dad listen to him with respect. First of all he's rolled up in a car, which is causing some excitement in the street: the car is old and decrepit but it's big. They're also impressed because he talks about show business as if he knows everyone and everything.

'What I propose to do is take him and a few others to talent-spotting competitions. He's a clever boy and his playing adds a bit of class. I think we can win money. You have half and I have half, I find the venues and take him there.'

Eddy looks with satisfaction at his awestruck circle of listeners; his face is greasy and again I notice the blackheads.

'It'll be good experience,' Dad comments.

The following week it's arranged that I'll be picked up by Eddy and taken to a theatre some twenty miles away. It's my first contact with a professional venue. This is no Sunday school or village hall, it's a great big theatre, the sort I've been bewitched in. I begin to suspect that the car is an old taxi, though I know too little about cars to be sure. It's capacious and impressive and a mode of travel that is entirely novel. I've hardly ever been in a car, only at the odd funeral, and I have a rather grand feeling as I get in. Eddy sits in the front next to the driver, a young man of similar age and unprepossessing appearance. In the back are now five people including me. Two sit on drop-down seats facing the other three. I'm not introduced, but simply smile nervously at them as I sit down. It feels very luxurious as I sink into the well-worn seat. As the car moves off, I look out and see some of my street friends looking on in awe.

'You're the pianist, aren't you? Eddy told us about you.' The speaker is a middle-aged woman wedged between the two other back-seat passengers. She's wearing a mixture of second-hand furs and jewellery which even I can recognise is cheap in both character and value. Her eyelashes are enormous and unnaturally black, and her cheeks are covered in powder and rouge. Her lips glisten with red lipstick. 'Fred and me are coming to listen.' She nudges Fred, a much younger man with a dirty-looking smile. His eyes flicker from side to side. He's smoking a cigarette, held between his fingertips and thumb. 'Veronica's a singer,' she adds by way of introduction.

43

Veronica gives me a knowing look. She's small but exudes a daring and dangerous aura. Her clothes, a brilliant emerald green, are not revealing, but her face has an experienced look I recognise without understanding. That look dismisses me as an immature youth.

The passenger next to me is a bored youth of my own age. I discover that he plays the ukelele. 'Have you been before?' I ask him. His reply doesn't make clear whether he has or not, and he shows no enthusiasm for continuing the conversation.

'We've been with Eddy a few times. Haven't we, Fred?' Doris sniggers.

'You may have bloody been with him. You'll bloody go with anybody anywhere.' Fred smiles his dirty smile.

'Who the hell are you talking to?' Doris pretends to be insulted, but Fred's comment has quite obviously pleased her. She preens herself. Eddy turns round to her with a leer.

'Eh, Doris, don't start causing trouble with your husband.'

I'm shocked to discover that they're married. They show no sign of the sort of serious relationship that has always seemed a sign of marriage to me.

'I wouldn't cause trouble, Eddy, I'm a good wife.' She speaks coquettishly.

'There's only one bloody thing women are good for.'

The driver of the car speaks up for the first time. 'I'll bet you're bloody good, eh, Doris?' He is a plumpish man and he shakes with mirth at his lewd suggestion.

Veronica wriggles and sniggers in the corner and ukelele Charlie stares ahead. The conversation continues in the same vein, and I listen, hoping for more sleazy disclosures, oblivious to the time and the journey, until the car slows down and I realise we've reached the theatre.

It's known better days but it's still impressive. We enter through the stage door and my imagination is increasingly caught up in the occasion. I experience the same kind of feelings I've experienced as a member of the audience.

Rows of empty crimson seats which have held thousands of people stretch into darkness. I look at the circle, with its highly decorated lower front. The stage curtains are drawn with black drapes and in front is an orchestra pit. There are boxes on each side of the stage, and banks of coloured spotlights. Hopes, dreams, aspirations. I'm overwhelmed by the weight of memories I feel in this old theatre, even though I've never been in it before. It's intoxicating just to walk up and down the aisles; even in all its shabbiness, the magic is still palpable.

Several people are absorbed in arranging light and scenery for the evening's entertainment. One group is assembling drums, a guitar and other instruments. Someone is singing quietly through a ballad. Everyone seems intent on pursuing their own interests. We're led on to the stage by impresario Eddy, and I'm surprised by its remarkably steep slope. I wander to the footlights to enjoy the sensation of being a real professional performer and look at the rows of seats, which are barely visible.

'Try the piano.' Eddy is like an indulgent father with his children on a picnic. It's the largest grand piano I've ever seen, but it too has seen better days and the sound in no way matches its size. It's scratched and battered and the keys are yellow, but it's still the first grand piano I've ever played. I sit and play a few bars. While I'm toying with it, rather than playing it, I notice an old, distinguished-looking man in very shabby evening dress. He is stooping and slight, his thinning hair grey.

'You a pianist, eh?' He speaks with a foreign accent I've never heard before. 'I also am pianist, but I have many difficulties over the past years. I was professor in Varshava – I'm sorry, I should say in Warsaw. I was very outstanding pianist there when I was fourteen, and I was made youngest professor. Then came the war and I lost everything, my family, my home in Varshava and I have to work in factory.' He speaks quietly, slowly and carefully. No one else is listening to him. Eddy and his friends are on the other side of the stage. The lights are low so nothing is too clear, but I can see the threadbare suit well enough. His story has a fairytale quality and yet it rings true. It's a dreadful, ominous dull ring; a bell of doom, of death and ugly failure. I want to shrink away from him as if he were a ghost of the future, some portent of my own career in music, but I'm too fascinated to run, I want to stay and listen to him. The old man trembles a little as he speaks, so I stand up and offer him the piano stool. The Warsaw professor sits down and starts to play. His hands are emaciated and his playing lacks fire and power, but there is enough experience in it to confirm that what he has said about his career in Warsaw could well be true.

He begins to indicate his extensive repertoire by playing excerpts from many famous works, and all the while talks in a voice that isn't quite discernible. I'm too embarrassed to mention this and simply nod and mutter approval of everything he says without understanding much of it. There is a dream quality about the occasion: the old theatre, the vast stage, the derelict grand piano and this ancient Polish professor pathetically playing like a ghost from the past. It's poetic, but I suddenly remember that he's come here to compete against me. After he's finished playing, he turns to ask my opinion.

'I thought I would play this piece.' He begins to play the *Warsaw Concerto*. It's quiet, like his talk, as if he's too tired to make a lot of noise, although his fatigue doesn't affect the speed at which he plays. While I'm listening, Eddy sidles up with a concerned look on his face. The old man stops.

'Or I thought to play this.'

He attacks the famous Chopin polonaise. He looks like a hero as he plays with his head thrown backwards. It's the spirit of his homeland.

'That's the best, definitely, the one you're playing now.' Eddy speaks up authoritatively. His interjection is so quick that it catches me off guard.

'You think so?' The old man pauses reflectively. He's never seen Eddy before but listens to him seriously, like a child to an adult.

'Are you sure, Eddy?' I'm surprised because I think the *Warsaw Concerto* would be a bigger hit.

'Absolutely positive. I know this game. I know what people want. It's my job, isn't it?'

The old Pole looks sadder and greyer as he sits in front of the piano. He starts to play the polonaise again as if to test the idea. He seems to satisfy himself that this is the right idea. Yes, the music of his homeland. He sits even more proudly and continues to play. I notice that he is talking quietly to himself.

Eddy pulls me to one side. 'Bloody good job I did that,' he laughs. 'He would have won the competition. The *Warsaw Concerto*'s really popular.' I feel implicated in this deception, but too unsure to do anything about it. I can neither tell the professor he's being duped, nor tell Eddy he's a crook. I feel ashamed of my lack of moral courage. I keep out of the Pole's way, not looking forward to the result of the competition.

A little later Eddy leads us to a nearby sleazy café, where we have a cup of tea. There's still enough about the experience to hold my interest, but inside I feel suddenly sickened by the ugliness of the people I'm with.

When we get back to the theatre it's filling rapidly with people, and as I go backstage with Eddy there's a vibrancy in the air. The theatre seems much less down at heel now the spotlights are on. There's also a new energy in the way everyone moves. Eddy takes the three of us to meet the compere.

'This is Harry Kenyon.' Harry is unpleasant-looking, heavy-jowled, middle-aged. He has little hair on his head but large bushy eyebrows, and an unsmiling face. The professional variety man's make-up that

46

transforms him into everyone's favourite uncle behind the footlights makes a grotesque impression off-stage.

'Let me give you a bit of advice. Make it short and sweet. Some of my best winners are only on thirty seconds.'

I think it might be true but I also suspect that Harry Kenyon is a little weary of his vaudeville life, and that short performances might just mean he can get home a bit sooner.

The talent-spotting competition is just one part of a normal variety show. As we stand in the wings, the curtain goes up and the show begins. I'm surrounded by buckets, ladders and ropes, and watch the magic of real theatre unfold before my eyes. The music, the chorus girls, everything is as tatty as the grand piano – and yet it works, the magic still works.

Several people stand in the wings, but I can't help noticing two squat, ugly men in particular. Judging by their dress, they're not here to take part in the show. They're both short and heavy-set and I wonder if they might be wrestlers. If so, this is obviously their night off, as they look like two men who will soon be enjoying an evening on the town.

As I watch, the chorus girls finish their dance and file past me in the wings. They're all preoccupied and ignore me completely, so I can look without feeling or causing embarrassment. I'm surprised at the dirty-looking, wrinkled skin. They've just been dancing as if they're the most desirable twenty-year-olds. I begin to learn the illusion of theatre and how far from reality it is. Two of the chorus girls – if anything, older and more wrinkled than the rest – have stopped in front of my two wrestlers. One girl is being introduced by the other, amid leers and giggles. As if to add point and purpose to the introduction, one of the men gets hold of his new acquaintance's right breast and squeezes it in his big hand. I freeze with horror, but the chorus girl continues to smile and giggle as if enjoying the coarse gesture. It's the act of a crude, ugly man; it's everything I hate in life, and I turn away in case someone notices me looking.

My turn comes. As I stride out to the centre of the stage, I'm conscious of some difficulty in walking at the right speed. The brightness of the lights completely obscures the audience, and the buzz in my own head seems to keep out all but a fraction of the audience's applause. With a grand gesture, Harry Kenyon motions me to sit at the piano and exits the stage, leaving me alone. My brain is now whirring at some supercharged speed. It seems to leave my body, so that I become a kind of robot going through an intricate but well-rehearsed routine.

47

It's quickly over. I bow to the applause and leave the stage, still bothered by my inability to walk in a natural way. All my life I've walked without thinking, and suddenly I can't do it properly. Eventually, after many more acts, I'm once again in front of the footlights. Harry Kenyon assesses the applause for each performer as he singles them out. The old Pole stands some distance down the line, of no interest to Harry Kenyon. He is introduced like a non-starter and shuffles back into line again, head bowed to the noise of half-hearted applause. I suspect it isn't this proud old man's first humiliation.

I don't understand the sequence of events, but I can see Harry's flashing smile as he gently chides the audience, and I can hear the audience applaud, and many people moving, and then I've won something, along with several others. I find four pound notes in my hand, and it's all over.

On the way back we have an extra passenger, so Doris sits on Fred's knee. It's approaching midnight, and I'm vaguely aware that the car is moving quickly. The darkness inhibits conversation. Gradually I recognise more and more landmarks, then the final stretch of almost deserted main road. The car sweeps off Blackburn Road into Haydock Street and I follow the headlights as they illuminate the houses. Everything is unusually still.

I'm home again and Dad is waiting up for me. Because the night out has been Dad's idea, there is no annoyance about having to stay up late to lock up. As I walk in, the quiet of the sleeping house discourages any conversation. Whatever has to be done is done quickly, and we go to bed. No doubt Dad is curious about the events of the evening, but so far his knowledge only extends as far as the two pound notes I've placed on the table. This is not a time for direct questions. Whatever he discovers will be discovered gradually and imperceptibly.

I undress, thinking of the night's experiences. I lie looking out of the window again. This is my favourite view, the black silhouette of chimneys against a glittering backcloth and the beautiful, pure, unemotional light of the moon. It's quiet and peaceful, and I fall asleep thinking of the next morning's practice.

6

Bus Ride to Heaven

I listen to *Children's Hour* regularly, as it features young musicians, but I know that my own playing isn't good enough to be considered yet. The standard of playing is very high and I'm amazed when I realise that they're playing live, knowing that every little mistake will be heard by thousands of people. But I've continued to compose, and wonder if any of my compositions would be considered. I decide to send a piano piece to the BBC in Manchester in the hope that they'll include it on *Children's Hour*. There is a particular pianist who plays on the programme, and I compose it with her in mind. I call it a study and it's written in the style of Rachmaninov. In the middle of the piece is a calm section with what I think is a daring discord. The outer sections are passionate and tempestuous and, as I've called it a study, appropriately difficult.

So many programmes have come and gone since I sent my piece that I've given up hope of hearing it, but at the end of one *Children's Hour* I'm stunned to hear it announced. I've hardly time to concentrate before it's under way. I shout out to Mam and Dad but they're too busy to respond and I'm frightened to miss it myself.

She's playing it more slowly than I intended and I'm disappointed by the effect this produces. I hear the discord in the middle and in no time it's all over. I feel excited but deflated. It wasn't what I expected. None the less, *my music was played on the BBC*. I feel a sense of importance and go out into the street to see if any of my friends heard it.

Almost as soon as I'm in the street I see a postman coming towards our house, a telegram in his hand. It's for me. I open it and read the pasted strips of words. It's from the BBC. 'Your piece will be played on *Children's Hour* tonight,' it says. Some use sending that, I think. If I hadn't been listening I'd have missed it.

Next morning when I go to school, several boys run up to me.

'We heard your music on the radio.'

49

'I didn't know you're a composer.'

'Mr Skuse says he wants to see you.'

Mr Skuse is the deputy head and history teacher. He's always been unpleasant to me. I knock nervously on his study door, afraid to make a noise. No answer. I knock again, louder. 'Come in!' Mr Skuse looks unusually affable. 'We were all delighted to hear your music on the radio. Unfortunately I didn't hear it but several of the teachers did. This is very good for the school. You must be proud of yourself.'

I'm taken aback at being someone of whom the school is proud. 'I've been wondering what we can do for you. A very good friend of mine called Frank Hamer runs an orchestra for young people, and I'm sure he'd be pleased to see you. If you're interested, they rehearse on Monday evenings in this school.' He gives me a card with the address.

I make my way out of his study still reeling from Mr Skuse's sudden turnaround. But in morning assembly I hear him say, 'I want to warmly congratulate one of the boys, whose music was featured on the radio last night.' I hear no more. My heart pounds and I begin to perspire as the blood rises in my face. This time it's a moment of glory, not shame. I'm being publicly congratulated as a composer. I'm beginning to believe that I will after all enjoy a glittering career as a pianist and composer.

The following Monday I'm walking to meet the conductor of the youth orchestra. I imagine playing the Grieg Piano Concerto. I have the music but it looks very difficult in parts, and I wonder if I'll ever be able to play it.

A temporary sign on the school door confirms that I've found the rehearsal venue. More signs take me through a flagged hall and up a stone staircase. As I near the rehearsal room, feeling increasingly nervous, I can hear a violinist playing the most wonderful passage of music. It's rhythmic and powerful and I'm intrigued to know the music and performer. As I enter, I see a group of musicians surrounding the young man who is playing this music. I also see a large, white-haired man, whom I assume must be the conductor. He's going round the music stands rearranging them, but when he spots me he immediately comes over.

'Mr Skuse told me about you. I'm so glad you could come.' He shakes me warmly by the hand. 'Have you met my son before?' He nods in the direction of the young virtuoso violinist. I indicate no. 'You've probably heard him on the radio.' The penny suddenly drops and I realise who he is. The conductor is Frank Hamer, so his son must be Gerald Hamer. I've heard him play several times on the radio and I think of him as someone already accepted in that privileged world of professional musicians. Now here I am next to him, talking to his father.

'Do you mind if I just leave you for a few minutes?' Mr Hamer leaves me to continue his arrangement of the stands. I join the group round Gerald and watch and listen in awe. I've never been so close to such wonderful playing before. All the playing I've heard has been on gramophone records, and now I'm listening to the real thing.

'Gerald, play the Paganini Molto Perpetuo.' Gerald immediately starts to play. The speed of the bow is unbelievable. The piece seems to go on forever, yet Gerald shows no sign of tiring. When he finishes he looks at me, to my surprise.

'You're the one Mr Skuse mentioned, aren't you?'

I nod, eager to be in conversation but not knowing what to say. 'Are you hoping to be a pianist? I play with Joseph Brown.'

I've never heard him play but am sure he must be brilliant. Gerald looks at me in what seems a disparaging way.

'I'm playing the Sibelius with the Hallé.'

He immediately begins to play the music with such assurance that I feel desperately inadequate. How could I have imagined that I could ever be good enough? My confidence in my future as a musician starts to wilt. I'm in awe of someone who is doing something I hardly dare dream of. How can anyone have the confidence to stand in front of the Hallé and play something so difficult? I imagine for a moment playing the Grieg concerto and wonder how I could cope with all the tricky passages when everyone is watching and listening. It seems terrifying and, if I'm realistic, impossible. Gerald resumes playing but Mr Hamer interrupts and calls everyone to order.

'Come on, take your seats, we've got to get started. The piano isn't very good but there's a piano part with most of the music we play, if you'd like to try it.'

I walk over to the upright piano and pick up the music. It looks quite simple. At least I can show that I'm a good sight-reader. The piano has been specially put in because of the shortage of brass and woodwind players in so many school orchestras. I've never played with other musicians and it's thrilling. We're playing a selection of ballet music, and although at first the noise of string players badly out of tune grates on my ears, I notice it less and less as we continue. Gerald leads the orchestra, playing so strongly and assuredly that he gives everyone confidence.

Mr Hamer looks pleased with me, and when we break he comes over. 'You're hoping to go to music college, aren't you?'

'I want to very much.' I daren't tell him that I dream about it night and day and I'm terrified I won't be able to get in.

'Have you applied for entry yet?'

'Er, no.'

'Well, you should write to them. Write to the principal and they'll send you the entry forms.'

I've been dreaming of going to the Royal Manchester College of Music but have never faced the practical issue of what to do to get in. It all seems so impossibly difficult. Mr Hamer suddenly gives me both the encouragement and the information to do it. He seems to take it for granted that I can get in.

'I wonder if you'd like to come to the Open Practice next Tuesday? Gerald's playing and he tells me that there are one or two brilliant pianists playing as well.'

'Thank you. Yes, of course I'd like to come.'

'Then meet me at the bus station at six o'clock and we'll go together.'

When I walk home after the rehearsal, there is extra energy in my step. I walk past the town hall and look at the great stone Bolton lions. Everything is bathed in moonlight and I look up at the stars. It's a beautiful evening and it's been made more so by Mr Hamer. No one else in the world can feel as excited about the future as I do.

I look up again as I pass St George's Church. I don't think I've seen the stars so clearly before. They're startling, scintillating. I go past my old school, recalling the day I discovered beauty and inspiration in the classroom there.

As I enter the house, Dad is sitting reading the paper, waiting for me so he can go to bed. I know it's dangerous to try to share my experience, but I'm bursting with the feeling that my life has jumped forward and I can't contain it.

'Mr Hamer thinks I should apply to the college. His son is a wonderful player and he's playing a concerto with the Hallé.'

'It's all right for them.'

'But Dad, he thinks I can get in.'

'What if you do get in? You've still got to make a living.'

'But I could make a living as a pianist.'

'Perhaps, if you play in a dance band.'

'I'll never play in a dance band.'

'When you've got a wife and family and bills to pay, you'll be glad to do anything for money.' As I listen I feel fear, but I also feel I'll never be forced to do anything for money. The more certain Dad is that I'll have to capitulate, the more certain I am that I won't.

'Don't forget you've still got the potatoes to peel.'

I'd forgotten, and the thrill of dreaming about my future is reduced to a feeling of despondency that it's all still so far away.

As I peel the potatoes I reflect on the way events are unfolding. I feel the need to express my growing ambitions. I suddenly realise the answer lies in work. I decide to get up at the same time as Mam and Dad, who are always up at six because the shop opens at seven and Dad has to light the oven. If I get up at six, I can practise for two hours before school.

'Mam, will you wake me up at six every morning?'

'What for?'

'I want to practise before I go to school.'

'I hope Mrs Oxendale doesn't complain.'

In the event, our next door neighbour doesn't complain but Dad moans about the music I have on the radio all the time.

'It's all banging, there's no tune in that music.'

'But Dad, listen to this.' I turn up the volume of the Tchaikovsky violin concerto.

'That's not a tune, it's all screeching.'

I can't believe he can't be touched by the sound that moves me so deeply. I feel frustrated by my inability to reveal it to him.

'It's a horrible noise.'

'I think so as well.' Mam is passing through and lends Dad her support.

I listen to this inspiring music and wonder what it is that makes it so incomprehensible to them.

'Turn it off!' Dad's had enough.

'Just let me leave it on till the end of this piece.'

'It's a depressing noise. I like music with a tune in it, like *Melody in F* or Handel's *Largo*. That music's all discords.'

'It's not! It's beautiful music.'

'It might be to you, but I don't like it.' Dad's constant barrage of criticism takes the pleasure out of listening. I turn it off and go back to the piano.

I begin to dream again about a life where I'm playing wonderful piano music and my audience is listening, entranced. Uncle Harold, Mr Marsh, Dad, all seem to enjoy making me feel my dreams are unattainable. I can't do tonic sol fa, I have no influence, and if I have a family I'll give up all my ambition, become second-rate and do anything to bring in money.

No, I won't abandon my dreams. I'll prove everyone wrong.

The following Tuesday I peel the potatoes as soon as I get back from school so I can leave without any fuss.

'What's happened to you?' Dad is surprised by my eagerness to peel potatoes.

'Mr Hamer's invited me to go with him to the college to hear a concert.'

'You'd best not be late back.'

'Why can't you go to bed and let me come in on my own?'

Dad looks angry. 'Cos I can't.'

'Why can't you?'

'Never you mind.'

I'm baffled by the illogicality of his attitude but recognise I'm wasting my time arguing. I say no more and leave the house to walk to the bus station. It's still light and the sky is clear, but the brown smoke from the foundry is staining the sky. As I walk along the street I pass a few friends.

'D'you want to play football?'

'I can't, I'm going to Manchester.'

'Are you going to play some of your music at the BBC?'

'No.'

'But you did do, didn't you?'

It's not true but I don't disillusion them. I enjoy the modest deception as a taste of the life I shall have.

Mr Hamer is waiting at the bus station and smiles as he sees me. 'Come on, this number eight is just leaving for Manchester.' I follow him on to the bus and we sit down. 'I'm sure Gerald would like you to accompany him.'

'Really?' I'm taken aback because Gerald seemed so aloof and superior when I met him. The prospect of playing with him is stunning.

The bus journey is like going to heaven. I'm so excited at the prospect of seeing and entering a college where some of Britain's greatest musicians have worked. When we get to Manchester we have to get another bus to Oxford Road. I look from the bus, mesmerised by so many large shops and strange, important buildings.

'That's the university. We're getting off next stop.'

We walk down Ducie Street, towards the building which proclaims in big gold letters: Royal Manchester College of Music.

'It was founded by Sir Charles Hallé, who founded the Hallé Orchestra. He was a pianist and the first principal of the college.'

I try to concentrate on absorbing the atmosphere of this holy place. We walk up a flight of wide stairs and enter the hall through half-glazed doors with shiny brass handles. I feel overcome with emotion. On one wall are glass cases from floor to ceiling, full of antique musical instruments. The platform is at the end of the hall on the right, and on it are two beautiful black grand pianos.

Already many of the seats are taken and we make our way to the middle of the hall.

'Can you see the keyboard all right from here?'

Mr Hamer is taking a lot of trouble to ensure that I enjoy my first concert in the college. I look around, hardly daring to imagine that I might one day be a student here. I notice that the front two rows are empty and wonder why. Mr Hamer tells me, 'All the professors sit in the front two rows.' I watch intently as they file in: long-haired men with exotic-looking clothes, and dramatically beautiful women. All of them, to my unsophisticated eye, display the sensitivity that is such an essential part of being a musician.

When I look at the programme I'm astonished to see so much difficult music. Somehow I imagine there will be a big gap between students and the professional pianists I hear on record. I realise with an ominous feeling that the gap is actually between me and professional pianists. I'm obviously nowhere near as good as the students here. I sit back, both enthralled and daunted by the most spectacular piano playing I've ever heard. One student comes on with a professor I noticed sitting down earlier. They sit at the two grand pianos and only the professor has music. They begin to play the Liszt Second Piano Concerto. The student is brilliant. I've never even attempted anything so difficult. I've never had a teacher who would consider giving me such music to play, probably because they don't know it exists.

The hopelessness of my playing begins to dawn on me.

When Gerald comes on to the platform I feel proud to be associated with him. He stands confidently and begins to play the Cesar Frank sonata with Joseph Brown. As I hear it I'm overwhelmed by the power of the piano and violin, and the passion of the music. Tears come into my eyes and I try to stifle them. After the concert, we go to speak to Gerald and I look in awe at the pianists, who are now standing talking to their friends. I stare at their hands and marvel at their hidden power. Can I ever be one of them, I wonder?

None the less, as we return to the bus station I'm elated. It's my first taste of the world I'm desperate to enter. I find it difficult to talk because I want so much to stay in the world of my imagination, which has me in its grip.

'Did you enjoy that?'

'Yes.' How can I explain that it was wonderful beyond words? We sit silently on the bus on the return home.

'Thank you for taking me.' I leave Mr Hamer at the bus station and walk home.

Dad gives me a surly look. 'You're late enough.' He goes upstairs, satisfied in his resentment. I find solace in the memory of the evening and look forward to next morning's practice, when I can try again to scale the rock face of virtuosity.

Any feeling of inadequacy is soon left behind as I dream about my future as a pianist. I'm living in a dream world of infinite possibilities and no moment has arisen which signals an end to the hope.

Whenever I feel the need for space to dream of a beautiful life remote from my urban environment, I find what I want on the moors. Whenever my spirits falter I walk there, my brain teeming with music and ideas, and abandon myself to the sweeping landscape, lost in my reverie of how things will be.

I vary my route according to my mood, and one day I find myself walking towards a particular village. The final stretch of road before the village has a row of detached houses, each with its own distinctive design and all different in size. I've always looked at them and wondered what sort of fortunate people can live in such comparative elegance so near the moors. I see a young woman coming out of one of the houses, and as I draw level with the garden gate she reaches it herself. I'm surprised to recognise Elspeth Williams, one of the senior girls from my school. She recognises me too. I'm the first to speak.

'I didn't realise you lived here.'

'Yes, I was born here.'

Out of school uniform, she's more attractive than I remember. She's always top in exams and I feel slightly envious of someone with so many advantages. We walk towards the village together.

'You're going to be a professional pianist, aren't you?'

'I hope so, that's what I want.'

'I'm absolutely sure you'll be a success.'

'It's not easy.'

'Everyone says you're a great pianist as well as a composer.' I feel abashed by the compliment but it gives me confidence.

'I'm just posting some letters for Mummy and Daddy and the last post goes in half an hour.' She puts the letters in the box and hesitates before making her move back in the direction of home.

On impulse I seize my chance. 'I was just walking round Scout Lane. I don't suppose you'd like to come?' I blush, convinced I've made a fool of myself.

'Yes, I'd like to come. I've finished my homework but I'll have to go back and tell Mummy or she'll be worried.'

We retrace our steps back to her house and Elspeth insists I follow her in. Her mother greets us with smiling, questioning eyes. Mrs Williams looks older than I expected, with grey hair and gold-rimmed spectacles. She holds out her hand and I take it delicately, anxious to make a good impression. The house is clean and bright and airy and every piece of furniture looks beautifully dusted and polished.

'Would you like a cup of tea and home-made fruitcake?' Before I can answer she insists, 'It's absolutely no trouble. I was just going to make myself a cup of tea, and the cake came out of the oven only half an hour ago.'

I'm only too ready to be persuaded. I can't help but contrast the serenity and comfort of this house with life in Haydock Street. Elspeth leads me into a sitting-room where a piano, burnished and shining, stands welcoming me.

I begin to play, and the cleanliness of the ivories is immediately apparent in the touch. It's the best upright piano I've ever played. While I'm playing, Mr Williams makes an entrance. He's a kindly-looking man with thick wiry hair. He says, 'Don't let me distract you,' but I immediately stand up and shake his hand, which is firm and welcoming.

'Elspeth tells me you're the best pianist in the school.'

I don't strictly deserve the compliment but I'm certain there's no one else there who loves the piano like me, and that's a valid distinction.

Mrs Williams comes in with a tray. I've never seen such pretty, gleaming cups and saucers. Everything looks immaculate and the cake is mouth-watering. It's all such a far cry from the rough and ready world I live in.

We all sit politely with tea and cake and I look at Elspeth, so comfortably ensconced under the eyes of her adoring parents. But for the return to tell her mother, we might now be strolling out on the moors. As it is, observing the care and attention that surrounds her is already making me think of our relationship as a serious one.

'Elspeth is hoping to read medicine at university.' Parental pride oozes out of them.

'I've got to get a place at university first!' she protests.

'I'm sure you will.' Her mother radiates absolute confidence.

It becomes obvious that being a doctor or surgeon is the ultimate goal in their social world. There's something smugly superior about families who have offspring destined for the medical profession. As the Williamses discuss their many friends in that position, the sense of collective superiority becomes disconcerting. My self-esteem is built on my musical ability. My mediocre results at school wouldn't allow me to join the charmed circle of medics. I already feel a nagging unease at being excluded.

By the time tea and cake is finished, the sun is setting and it becomes obvious that it's too late to enjoy the walk I had hoped to share.

'You're very welcome to practise on our piano if you like.'

'Yes, do. The piano needs playing and if it's better than the one you have at home, you may as well.'

'Thank you.'

'Why not come on a Wednesday after school and stay for supper? We eat at about seven.'

Elspeth adds her own encouragement. 'I can do my homework in my bedroom. The piano playing won't disturb me.'

'Thank you. I will then.'

I feel very attracted to the idea, not least because in the passage of just a few hours I'm drawn towards Elspeth. She's intellectually alert and her acceptance of my musical ability neutralises any agony I might feel about her undoubted academic superiority. I'm impressed by the way her parents have taken an interest in me, and I'm sure it can only be beneficial.

Elspeth walks out of the front door with me. For the first time I notice that she's wearing a beautiful-smelling perfume. It has become a serene evening and she looks more attractive than ever.

'Would you like to come for a walk tomorrow?' My enthusiasm is uncontrollable.

'I can't tomorrow. I've got a special project at school that needs doing.' The mundane practicality of her reply deflates me. 'But I could meet you on Saturday afternoon.' My spirits are instantly restored.

'That's perfect for me.'

'And don't forget, Mummy and Daddy would really like you to come here to practise, so do come next Wednesday.'

'I'll come.'

I feel an awkwardness about parting, but after a few hesitant seconds I leave and stride out in the direction of home.

Immediately I'm on my own, my head fills with joyous music. The stirring strains of Tchaikovsky's Fifth Symphony resonate through my whole being. The future is more enticing than I could ever have imagined. As I walk along Haydock Street, I can't wait to start living in it.

7

Back Down to Earth

I become increasingly convinced that I'm not Mam and Dad's child. This conclusion has crept up on me by stealth. Nothing I have experienced suggests any possibility of my having other parents; and yet the feeling that I don't belong to them grows day by day. It gives me increasing pleasure to daydream and speculate about my imaginary origins. I lose myself in a world where intense mystery surrounds me and where it becomes unthinkable, absurd, shameful to think I could ever have considered them to be my parents. It's so puzzling. They've given me so much love as a child but now, in adolescence, their resentment and antagonism surfaces.

As my dreams of the future grow, Mam and Dad seem more and more peripheral. Their lack of interest in my world of music is motivating, their scepticism and negativism is energising. I now have another human being as close and warm as Mam once was. But where Mam is puritanical and inhibited, Elspeth is natural and open. Elspeth doesn't share my passion for music; she seems to like it in a way I find difficult to understand, but she takes for granted my obsession and my determination to become a pianist. Her own intention to be a doctor seems more in response to her parents' wishes than to any deep desire of her own. It's this uncomplicated response to other people's needs that makes her a perfect girlfriend. If I need something, it's unthinkable for her to have any reserve or objection.

It's Easter and we're walking above the village near Elspeth's home. We're holding hands as we walk. Her dark hair is loose and blown gently by the wind. Her skin, so fresh and healthy and vital, gleams in the sunshine.

We follow a path that carries us to the top of the valley. We leave the trees below us and heather covers the ground. The sound of the birds changes. I see a skylark and think of Vaughan Williams' *Lark Ascending*. I push my luck and try to intellectualise about it.

61

'There's a piece of music by Vaughan Williams, about a skylark climbing high in the sky and returning to earth. Nature seems to provide inspiration for so many artists. Maybe it represents a kind of perfection we can only aspire to.' Elspeth listens without commenting. I keep going. 'Perhaps the greatest art is nature, and all we can do is to reflect the emotion it stirs in us as best we can.' Still no comment.

As I'm talking, we reach the summit and look down into the valley, where we can distantly see and hear cars on a road. The noise of each car stops as it disappears briefly behind a complex of stone buildings.

We find a grassy hollow, secluded and private, where we can kiss and embrace. The sun shines sporadically now as clouds pass overhead. It's noticeably colder without the warmth of the sun, but we're close and comfortable enough together not to be bothered by it.

Elspeth breaks the silence. 'What can you see that tells you that light is faster than sound?' I'm so used to taking the initiative that I'm caught on the hop. What can she mean? I wrack my brains for an answer, but without success. I concede defeat, hoping the answer won't expose me as an idiot. Without indicating any superiority on her part or stupidity on mine, she says: 'Watch the cars. When they disappear behind the buildings the sound continues, and when they reappear there's a time lag before you hear them again. The light waves reach us, but the sound waves are slower.'

I recall the jealousy I felt when her best friend confided, 'Hasn't she told you she got all A's in her School Certificate?' She was the most brilliant pupil in the class. I think of my own miserable performance and justify myself: I didn't really try because I'm a musician. I could have done better if I'd wanted...

But I couldn't deny the hurt I felt.

It all served to confirm that music was my future. Although I'd done so badly in every other subject, at least in music I could demonstrate what I was capable of. Being a pianist has compensated in most people's minds for my mediocre performance in everything else. It's as if being exceptional in one thing is more than enough, and I'm excused for being so bad at so many other things.

I hardly dare believe it's possible for me to enter the Royal Manchester College of Music. Since first visiting it with Mr Hamer, I think of little else. I'm terrified that I'll be rejected when I go for an interview because my playing still falls short of the standard I believe is needed. I'm obsessed by the piano, both as performer and listener. The performances I hear create a yearning to sit and recreate the sounds that so captivate me. I imagine holding an audience in the palm of my hand as I play with unerring confidence. The names of great pianists now dead, immortalised on record, resonate powerfully in my imagination. I want to join their ranks more than anything in the world. The only hope I have is to enter the holy institution which has been home to so many great musicians.

I vacillate about what to play when I go for my interview. One day I play one piece, believing it the perfect choice; the next day I pick up another piece and change my mind. An element of panic sets in as I realise that indecision will result in nothing being well prepared. One evening I listen to a record of Schnabel playing the Beethoven *Appassionata*. The opening is so mysterious and mystical, and I'm so inspired by the music, that I decide: this is it. I'm also practising Bach's preludes and fugues, and decide on the D Major from Book I. These two pieces become the focus of frenzied practice as I prepare myself for the most important day of my life.

My piano playing is improving as a consequence of using Elspeth's piano, and her confidence in me is another powerful aid. Mr and Mrs Williams seem to take genuine pleasure in my playing. When we're together and there is a piano somewhere near, whether in a private house or a public place, Mr Williams encourages me to play like a proud father. 'He *can* play, actually.' He says it very confidently, to reassure the owner of the piano, as though bad playing could damage the piano as well as the music.

To my excitement, a letter arrives from the Royal Manchester College of Music offering me an interview with the Principal, the famous pianist R.J. Forbes. I read it again and again before it sinks in.

'Who's that letter from?' Dad asks, in a tone of voice that suggests he knows he's not going to like the answer.

'It's the college. I've got an interview.'

'You'll have to help in the bakehouse when you start.'

Yet I'm surprised a few weeks later when they give me a new brown leather music satchel. I'm moved by the gesture because it's so out of character.

When I next see Elspeth I tell her the good news. She responds immediately: 'I'll come with you.'

'Are you sure?'

'Of course I'm sure.'

I feel less sure, as I wonder what they'll think of me turning up with a girlfriend. None the less, on the day of the interview I retrace the journey I've taken once before with Mr Hamer. Knowing how to get there is a big advantage. Recognising buildings en route gives me confidence, and as we take the second bus past the university, Elspeth points out the medical school. It has already given her a place.

We enter the college through the double doors. I report my arrival to a woman who is on the lookout for interviewees. In what seems very little time she collects me and takes me into Mr Forbes' private study.

My interview with R.J. Forbes is not the ordeal I expect. He's a kindly man in a three-piece suit with a gold fob; brown, round-rimmed spectacles sit on his large nose, and his quiet dignity suggests a thoughtful, studious mind. More than anything I notice his broad, large red hands and imagine them playing the Ravel I heard on the radio. The interview is in the room just off the hall where I heard such wonderful performances. The knowledge that Sir Charles Hallé and Adolph Brodsky have taught and played here makes me feel abjectly inadequate.

I look at the beautiful brown Steinway, shining and perfect. Mr Forbes looks at me with kindly eyes. 'What are you going to play?' The presumption and near-impossibility of what I'm proposing to do weigh in on me. I pull my music out of my bag because I've suddenly lost confidence in my ability to play from memory. The keys of the piano have a quality I've never seen before: their pearly-white surfaces glisten; they demand accuracy. I sit down and play. My performance is far below what I had hoped to achieve. The strangeness of the keys and the daunting nature of the experience combine with an awareness that for me, the outcome is life or death. I can't bear to contemplate rejection, yet as I play I can't imagine any other outcome. Perspiration makes the keys slippy.

R.J. Forbes stops me. 'Don't let your hands go so floppy.' One of my teachers had tried to instil his interpretation of the Tobias Matthay method of piano playing, the main object of which – according to him – was to relax the hands at all times. In an instant, R.J. Forbes brings me to my senses. He demonstrates that a firm hand is indispensable to effective piano playing. I suddenly realise that the way he plays is the way I've wanted to play all along, and I deeply regret all the time wasted going down a road to nowhere, constantly trying to perfect a technique that fits someone's inexact idea of what someone else may have intended.

I start again and immediately my playing feels better. As I continue, my confidence grows and I begin to play to a much higher standard.

Mr Forbes has improved my playing more in that one moment than any of my previous teachers have ever managed.

In an almost casual way he indicates that I've been accepted, even before the interview has finished. I hardly dare believe it's true. I feel all the strength leave my legs as the excitement of being accepted overcomes me.

R.J. Forbes leads me out of his study across the hall to meet another professor, and I see Elspeth looking at me expectantly. My excitement is bubbling, and without a word or obvious sign I'm sure she understands that I've been successful.

On the way home we hold hands, both of us poised on the first rung of our individual ladders.

I prepare to enter the college of my dreams in a state of high enthusiasm and anticipation, but with limited technique and understanding. As knowledge of my acceptance at the college spreads, I receive a letter from a fellow Boltonian, Harry Eccles, who is an organist and composer and in his third year at the college. He invites me to his house several times during the summer of 1947. He introduces me to Stravinsky's *Symphony of Psalms* and we listen together in a state of near-religious reverence. He is constantly composing, and each time we meet shows me page after page of new composition. We go to a café one evening, and while we're there he writes a complete piano composition. I contrast his facility with my own agonisingly slow efforts.

When we talk about life in the college it becomes obvious that he admires a pianist and composer called Stephen Smith, who it seems has prodigious gifts and an utterly compelling, if controversial, personality. It's obvious that Harry regards him with greater respect than any of his teachers.

He sounds like the artist I so much want to be.

My first piano lesson at the RMCM is to be with a newly appointed piano professor from Dublin. His name is Claude Biggs and he is, I'm reliably informed, chaotically forgetful and yet has a prodigious memory. His favourite hobby is learning off by heart Bradshaw's, the bible of train timetables. If you ask him for a train from, say, Newton Abbott to Newcastle on a Sunday, he'll blink furiously behind his opaque spectacles, take a pull on his pipe and then start: 'Catch the 10.13 from Newton

Abbott, change at Birmingham New Street and catch the 1.45 to Leeds. Take the 5.15 to York, change there and catch the 7.05 to Newcastle, due in Newcastle at 10.55. Would you like to know the trains on a weekday?' This comparatively useless information gives him enormous pleasure.

I'm the first pupil Claude is given at the college. I turn up at 10.30, excited at having a professional pianist as a teacher for the first time. I'm surprised how old he looks and realise that he's at the end of his career, not the beginning.

'Play me something.'

I start to play a Beethoven sonata. After only a few bars he stops me. 'Can you play it like this?'

He starts to play it himself. It sounds remarkably similar to what I thought I'd played.

'It's important to play these opening notes very quietly.'

I know that, and I've been trying to play them as quietly as I can. I feel a sense of frustration rather than any sense of discovery.

I had hoped for some revelation which would transform my playing, but I'm to be disappointed. Claude is a kind, benevolent man with a deep love of music, but he has no secrets to confide, no master plan, no suggestions which change my limited understanding of piano technique. I'm given music to play, but in a random way which gives the lessons no coherence. Often the lesson time will be taken up by Claude playing excerpts from his own repertoire.

Yet despite him, my piano playing flourishes as never before. There are other, more ambitious pianists there, playing more difficult music than I have ever attempted, and it seems as if simply working alongside them is enough to push my playing to a higher level.

From the moment I arrive, I hear the sound of wonderful piano playing coming from all the rooms. Solo playing, piano quartets, two pianos. All the pianists I hear sound considerably more able than me. I marvel at their dexterity, but more than anything I marvel at the music they're playing. I scrimp and save and begin to buy all the great piano music I never thought I could ever play. The undeniable evidence of so many people playing it suggests that it is after all achievable. I take it back to Haydock Street piece by piece and spend my days attempting the impossible. I only have two days a week in college, when I have my piano tuition and lessons in theory; the rest of the time I work on my own. Claude's expectation of how much music I should prepare each week is not high, and I might have lost momentum but for one thing.

One day, three weeks into my first term, I notice a student more striking than any I've yet seen. He's talking to Harry Eccles. As soon as Harry notices me, he walks over and introduces me to the Stephen Smith he's told me so much about. Within minutes I'm led to a practice room.

'Play something,' says Stephen. The order implies a test and I feel my confidence shrink. I've built up an image of him as the complete virtuoso and I know I'm far from that. My hands are cold and my technique unpredictable. I know that nervousness will reduce my ability to its lowest level. I try to avoid playing.

'I've nothing prepared. I'm just working on a new piece.'

'Then play the piece you played for the entrance exam.' I'm cornered. How can I now refuse? In my present defeatist mood I know I daren't play the first movement of the Beethoven *Appassionata*: soon after the quiet opening there is a loud eruption of notes in the right hand, which are obviously and gloriously right or obviously and disastrously wrong. It's a moment of truth that either reveals a confident, brilliant pianist or cruelly exposes a lesser one. Make a mess of it and you're still an amateur. Get it right time after time and you're well on the road to being a professional. One thing I know instinctively is that getting it right demands confidence, but without the *certainty* of getting it right it's impossible to feel confident. I just know that if I attempt it now, it will be a disaster.

I decide to play some of the last movement, which has no such moment of exposure. It opens with a quiet, tranquil figure in the right hand, which demands smoothness and equality, with gentle crescendos and diminuendos. I start to play cautiously, anxious not to ruin it, but this approach in fact prejudices any chance of doing it well: what I don't know is that several notes on the piano Stephen has led me to are difficult to depress. My nervousness and the unplayable keys reduces my performance to a shambles. Both Stephen and Harry attempt to conceal their sniggering. I come to a halt and they don't encourage me to continue. I feel humiliated and exposed as a tenth-rate pianist. But the torture isn't over yet.

'Harry tells me you're a composer. Play one of your compositions.' The idea of parading one of my juvenile efforts is so unthinkable that I instantly and flatly refuse. Stephen doesn't persist but he still manages to expose me as a composer of no value.

'Perhaps you could improvise in the style of your composition?' he asks slyly. I'd never thought of it before, but it seems something any real composer should be able to do – and I can't.

My relationship with Stephen is fixed at that moment. He is the leader and I the decidedly inferior follower. He has taken my confidence away, but accepting me as an acolyte gives me some of it back. Could it be that, despite the lack of any exceptional skill in my playing or value in my composition, he senses some quality worth encouraging? With his leadership, could my failure be transformed into success?

I seem to be facing reality for the first time. I sense that acceptance of my low standing is something positive rather than negative. It dawns on me that I've been fooling myself, living in a dream world, imagining myself to be better than I am, playing to people who are easily impressed because they have little knowledge of music. For the first time I face the fact that I'm not as good as they or I thought. Meeting Stephen has brought me down to earth, but it gives me a sense of what I need to do and where I need to go. Accepting what and where I am seems to make the ground firmer beneath my feet, and I can see for the first time what is required.

It's strangely exhilarating. To accept that one is no good, but at the same time to believe that one can become very good, is empowering. In my defeat I find the key to success.

8

Pebbles on the Beach

An eerie quiet prevails in Haydock Street. It's Wakes Week, and the first time I've been left at home alone. The shop is closed, the bakehouse oven cold, and the absence of bustle and bad temper creates an uneasy serenity.

I notice how dusty and untidy the house really is. It's a warm day and the living-room is stifling. The monotonous buzz of flies is a constant background noise but I'm eager to seize this rare opportunity to get through much more work than usual. I want to fill every moment with piano playing and composition, but I'm finding it harder than I expected. I realise how much I've come to depend on interruptions and noise and clamour. I never understood before how much I've been helped by obstacles and hindrances. I've grown fond of adversity; achievements against its background are seen by others as remarkable.

I've been working for several hours, determined to persist despite tiredness and a feeling that I'm going round in circles, when I hear a knock on the door. I'm astonished to see Harry and Stephen standing there. I'm embarrassed but also hugely pleased that they've come to see me. As they stand framed in the doorway, I'm struck by how chalk-and-cheese they are. Stephen's superior status is emphasised by his more striking appearance. His long, blue-black hair and prominent eyes dominate a tanned, gypsy-like face. Harry, by contrast, has a mop of blond hair verging on white above a florid, pimply face.

They're plainly in ebullient humour and I feel awkward as I lead them through the small shop cluttered with vegetable boxes, which we step over. I hope they won't notice the large, sickly print of the Virgin Mary, which Mam insists on hanging over the piano. I reflect on those magical, unreal occasions I've read about when Chopin, Liszt and Schumann gather together to play to each other. I feel suddenly uncomfortable, as if outside the circle. I imagine they sense the honour they're paying me by calling.

69

'I've just been playing at one of the examination concerts. I was playing Opus 101,' Stephen explains. I know this is one of the last great Beethoven sonatas, but I've never heard or played it.

'Yes, it was rather good,' says Harry. 'I particularly liked the way you played the fugue.'

Harry makes no attempt to sit at the piano, but stands and taps the theme of the fugue on its wooden lid. That's all the encouragement Stephen needs to sit down and play the fugue right through. He plays with total confidence and enormous power, hitting the keys with all his considerable strength. The piano rocks as he hammers out the climax. I'm mesmerised. I've read about musicians gathering to talk and play music together and here it is, happening now, in my own living-room.

'Do you know the Chopin nocturnes in G Minor?'

I don't, but secretly resolve to get to know them as soon as I'm on my own. Once again I feel caught out. I long to be able to demonstrate my commitment, to be asked a question I can answer, but somehow I know that Stephen will deliberately not ask questions he senses I can answer.

Harry is playing a wonderful role as foil. 'Play some more Opus 101,' he suggests. Stephen again sits down at my piano, but now seems unable to concentrate for long, and in only a few moments he leaps up to interrogate me again.

'Have you ever read Kaikhosru Shapurji Sorabji?'

Yet again I have to admit my ignorance. He pulls out a book from his music case and starts to read: 'When is a concerto not a concerto? When it is struck by the crass stupid infantile moonshine of Hollywood.' Sorabji's essay continues in this vitriolic vein for some time. I cringe as I recall my numerous winning performances of the *Warsaw Concerto* at talent-spotting competitions, and imagine that Stephen is reading the essay to punish me for the bad taste and ignorance of my early years.

Despite the absorbing conversation and music, I feel the need to be hospitable and go into the kitchen to brew a pot of tea. My queries about milk and sugar intrude incongruously on a profound discussion about the influence of religion on music.

'The real break away from religion happened when the contrapuntal element in music declined,' proclaims Stephen with total assurance. 'And polyphony reached its highest level in church music when Bach wrote his *Mass in B Minor*. Would you call Mozart a secular or religious composer?'

'Surely he was one of the great contrapuntal composers?' says Harry.

I hand round two cups of weak-looking tea and go to get a cup for myself. Stephen expresses his enthusiasm as he talks by bouncing up and down on the piano stool, which he has adopted as his throne. His tea is slopping into the saucer. I watch him with a mixture of fascination and trepidation as he behaves with carefree abandon in our house. His bouncing grows in intensity until, to my horror, with one great whoop he flings the remains of his tea at the living-room ceiling. He shows no sign of remorse, but giggles with self-satisfaction.

Almost at that exact moment I hear the ping of the shop door and Mam, Dad, David and Jack troop in. I can hardly believe what's happening. It's only Wednesday and they're not due back until Saturday. The sudden gathering together of so many conflicting influences in my life plunges me into confusion. The wall I've erected between life at home and life at college is in an instant reduced to rubble. I gaze with embarrassment at my family, who look collectively pathetic and are dressed like badly tied-up parcels. My dismay is obvious in my voice as I ask, 'Why have you come home, Dad?'

'It's been raining ever since we left,' comes the simple answer. My heart goes out to them, and I picture my brothers squabbling and Dad and Mam bickering in the boarding house at the side of the gasworks. The tea is dripping gently on to the radio from the ceiling, which now has a big wet patch on it.

Stephen's giggling subsided the moment my family appeared, and I now feel an urgent need to get my friends out of the house. As quickly as I can, I make my excuses and we exit through the shop and start walking along the street. Stephen's high spirits reignite immediately and he swings round every lamp-post we pass. This is the behaviour of someone younger than my own seventeen years, let alone his twenty-one, but the more passers-by stare, the more vigorously and vocally Stephen behaves. Harry and I shuffle ineffectually by his side, associated with the eccentricity but tamely conventional.

Stephen suddenly suggests that we accompany him to a concert he's been invited to in Blackburn, his home town. I have very little money on me, certainly not enough for a railway ticket, but at the moment I can't imagine anything more enticing than going to a concert with my two college friends. 'Don't worry about money,' Stephen says, 'I've got some train tickets.' But he doesn't reduce my concern. How can he have tickets apart from his own? When we arrive at the railway station he tells me to buy a platform ticket. 'I've got a few tickets in my bag and I'll sort them out when we're on the train. My father works on the railway and he gets concessions.' With a strong sense of guilt, I hand in my platform ticket at the barrier. The ticket collector looks at me suspiciously but lets me go. When we're on the train, Stephen rummages in his pockets and produces two tickets. 'They're a bit out of date, so when you give them in at the other end, run like mad.' He laughs at my look of panic. My stomach churns at the prospect of running like a thief when we get off the train, and I find it impossible to concentrate on the conversation.

'What do you think of Paderewski's playing?' quizzes an oblivious Stephen. I can think of nothing more inspired than a distracted, 'I like it.' I haven't actually heard enough Paderewski to have an opinion, but I know the answer has to be positive. Stephen shows no interest in my response, but I know it's been the wrong one. I feel my heart sink again. Stephen pronounces: 'Paderewski is a god. His was the playing of one of the last great pianists. He behaved like a god and he played like one. He was the prime minister of his country and a social lion. He was fawned over, worshipped, idolised. He was a link between the nineteenth and twentieth centuries. He stood in the line of the great virtuoso pianists, Liszt, Thalberg and Busoni. He not only believed in himself, he was surrounded by people who believed in him. Schumann says in one of his aphorisms, "Only mix with talented people. Today, pianists look and play like bank managers."'

I now understand that in asking the question, Stephen has simply created an opening to hold forth on one of his favourite themes. Yet I feel utterly convinced by what he says.

'When we get to my house I'll play you some of Paderewski's records. He can play music slower than everyone else, yet make it sound faster and more exciting at the same time.'

I look forward to listening to this miraculous achievement.

'I particularly like the way he plays the Chopin mazurkas,' chimes in Harry. 'You know, that sort of clog dance.' He tries to convey what he means by playing an extract on an imaginary piano. Stephen nods dismissively. I only half listen, too apprehensive to join in.

The train draws into Blackburn station and my stomach begins to flutter. Afraid to appear a coward, I put on a show of bravado as we approach the ticket barrier. The instant I hand over my ticket, I run off as advised. Once I'm safely outside the station I begin to enjoy my minor moment of daring, and resolve never to be worried by such a trivial thing again.

* * *

72

Stephen's house is within walking distance of the railway station. It's in a terrace, but the quality is superior to Haydock Street. All the houses have small front gardens and are neat and clean. The paintwork looks fresh and the street is unusually quiet, in sharp contrast to my part of Bolton.

Stephen's mother greets us at the door. She's obviously very attached to her younger son and beams as soon as she sees him. She smiles fondly at Harry and me.

'You're at college with our Stephen, are you?'

'Yes, that's right.'

'Are you a pianist too?'

Harry answers, 'I play the piano but I'm really a composer.'

'Our Stephen's daft about piano playing, aren't you Stephen?'

Stephen completely ignores the question and leads us into the front room. I look around in wonder and envy. There are two pianos, a grand and an upright. Bookshelves cover one wall, crammed with books about music and art. On the other walls are framed photographs and drawings of famous pianists including Liszt, Paderewski, Rubinstein, Busoni, Thalberg, Vladimir de Pachmann and Leopold Godowsky. There is little room left over, but to me it's a musician's paradise. We sit down. Stephen begins to play his latest composition.

His teacher has been a Mrs Baumler, a German refugee whose career combines teaching and playing and who is married to a medical specialist. She also plays a prominent part in local music activities, and the concert we're about to attend is one she has organised for a world-famous violinist. She has invited Stephen as a successful past pupil, not just to the concert but to the party afterwards. She has even suggested that he might perform one of his own compositions. We gather that her party invitations are bestowed as a form of privilege; the entry qualifications are normally social rather than musical.

We all three attend the concert without seeing Mrs Baumler, but as soon as it's over, Stephen decides he ought maybe to alert her to the fact that he isn't alone as expected. Harry and I keep at a discreet distance while Stephen seeks her out to ask for two extra people to be admitted. It's a simple enough request, but the length of their conversation suggests that the answer isn't straightforward. The frequent and not at all complimentary glances which Mrs Baumler throws in our direction suggest the reason for the delay.

After a few more minutes, Stephen rejoins us.

'She wasn't keen on you coming,' he reports, somewhat superfluously. I would have been happy to call it a day there and then.

'But you persuaded her?' presses Harry.

'I told her it was the three of us or I wouldn't come. I think she's already told some people I'd be there, so she didn't have much choice.'

Judging by the look on his face, he's enjoyed getting his own way. But to me his egocentric success is acutely embarrassing. In all honesty I would have been much happier to hear that she'd refused us point blank. My upbringing has made me over-sensitive to being regarded as a poor relation. I have considerable misgivings about the forthcoming party.

Most of the party invitees are in cars, but the Baumlers are too preoccupied to think of arranging a lift for us. As we make our way to the nearest bus stop, all three of us are unusually silent. Even Stephen knows we'll soon be in an environment where we'll feel inhibited and unable to be ourselves.

It takes nearly thirty minutes to get to the house. We walk along a drive bordered by rhododendrons and laurels. It's a beautifully clear summer evening and as we walk, we instinctively slow down to enjoy its sights and smells. It's impossible, for me at any rate, not to think of the languorous quality of Delius. The music of *A Summer Evening* comes into my mind. The moment seems perfect; and after all the pretension of the concert, where people have clearly been more interested in the occasion than the playing, it's refreshing to re-establish our own love of music and its pathway to paradise. I start trying to put some of this into words, but Stephen stops me.

'You've got a special and remarkable feeling for atmosphere, but you must be careful. I think it could be a very dangerous thing.' He speaks with the wisdom of a thousand years in his voice. I listen without resentment; I actually feel gratitude for the warning.

As we approach the house, we pass a long line of expensive cars shining in the moonlight. We look at these symbols of power and affluence as if they're no more significant than pebbles on the beach. Any way of arriving other than walking through the garden of heaven seems mundane.

We push the doorbell. A maid quickly opens the door and shows us into a brightly lit entrance hall, full of large vases of exotic flowers, silver candelabras, ornate lamps and rich fabrics draped against the walls.

'Do come in!' Mr Baumler walks towards us. His welcome is too effusive. His smile, artificially large, reveals shining white teeth with a number of gold fillings.

'Ah yes, one of you must be Stephen.'

Stephen steps forward, but Mr Baumler doesn't seem over-anxious to regard us as individuals and quickly herds us into a large music-room, as ornate and opulent as the hall. A beautiful grand piano stands in one corner, on which are many photographs, all of famous musicians and all dedicated to Mrs Baumler in gushing terms. It's impossible to read these eulogies without suspecting their sincerity, and their ostentatious display seems highly revealing about Mrs Baumler.

We stand in isolation in our corner; the rest of the guests ignore us completely.

'Would you care for a drink?'

Mr Baumler asks the question with a subtle intonation suggesting that any answer but no will be unwelcome. I look around the room and see the solo violinist doing his best to enjoy the occasion. He's standing talking to a group of admirers in a tone of somewhat strained conviviality. I'm far more interested in listening to their conversation than joining in, particularly as they're discussing music. 'I'm very fond of playing unaccompanied Bach but audiences usually get a bit fidgety after the first five minutes.' He laughs heartily. 'If I play any, I always throw in something light afterwards to liven them up.'

'You must get frightfully tired sometimes?' The question is asked by a star-struck young woman.

'It depends on what I'm playing. Bach needs concentration, but in romantic music I let myself go.' He looks at the young woman, his voice insinuating other ways of letting himself go.

'Do you play the Bach chaconne very often?' asks another woman in the admiring band.

'Not very often, I usually play the Vitalli chaconne.'

'Oh, I don't know that one,' says a third woman, anxious to join in.

'It was in tonight's programme, actually.' The violinist looks at her superciliously. I realise that he is as egocentrically ruthless as Stephen. I'm fascinated by the conversation when we're suddenly interrupted by a maid carrying a silver tray covered with what I discover are canapés. Harry's choice is a rather precariously assembled puff pastry delicacy which collapses on him before it reaches his mouth. Bits fall on to the thick, moss-green carpet. Harry hastily bends down and picks them up, but having no side plate it's only a moment before he realises the only way to dispose of them is to eat them. Stephen and I are careful to avoid Harry's error and choose specimens that look flat and safe, but this minor mishap is enough to make us feel thoroughly out of place.

It isn't long before Mr Baumler, with evident pride, is suggesting that his wife and the violinist play some music. The violinist moves to pick up his violin case, while Mrs Baumler sits on the piano stool and prepares to play. She unexpectedly turns to Stephen.

'Perhaps you could turn over for me?'

She smiles, and her smile looks astonishingly like her husband's. Stephen seems perilously close to ignoring her, and I find myself saying, 'I'll turn over.' I want desperately to do something that will make me a welcome guest rather than a pariah.

Mrs Baumler is far from enthusiastic but has no alternative. I now have an opportunity to prove my worth, but despite the simplicity of the job I'm aware of the dangers.

'Don't turn here until I nod.'

With more than a hint of bad temper she points to the middle section of the piece, where the violinist plays a very long passage, almost impossible to follow. During this passage the piano makes very little contribution, but immediately after the page is turned there is a loud repeat of the opening theme by both instruments.

The performance starts, and after the triviality of the cocktails and conversation the intensity of the music in this intimate atmosphere seems to cleanse the room. As the music progresses towards the critical page, I begin to look more intently at the score. When we reach it, I look at Mrs Baumler with an unwavering gaze that would have been considered objectionable under any other circumstances. I look at her profile, anxious not to miss the tell-tale nod, and ready to explode into action. The music increases in intensity, and although the piano part is almost nonexistent it does contain an irregularly repeated octave in the left hand which increases in both sound and tempo. To my consternation, each octave is accompanied by something suspiciously like a nod. I watch with growing concern; I lean forward; the quasi-nods become more vigorous; I lean further forward and the nods become agitated – but I can't be sure. Does this mean turn, or not? I'm now as agitated as her, and put my hand at the top of the page. The nods, now almost frenzied, climax in one extra-special, angry nod. My reflexes are so keyed up that I react instantly.

I know it's wrong the moment I turn, but it's too late. In place of what I hoped would be a moment of minor glory, I feel disgraced and useless. Instead of appreciative thanks from Mrs Baumler, I get angry glances for the rest of the evening. Several more salon pieces are performed, which Mrs Baumler decides need no turner-over.

During all the performances there is a remarkable exchange of what I begin to recognise as especially dental Baumler smiles between husband

and wife. It's particularly noticeable during heroic and romantic passages, when their relationship seems to become a public display of intimacy. Mr Baumler looks at his wife with unwavering adoration. I suspect he regards the occasion as no more than an excuse to show off the talents of his brilliant wife and the affection they have for each other.

After the violinist has put down his instrument and picked up another drink, Mrs Baumler turns to her protégé.

'Will you play for us, Stephen?'

Stephen moves over to the piano, pulls a manuscript from his bag and sits down. He plays his first piano sonatina, which I've never heard before. It has the most intricate contrapuntal and yet totally satisfying opening passages. As I look at the manuscript, it's clear that the music has been wonderfully crafted. I listen with growing delight and admiration, but when the performance is over there is an uncomfortable silence. Harry and I are incredulous that our feeling isn't general. I then realise that the rest of the room will only know what they think once the violinist has expressed his opinion. But he sidesteps his responsibility adroitly. He picks up the manuscript and scrutinises it carefully. 'Wrote this a few years ago, did you? Perhaps your manuscript writing is a bit more professional now, eh?' He laughs, 'My old friend Willy Friedman showed me some of his early compositions the other day. Remarked how much less legible his later ones are. Do you know his music?' No one does.

After what seems an interminable, embarrassing period following Stephen's unacclaimed performance, we find ourselves out in the open air once more. It's no doubt as much a relief to our hosts as it is to us. We retrace our steps past the pebbles on the beach, looking up at the sky and the stars, which seem brighter than ever. Despite circumstances which on the surface might have deflated us, our spirits are surprisingly intact and growing more exuberant by the minute. Before long we're back among the terraces of houses which are more like home, and Stephen is circling lamp-posts again. Fortunately, Harry has enough money for two bus tickets, and we're just in time for the last bus to Bolton. With a feeling of heady happiness we make our way home.

9

Stephengali

Following his visit to Haydock Street, I see Stephen by chance in the college hall and am flattered that he comes over immediately to speak to me.

'Are you busy at the moment?'

I am, but I say no.

'Come with me to see the Blakes.' I'm not sure what he means but I follow obediently. We leave the college and walk a short distance to a scrubby park that contains the Whitworth Art Gallery. Two uniformed attendants sit on guard amid the familiar museum fustiness, the polished wood and gleaming brass, and look at us as if we're intruders. Standing on a pedestal is a vase with white lilies. Stephen walks over to it and ostentatiously smells the flowers. The two attendants stiffen, obviously afraid for either the flowers or the vase.

After what seems an embarrassingly long period of sniffing, Stephen moves on from the flowers to the gallery proper. It's quite clear he knows where he's heading. The focus of his attention is a small painting.

At first glance the male body that dominates the painting seems deformed in some way. Closer, I realise it's Zeus leaning over with his long arm pointing beneath him, his thumb and forefinger creating a great bolt of lightning. I read the title on the mount of the picture: *The Ancient of Days*. We both stand and gaze for a longer time than I've ever stood looking at a picture. It's a moving and memorable experience.

As we return to the college, Stephen pulls a small book from his pocket and hands it to me: Blake's *Songs of Innocence and Experience*.

'I'm setting some of the *Songs of Innocence*. I'll play them to you on your next visit home.'

I'm keen to hear Stephen's music and can hardly wait to read the poems. This is the start of my interest in William Blake, and I feel that growth of mind and spirit that follows a glimpse of heaven.

After this meeting, Stephen takes more and more interest in me and I happily allow him to appoint himself my teacher and guru. He invites me to visit him at his home, and in this way I become his pupil. I learn so much from him that I spend more and more time in his company. He conveys a powerful feeling that his relationship with me is more important than any other. He confides in me his most important secrets. One is that he has discovered the music of one of the greatest piano virtuosi of all time, Ferruccio Busoni, and speaks about it and plays it as if he has a unique relationship with the music. He becomes both a disciple and evangelist, and through him I begin to share the sense that Busoni's music is of a very special order.

On each visit Stephen reveals more and more photographs, the Dent biography, Busoni's letters to his wife, and above all else the music, which is out of print and so has to be borrowed from several lending libraries. It seems as if access to this extraordinary composer can only be through Stephen. His understanding of the music and his advocacy affect me deeply. Yet he makes no attempt to play any Busoni at any of the concerts in college, as if it's too important to risk exposing such precious sounds to an unworthy audience. All of this makes his sharing of the music with me all the more remarkable.

He seems immune to external distractions, and has discovered long ago that any relations with other people can always be manipulated to further his own career. Every moment he spends with other people has one purpose, and that is his purpose – and extraordinarily, other people, including me for the time being, are ready to accept a supporting role. He has developed the artist's focus before he has developed a career.

His overweening confidence is in marked contrast to the diffidence most students exhibit. It's as if he is aware of his mission before it has been recognised by others. This absolute certainty has given him command of all his relationships. I can see that he's been feeding his ego with exploitative master-pupil relationships over the past few years. But somehow his overwhelming confidence makes this subservient status acceptable to the sensitive and intelligent minds of his friends. In short, I realise he needs disciples and I'm content to allow myself to become one.

But I'm no mug. I'm instinctively aware of the dangers in serving someone else's ambitions, and never doubt my ability to break the bonds when it suits me. We're attracted to those who inspire our admiration because we hope that by emulating them we can in turn inspire the same devotion from others. But there is equally a great danger of simply surrendering our own individuality and our own dreams. Nowhere is this more evident than in the practice of the masterclass. How many students have emerged feeling devalued and inadequate, and how many masters have emerged feeling superior and more confident? Whose purpose does the masterclass really serve?

Stephen is the master, and from the beginning I risk being exploited and even destroyed, but I develop a split personality in order to benefit while protecting my own self-worth and ambitions. In my outer world I remain a devoted disciple, admiring, listening and observing, but in my inner world I keep intact my allegiance to my own career, secure in my ambition, and needing nothing in the way of reciprocal admiration or interest.

It gives me a growing sense of confidence to know that while my admiration is important to Stephen, I need none in return. I'm able to take advantage of his knowledge and insight. My role is to add to his sense of power and purpose, but I can learn a great deal from him. It's a delicate balance, but I'm confident I can maintain it.

Why is he so valuable to me, despite the dangers? Because up to now, all my music teachers seem to want to curb my ambitions. Stephen, by contrast, conveys a sense of limitless possibilities. His record as a student at the college has in truth been comparatively undistinguished. His larger-than-life personality is not particularly welcome in the conventional world of a music college, but his powerful sense of purpose and his unswerving confidence – indeed, arrogance – that he knows better than his teachers are the qualities which free him from the constraints of their opinions.

I soon discover that his ideas on many subjects are highly unorthodox. He will, for example, play Bach preludes at twice the normal speed, a display of audacity that turns almost every teacher against him; but all this alienation does is make him believe even more strongly in the rightness of his view. On one occasion a well-known singer is taken aback when Stephen, playing the piano accompaniment of a Hugo Wolf song, suggests a radical rewrite of the piano part. 'He thinks he knows better than Hugo Wolf!' the half-contemptuous, half-admiring singer hisses in my ear. But this kind of situation only reinforces my admiration for Stephen's courage and daring.

My visits to his house are both a privilege and a pleasure. Stephen has such certainty about everything he does. He carries a volume of Blake's poetry, which he dips into and quotes from time to time. He gives my life a feeling of importance and purpose it has never had. He is able to create an aura around his own life which makes me want to imitate everything I can.

We sit together in his music-room and he shows me his latest composition. The music is beautifully written, with faultless precision, and the style of writing is more elegant than I have ever seen. He plays a new piece of piano music.

'I've written this on three staves because the music demands it.' His hands slip under and over each other, suggesting as they strike the notes and chords some limitless expanse of cosmos. I sit, feeling privileged to hear it. When he's finished he says, 'By the way, I'm giving a piano recital in Blackburn. Would you like to come?'

'Of course.'

I write down the date and venue, and resolve to invite Elspeth so she can meet Stephen.

When I'm with Elspeth's parents, anecdotes about Stephen become a way of describing a lifestyle I want for myself. However, the consequence more often than not is ridicule.

'A lot of poppycock,' jeers Mr Williams.

Every time I mention any of Stephen's ideas to Claude Biggs, he looks at me with sceptical amusement. 'How extraordinary,' he says, meaning he thinks nothing of the idea. But I become more and more convinced that Stephen is a remarkable composer and musician, and the consequence of so much indifference from everyone else doesn't shake my confidence in my judgement.

I'm fascinated to attend Stephen's concert because I've never heard him play publicly except at the Baumler party. Elspeth readily agrees to come and I arrange to meet her at six at the bus station.

As we approach the venue, I discover that it's only a church hall. Yet I'm surprised to see many people clustering around the entrance, most of them looking very different from normal concert-goers. They stand around in groups, talking and smoking. I get the impression they're all friends and family, and I wonder whether his brother George, who I know works in a mill, has persuaded a lot of his workmates to come.

We collect the tickets Stephen has left for us and enter a hall that is quite small but has a balcony. There's a stage with a grand piano, and already the seats are filling. The hall is gloomy, apart from a spotlight shining on the piano. There is no sign of Stephen, and I assume he is keeping out of sight before the concert. I decide to sit in the balcony on the keyboard side of the piano, so I can see everything.

Just as we're making our way towards the staircase I see Mr and Mrs Baumler, who look distinctly out of place. I'm not at all sure what to do. Impulsively, I walk over to Mrs Baumler and try to introduce myself.

'I came to your house with Stephen.' She looks icily at me.

'Really? I don't remember.'

I remind her about the violinist.

'Oh yes.' She evidently has absolutely no interest in either being reminded of the occasion or of continuing any sort of conversation with me. Mr Baumler looks even more detached. I've gone too far to withdraw, so decide to persevere.

'By the way, this is my friend, Elspeth Williams.'

I turn to bring Elspeth into the conversation, believing that a medical student will improve my standing in their eyes. They barely acknowledge her and at that moment see someone else in the distance. 'Oh, do excuse us.' They rush off. Obviously I need more than a budding doctor girlfriend to impress them.

We carry on up the staircase and choose seats directly over the piano keyboard. I can see Stephen's parents and brother George, all radiating family pride and good humour. His mother is turning her head from left to right and front to back continuously. She's wearing a dress I imagine has been bought for the occasion. It has an elaborate sash which looks too big and out of character, but it's a brave attempt to play the part of a virtuoso's mother. In no time at all the hall is heaving with people, and as the starting time approaches, the hubbub drops to a murmur. I squeeze Elspeth's hand in excitement.

For the first time I have the chance to look at the programme, which is printed on one sheet of paper. I'm astounded to see a long list of popular piano pieces, without any major work. There seems to have been no attempt to bring coherence to the programme. It's obviously been picked to give the maximum number of people with limited musical knowledge the maximum pleasure. It is in fact a pot-pourri of the most vulgar kind, containing every piece one could expect in a programme shamelessly devised to suit the lowest common denominator: *The Moonlight Sonata, Clair de Lune, Invitation to the Dance*, Chopin's *Military Polonaise, Liebestraum, Song Without Words* ... and so it continues. No popular stone has been left unturned. I'm perplexed. I can't relate the Stephen I know to this programme. I say nothing of this to Elspeth, as I don't want to prejudice her against him.

Then Stephen enters and walks to the piano. His white tie and tails look strangely old-fashioned. He puts his left hand on the piano and bows very slowly, as if he's practised it many times. His long hair masks his face as he bends. We all applaud, but my own enthusiasm is inhibited by the excessive adulation of many people in the audience who almost certainly have little or no understanding of piano music.

He begins to play, and again I'm astonished – this time by the erratic rhythm and a feeling of insecurity in the playing. This is so very far from what I expected. But the audience greets each solo with rapturous applause, and as none lasts longer than a few minutes it becomes an exhausting sequence of clapping. I feel more and more uneasy about Stephen's playing, and wonder what he's thinking of it himself.

The audience insists on encores, which to me is a crushing affirmation of ignorance. I feel embarrassed for Stephen, though he displays nothing but pleasure as he takes his bows. As the audience reluctantly allows him to leave, I turn to Elspeth. She senses I'm not euphoric, but is clearly puzzled.

'I thought you were a great admirer of his.'

'I am, I am.'

'So why aren't you as enthusiastic as everyone else?'

'I don't want to spoil your pleasure, but I'm surprised and disappointed in him.'

I speak quietly, conscious that we're in danger of being overheard. One woman looks at me with fierce disapproval and I blush, suddenly aware how hot the room is.

'You'll have to go and say hello to him, you can't just leave.'

I feel embarrassed, wondering what I can say that won't be blatantly dishonest. When we reach the corridor leading to the dressing-room, it's packed with people waiting to get his autograph or congratulate him.

'Wasn't it wonderful?' someone says.

'All that playing and no sheet music.'

'His brother works in the same mill as me.'

'His mother says he's always been mad about the piano.'

Eventually we get to the door and look in. He's sitting in the centre of the dressing-room, still wearing his tails even though his brow is dripping with perspiration. His mother and brother are with him, looking on with great pride. Stephen suddenly catches my eye and brushes aside the people waiting to speak to him. He clasps my hand and shakes it warmly.

'Thank you for coming.'

'You've not met Elspeth but I think I've mentioned her to you.'

Stephen puts his arms out and embraces Elspeth as if she's an old friend.

'I do hope you enjoyed the concert.'

'I thought it was wonderful!' I groan inwardly, but to my amazement Stephen accepts the compliment as no more than his due.

'I'm very glad you came Elspeth, and I hope I'll see a lot more of you.'

'Would you sign this?' Elspeth hands him the programme. Stephen takes out his pen, sits at the table and begins to write in a style that I recognise as Busoni's. With a great flourish, he begins, 'To my dear friend Elspeth, on the occasion of my recital, with great affection.' He writes the date, with the month in Roman numerals. He then signs his name with even more flourishing strokes than usual. Elspeth, moved by this emotional outpouring, takes the programme with evident pleasure. I on the other hand am unmoved by what I regard as a display of synthetic feeling manufactured for the occasion. Stephen looks at me.

'What did you think of it?'

'It was different from what I expected.'

Fortunately for me, at that moment several new admirers burst into the room and divert his attention. My ambiguous answer remains unchallenged and unexplained. I feel proud of myself because I haven't had to lie. As it is, I've managed to answer truthfully.

Elspeth and I turn to leave the room, as Stephen and his admirers are now totally absorbed in each other. As soon as we're outside, Elspeth says, 'Did you see his dress-shirt?'

'No, what do you mean?'

'I've never seen anything so badly ironed. It was absolutely disgraceful.' As she speaks, there's a look in her face that reminds me strongly of her parents. I feel something inside shrivel at this evidence of lower-middle-class respectability. For good or ill, Elspeth is certainly the product of her environment.

We walk back to the bus station still holding hands, but my feelings have cooled somewhat and our conversation on the journey home is awkward. It's difficult to reconcile her delight in Stephen's mediocre piano playing with her fixation about the creases in his shirt.

Stephen's performance ought to have damaged my regard for him, but it was quite the reverse. I couldn't resist saying to him, when the occasion

85

seemed right, 'Your rhythm sounded very erratic sometimes.' I couldn't bring myself to say 'all the time'.

'That's very bad.'

But he says it in a way that tells me he isn't at all put out by the comment. The way he accepts my criticism while remaining untouched by it makes him seem invulnerable.

A few weeks after the Blackburn concert I bump into Stephen in college and he invites me into a practice room with a particularly serious air. He pulls a letter out of his pocket, opens it slowly and carefully for dramatic effect, and passes it to me. I read and reread it in quite genuine amazement.

> Dear Stephen,
>   Thank you very much for sending me your beautiful composition.
>   Jan Sibelius

Although I know Sibelius is alive, the greatness of his symphonic writing makes him seem as remote as Brahms and Beethoven. Stephen hasn't mentioned any intention of writing to him, but I've already seen the manuscript of the composition. Stephen's manuscripts are always elegantly written, and this particular solo piano piece is particularly beautiful to look at. It's an extraordinary compliment to receive such a reply from such a great man. Few people, myself included, would have dared even to think of writing to Sibelius, and as I look at the letter I ask myself whether that lack of boldness is a weakness that means I'll never succeed.

I'm further astonished to learn that once Stephen's teachers hear about this letter, they totally disregard the compliment it contains and instead consider Stephen to be insolent in presuming so much. The very qualities I so much admire are condemned by them as evidence of someone with an inflated opinion of himself and his limited talent. For my part, I continue to be inspired by Stephen, and in particular by his ability to rise above what he considers the limitations of his teachers. To see him so untouched by their low opinion is hugely reassuring.

He has already conditioned himself to believe that those in authority are often wrong, indeed rarely right. As evidence he cites Paderewski's rejection by the Warsaw Conservatoire when he first applied. Proof that the opinion of a body of the most distinguished professional teachers can be so wide of the mark was yet more invigorating proof that negative judgements have no power to curtail dreams and ambitions inspired by great art. What matters is the depth of feeling, the passion, the dedication, the commitment. This way of thinking provides me with an immensely solid launch pad for my career.

Stephen's massive egotistical confidence creates a protective shield, and his limitless ambitions fire my own. Every meeting with him adds to my own sense of purpose, every idea that spills out of him is greedily absorbed. His radical views are particularly attractive when they're in conflict with all the teaching staff. His isolation only increases his sense of the rightness of his views. Opposition is, to him, a sure sign that he is on the right track.

One day he comes to see me when I'm in one of the practice rooms. He sits down at the side of the piano.

'I've been inspired with an ambition that's almost terrifying.'

He hesitates, as if afraid to share the idea even with me. He asks to sit at the piano.

'Last night I decided to perform the Twelve Studies Opus 10 of Chopin.'

He plays the beginning of the First Study in C Major, toying with the piece as though toying with the idea. His conspiratorial manner and the boldness of the idea affect me powerfully. To this day I recall the room and the thrill of the idea. Up to then, every teacher I had known had delighted in discouraging ambition and creating a feeling almost of guilt at the impudence of it. Every lesson seemed calculated to prevent you from having ideas above your station. Pupils had somehow to demonstrate their worthiness for tasks, but without ever being given the responsibility of carrying them out.

In that moment with Stephen I discover the irresistible power of audacious ideas. Our fear of failure, our innate modesty, the awareness of our limitations, all conspire to hold back our heartfelt yearning to soar with the angels. An audacious idea demands a surrender of the security of mediocrity. Being close to the ground reduces the fear of falling, but we can see little. To embrace the impossible is to put our faith in a power which lies beyond us but can release us from our self-imposed limitations. To have an audacious idea is to make a bid for freedom.

10

Only Common People Have False Teeth

Gerald Hamer is undoubtedly one of the most gifted young violinists in the North. I'd already decided that before I met him, because I'd heard him playing on the radio and had often seen his name in the newspaper. But meeting him and hearing him play has increased my respect and regard for him. He combines confident virtuosity with a compelling dynamism and vigour. He's made it clear at our first meeting that he knows he's superior to me, and I can only agree. But from the moment I meet his father, it seems that his father's opinion of me is based on what he thinks I can become, not what I am. Perhaps Mr Skuse told him about my background before I attended the first rehearsal, and Mr Hamer is taking into account the difference between my beginning in music and his son's.

Now I'm at college I occasionally see Gerald, who is now markedly more friendly and conversational, possibly encouraged by his father's benevolent attitude towards me.

'My parents decided I was going to be violinist when I was still in the cradle. They shoved a violin under my chin as soon as I could walk.'

I'm surprised to detect a slight tone of resentment in his voice.

'Is your mother a musician as well?'

'She plays the piano, and she's always made sure I do my practice. She's worse than my father at nagging me. She used to come to all the lessons and play the piano for me. When I started with Henry Holst, I was still in short trousers. He was a wonderful teacher and I got on very well with him, but however well I did, my mother was never satisfied.'

I'm fascinated to learn that his exceptional playing began in this way. This is not always the outcome. Many parents with similar aspirations only succeed in disappointing themselves and frustrating their children. After several years of pushing and pleading, encouraging and bribing, they eventually surrender to the inevitable as their children mature and assert their own wishes. Their dream of having talented musicians as children is abandoned. But sometimes the mixture is right. The temperament and inclination of the child, and the temperament and ambition of the parents, form a whole that results in an exceptional talent. In Gerald's case, the consequence has been to turn him into an outstanding violinist.

Gerald is in his last year at the college when I start, just like Stephen. At first I assume they'll be close friends because they're both so talented, but when I mention Stephen, he pulls a face. 'He's the most big-headed, arrogant pianist in the place and I don't think much of him. He's always trying to push himself forward when people with more talent are too decent to say anything.'

'What do you think of his composition?' I tentatively ask.

'The ramblings of a megalomaniac, in my opinion. He's totally obsessed with Busoni. I think he's a bit unhinged.'

I'm bewildered by this destructive view of someone I've come to admire so much. Gerald goes on:

'Ever since he started, he talks to everyone as if he knows more than anyone else. I just don't think he's that good.'

I decide that it's prudent to conceal my admiration for Stephen, as I'm afraid of prejudicing my growing friendship with Gerald.

During the first few months in college I see Gerald only occasionally, as he's getting more and more professional engagements. College has become central to my life, but it's now peripheral to his. However, I'm delighted when Gerald attends an Open Practice concert at which I'm playing the Brahms First Piano Concerto, with Claude Biggs at the second piano. I find it difficult to believe that my technique has improved so much and Gerald seems reasonably impressed.

'You played that well,' he grudgingly admits. 'If you're interested, come home one evening and we can try a few pieces through.'

I suppress my elation. 'If you let me know what pieces to prepare, I'd be delighted to come whenever suits you.'

I wonder if the offer might be forgotten, but a week later Gerald says, 'How about coming up next Tuesday?'

'What music would you like to play?'

'Let's work at the Fauré A Major Sonata, the Brahms Third Sonata and the Beethoven Opus 96.'

I feel so excited at the prospect of rehearsing these great sonatas that I rush to the Henry Watson Music Library to borrow the music.

The following Tuesday afternoon I catch a tram to Tonge Moor. The avenue he lives in is lined with trees and all the houses are semi-detached. His mother opens the door before I even have a chance to knock. A round-faced woman with no warmth or smile in her welcome, she leads me into the front room where an upright piano awaits.

'We're waiting for the tuner so it's less than perfect, but I hope you can manage.' She's disconcertingly matter-of-fact and curt.

'I'll go and get Gerald.'

As I look round the room, I feel a total lack of warmth in the furniture and furnishings. Everything is 'respectable' but somehow it isn't a home. I play the piano quietly. It's better than I expect, but not wonderful. A volume of Schubert piano sonatas is on the music stand, a big pile of music on top of the piano. There's also a photograph of a young woman, and I wonder if it could be Mrs Hamer. I'm embarrassed by the thought that Mrs Hamer may be listening critically and may be able to play the piano better than me.

After a few minutes Gerald enters.

'Is the piano all right?'

'Yes it's fine.' What else can I say?

'Most pianists who try it say it's a very poor piano.'

So that's what I could have said. I'm now afraid my dishonesty will reflect badly on my musical judgement.

'Do you want to practise now?' I'm puzzled by the question because that's why I'm here.

'Yes.' I say it hesitantly, in case I've not quite understood something.

Gerald puts rosin on his bow and starts to tune his violin. The sound is powerful and thrilling. Unfortunately the piano sounds nowhere near as good. In my effort to make a sound to match the violin, I play too many wrong notes. I blush and perspire, as I imagine Gerald thinking I'm playing badly. But during a pause he says, 'You're doing very well.'

'Do you think so? I think I'm doing very badly.'

He looks seriously at me. 'If you're doing badly anytime, *never* say anything. Always keep it to yourself.'

We resume and I begin to do better. Gerald has given me enough confidence to improve. I begin to enjoy myself. After we've been playing for about an hour, Gerald suddenly stops and puts down his violin. He stretches out in an armchair and puts his feet up on another chair.

'What's the matter?'

'Nothing. My mother's just gone out.'

I'm incredulous that his mother is such a powerful influence on his

91

practising. I've never ever heard Mam and Dad suggest I should practise the piano. It's always entirely up to me. With Gerald I suddenly realise that his brilliant playing is sustained largely by his mother.

'Does she keep track of how much you practise?'

'She does. One day I did twelve hours and I thought she'd be pleased. Do you know what she said? "Yes, but you haven't done any *piano* practice, have you?"'

After an extensive break we resume playing, and I feel he's pleased at the way I intuitively follow his lead in going more quickly and slowly. As I prepare to leave he says, 'My school has asked me to give a recital and I wonder if you'd like to play for me.' In asking the question I have no doubt he realises he's giving me a chance I'm desperate for. He tells me what the programme will be and gives me the music to practise.

I leave his house in a state of exhilaration. My dreams are becoming reality. The invitation to play with Gerald gives me an enormous boost. I feel renewed energy and purpose, and I work strenuously at the piano parts.

I'm so proud to be playing with Gerald that I can't wait to tell Elspeth. She looks at me with admiration. 'I've heard about him. I'm sure Mummy and Daddy would love to come.' I can hardly contain the pride I feel at the prospect of having them in the audience. Despite my unpromising background, my piano playing seems to have bridged the gap in our respective social standings and Elspeth's parents are becoming warmer towards me.

During the summer months our walks on to the moors become a regular feature of our lives, where our growing physical intimacy can find expression. The shame attaching to forced marriage is so powerful that we do everything except that ultimate act of making love. But we don't seem to miss anything, and our relationship is deeply satisfying. Elspeth's parents are terrified that something will come between their only child and her career, and that they may be humiliated by becoming the parents of an unmarried mother. At every opportunity they recount stories of mishaps that have ruined the lives of some of their closest friends. I know these stories are being told for my edification. Their pride in Elspeth and her future career is always being expressed in order to make it clear to me, I'm sure, how much it matters to them and what any irresponsible behaviour could destroy for them. However, they prove to be of enormous value to me in many ways. One day I mention toothache.

'Your teeth need filling,' says Mrs Williams with amused condescension.

'Why not go to see our dentist?' says Elspeth.

'Yes, do go to see him,' encourages her mother. 'The last thing you want at your age is to lose your teeth.'

I feel the implied inferiority of my own family. Mam and Dad have a definite and very different view on teeth.

'You're better off as soon as you can get rid of them. We both had false teeth when we were eighteen.' Mam has always said this when I complain of toothache. Dad tells how his teeth were extracted.

'I'd go to the circus for a penny pull. They had a brass band and a fellow with pliers. When he gave the sign they played a deafening chord and he pulled the tooth out. He were clever, he whipped it out before you knew what was happening.'

Suddenly I feel ashamed of Mam and Dad's innocent simplicity. Mrs Williams makes me feel that only common people have false teeth.

I become more aware in all kinds of small ways of the difference between life in Elspeth's house and mine. A bathroom, toilet paper, shades on the lights, professional papering and painting, meals at the same time every day, regular early bedtimes for young children, attractive gardens, simnel cake at Easter, beautifully wrapped parcels and presents. The contrast between this world and Haydock Street becomes increasingly painful. I suggest earlier bedtimes for my younger brothers but Mam is annoyed.

'There's nothing wrong with them going to bed when they want.'

'But Mam, they're too tired in the morning when they go to school.'

'What does that matter?'

'It matters because they can't do their schoolwork.'

'Your Dad and me have done all right, even though we had to start work in the mill when we were eleven. I think it's a waste of time going to school. They'd sooner stay at home.'

I feel desperate to change everything but I know it's impossible to influence Mam. The increasing contact I have with Elspeth makes me more and more uneasy about so many things I have up to now taken for granted. I had never worried about table manners or bedtimes, about schoolwork or clothes. Now I begin to feel an acute sense of my family's social inferiority. My relationship with Elspeth and her parents gives me a growing sense of comfort, but it also gives me a corresponding sense of dissatisfaction at home. I find it increasingly difficult to overlook so many details I would never previously have noticed.

I long for a more civilised way of life. A world of beauty, of order, of ceremony, of consideration, of romance, of refinement, of exclusivity – a world in which people express interest and knowledge and where ambition is not feared, but welcomed. A world in which everyone is better looking, mainly because they take better care of themselves.

In my own background, relationships are so strong that they become an excuse for showing no consideration or courtesy. The closest relationships often result in a complete absence of any kind of politeness. Social niceties are considered an irrelevance. There is no need to copy the habits or manners of others; indeed, there is a defiant adherence to inherited ways, even if they're uncouth. Eating with an open mouth, slouching over the table, taking without first offering, sitting anywhere, are considered the norm. There is something about this contentment with low standards, this refusal to aspire towards anything better, which now jars. I yearn for a better world, made better not by money but by effort and consideration. My relationship with Elspeth is the start of a journey that takes me to this better world.

11

Weathering the Storm

We're walking above the village where Elspeth lives, holding hands and enjoying the caressing of fingers meshed in mutual adoration. The sound and feeling of Delius reverberates unceasingly through me. His music seems to express perfectly my ambition to be a musician and my passion for Elspeth. The yearning and beauty, the surging emotion and the purity of nature all combine as we walk together through our own paradise garden. It's a beautiful summer's day, made perfect by love.

Our destination is always a protected hollow where we can lie and embrace, hidden from the world and oblivious to everything except each other. Birds serenade us from the trees and bushes as we cling and caress without inhibition, living through feeling. It's as if we're walking into the Paradise Garden of Delius's *Village Romeo and Juliet.* Nothing can be more perfect.

We lie for a long time, only dimly aware that the sun has given way to a menacing darkness in the sky. The birds are no longer singing as the darkness intensifies, but we're still unconcerned. As we lie together I feel an enormous raindrop on my shirt sleeve, and in seconds we're under a torrential rain storm. We shelter as best we can under the nearest tree, but the rain is too heavy for anything other than a stout roof to do much good. Our summer clothing becomes sodden. We cling to each other as the lightening flashes frighteningly around us, followed by deafening volleys of thunder.

The ferocity of the storm eventually abates and the rain becomes gentle and warmer. The sky grows lighter, and as a watery sun shines through, birds begin to sing again. The cold damp of wet clothes becomes more noticeable. We decide to seek help at a nearby cottage. An amiable-looking woman comes to the door and immediately recognises our problem.

'You poor things, come in.' We follow her into the living-room and she pulls out an ironing-board.

95

'At least you can dry your clothes with an iron. Dry yourselves with these towels and I'll light a fire.' I'm touched that a complete stranger is showing us such kindness. She provides Elspeth with a dressing-gown and gives me pyjama bottoms. I stand near the fire and watch Elspeth with my shirt, ironing it more carefully than it has ever been ironed. It seems ironic that the consequence of such a violent storm is this peaceful domestic scene. The tenderness and care in Elspeth's regard for my clothes is my first experience of a domestic life of my own.

Eventually everything is dry and I dress in clothes which are now smarter than before the storm. We thank the woman profusely for her kindness and walk back to Elspeth's house. No longer insulated from an awareness of reality by our passion, it begins to dawn that Elspeth's parents will have something to say about this, especially as we've spent more time than we realised in the cottage. We walk more quickly, increasingly certain that we'll have an unpleasant reception.

By the time we get back it's dusk and lights are shining. As soon as we enter, I can see that Mr Williams is furious.

'Where on earth have you been?'

'We got caught in the storm.'

He looks at me with a sarcastic smile. 'How could you get caught in a storm that was brewing up for at least two hours? Anybody with the wit to look at the sky could see it coming.'

I can't tell him that we didn't notice because we were enraptured with each other, but his anger suggests he may have worked this out for himself.

'But Daddy, the rain came so quickly that we had to shelter under some trees. We thought it would stop in a few minutes but it didn't and we got soaked to the skin.'

Mr Williams looks at Elspeth as if she has disappointed him. Mrs Williams comes into the room carrying a tray. 'Sit down and have some tea,' she orders, to calm the situation. 'You'll be lucky you don't catch your death of cold.'

'But Mummy, we called at a cottage and the lady there was so kind. She asked us in and we dried ourselves in front of the fire. She let us use her iron and ironing-board.'

Mr Williams is in no way placated by our romantic story. He clearly remains convinced that Elspeth would have had more sense but for me.

After the tea I sit as a mere spectator, excluded from the mundane family conversation. I feel something oppressive and destructive in this obsession with order and reason, and begin to wonder if my mission of being a virtuoso pianist is under greatest threat from suburban middle-class life. This is the kind of respectability that would never allow one to be trapped by a storm. One would instead anticipate it well in time. The consequence of the rainstorm seems to me like a poetic adventure, but to the Mr Williamses of this world it's a clear demonstration of contemptible irresponsibility.

I listen to him and his wife discussing the appalling lack of social awareness in a mutual friend.

'Can you believe it, she sent the letter addressed "Mrs J. Watkins"?' There is incredulousness in her voice. 'She obviously doesn't realise that you always use the *husband's* initial. It should have been Mrs *P.* Watkins, unless of course the husband has died, then it's correct to use the woman's initial.' I wonder whether this laboured lesson in etiquette is for my benefit as a potential son-in-law. These nuances mean so much to them that I begin to wonder whether I could survive in this claustrophobic world of genteel respectability.

I decide that I can't waste any more time sitting listening to their conversation. I have a pile of manuscript papers with me and music that needs copying out, so that's what I do. As I'm obviously distancing myself from them, I sense an awkwardness in the air, but I carry on relentlessly. Somehow I imagine that my demonstration of the commitment I feel towards my career will inspire the respect in them that it would inspire in me, but it turns out to be quite the reverse.

I walk out to the front gate with Elspeth at the end of the evening. She awkwardly tells me, 'Daddy is furious with you. He said he felt like punching you.'

'Because I've been working?'

'He thought you were very rude.'

Elspeth's manner implies that she is neutral. She is noticeably distant as we say goodnight. I stride out in the direction of home. The expensive houses are soon left behind. As I near the tram terminus the countryside gives way to more housing, now closer together and smaller. As I walk further into Bolton the houses get progressively smaller and more close-packed, but also more familiar and somehow more reassuring.

On the morning of the concert with Gerald, I begin to feel the mixture of excitement and nerves that heralds every public performance. I spend the morning practising in the hope that my playing will be impeccable. According to one of the professors at college, the difference between the amateur and the professional is that the amateur practises to get it right and the professional practises never to get it wrong. I'm desperate to perform well and demonstrate to Gerald that I'm a worthy partner. We've arranged to meet at two, and as the time approaches I pack my music and my clothes and set out for the concert.

It's a school I've passed many times before. It's set back from the road, with neatly cut grass surrounding several stone buildings, all a uniform soft sand colour, with attractive leaded diamond window panes. A quality of serenity seems to emanate from the whole. I know that this is a school for the wealthy, and as I pass through the main entrance a warm feeling of privilege engulfs me. As I enter the hall, the smell of polished wood combines with the sound of violin playing. Gerald is on the platform, playing with great confidence, and nervousness suddenly saps my energy. He stops playing as I approach.

'I've been told it's a good piano.'

I sit down and try it. I'm delighted to discover that it's first class, and as we begin to practise I'm re-energised by the sound, the venue and the occasion. Several of the pupils, predominantly girls, gather admiringly round the piano as we play. The hall is a magnificent wood-panelled auditorium, and sunshine streams through the great windows and reflects on the polished wood.

From the very first notes I'm astounded by the richness and power of the sound. I've never experienced the thrill of playing chamber music before. The sound itself begins to inspire even more effort on my part. The bass of the piano is so rich and sonorous that I can feel it up and down my spine. We play through most of the programme music and we both seem to grow in confidence. After we've been playing for over an hour, the school's music teacher invites us to tea and biscuits in a room off the hall. As we settle into the room, I realise that we're in the headmaster's study. How much music is doing for my life. Before now, a visit to the headmaster's study was something to be feared. Suddenly, through music, I'm here as a privileged guest.

I look at dishes covered with ham, beef and chicken sandwiches, all garnished with fresh green leaves. Tea is poured, we take plates, we begin to eat. I've never before experienced such a special feeling of hospitality. It's not just the food, but the fact that we're being fed as musicians. Just as we're finishing the tea I hear a knock on the door, and as it slowly opens I see Elspeth's face, full of warmth and interest.

'I hope you don't mind me coming, but I thought I might be able to help in some way.'

I'm delighted to see her and proud to introduce her as my girlfriend to Gerald.

He looks at her with surprise and admiration.

'Are you coming to the concert?'

'Yes, I'm coming with Mummy and Daddy.'

She is confident without being in any way presumptuous. Her physical presence is so comforting, and I long to be alone with her.

'Do bring them to the dressing-room after the concert.'

Gerald is so much at ease with her that I feel surprisingly jealous. It's difficult to feel entirely secure, knowing how much better a musician he is than me.

'Shall we meet here about half an hour before the concert?' I ask, hoping to forestall any question about our arrangements.

'That's fine. Don't worry if you're a bit later.'

I feel relieved that Gerald is putting no complications in the way. As Elspeth and I leave, I pause to look at the poster advertising the concert and feel a frisson of excitement as I read my name.

We walk along the road at the side of the school, hand in hand. There are so many beautiful trees covering the area that they convey a sense of privacy. We stand beneath one of the trees, and Elspeth raises her mouth towards me. I gently press my lips to hers, oblivious to everything now except the warm sensuousness of her mouth. We embrace, shielding ourselves from the outside world with the power of our feelings.

Only my pre-concert nervousness can intrude into this world. I try to repress it, but in the end I have to disturb our serenity.

'I think I'd better get ready for the concert.' We walk slowly back to the hall, and as we enter Gerald is playing a beautiful piece of Kreisler. The sweet, plaintive mood of the music seems to express the happiness I feel. He stops as we approach him.

'Don't forget to bring your parents round after the concert, will you Elspeth?'

'They're both looking forward to meeting you very much.'

'I'm looking forward to meeting them.'

Elspeth gives me a discreet squeeze of the hand and whispers 'Good luck!' as she leaves. Gerald and I change into our dress clothes ready for the concert. The noise of the audience increases as the time approaches.

We walk on to the platform to applause, and see that nearly every seat is full. As I repeat the A on the piano so that Gerald can tune his violin, we exchange looks and Gerald gives me a reassuring smile, as if he's confident that everything will turn out well.

99

As soon as we begin to play, I feel a sense of exhilaration and excitement that I have never felt before.

The great violin sonata that opens the programme seems to put the seal of success on the evening. Gerald's solo pieces astound me, and my subordinate role in accompanying them gives me a sense of sharing his brilliance. After a couple of virtuoso violin encores we leave the platform to rapturous applause.

As we retire to the small changing-room, enjoying our success, I look at myself in the mirror and unnecessarily adjust my white tie yet again. My hands are damp with the exertion and heat of the evening, and I wipe them constantly on my handkerchief.

Elspeth and her parents walk in shyly, as if afraid to intrude. Gerald immediately goes over to them and introduces himself. His self-assurance increases my own sense of awkwardness, but after a few minutes talking with Gerald, they walk over to me, smiling and expressing their pride and pleasure.

'Everyone really enjoyed it. It was a good concert.' Elspeth puts her hand in mine as if to confirm her words, but by now so many people have crowded into the room that it's impossible to ignore them. What would, under other circumstances, have developed into a private, intimate, happy family meeting becomes an uncomfortable display of personal feelings, out of tune with the surroundings.

Almost as soon as our hands separate, I become aware of a newcomer who stands out from the rest of the people in the dressing-room. She is a handsome, aloof, middle-aged woman who looks down her nose as she speaks as if she is conferring some privilege on a favoured few. Her face is vital and her eyes flash with energy, but she is without warmth. She seems to sweep aside Elspeth and her parents as she addresses Gerald and me.

'My name is Mrs Gainsborough. How do you do?' She drops a gloved hand in front of us. I take hold of it first and shake it, but it remains lifeless and unresponsive.

'I wonder whether you'd be interested in spending a weekend at my house, playing at a concert I'm organising. I sing quite a lot and I'm frightfully keen on music. I'd so like you to come.' She names a date, speaking in such a commanding way that it seems impossible to say no.

'This is my address and telephone number. If you let me know the time your train arrives on the Friday afternoon, I'll have my car pick you up.' She leaves us both looking at a card which reads:

Mrs Gainsborough
Leyton Hall
Carnforth
Lancashire
Telephone: Carnforth 348

I show the card to Elspeth.

'I thought we'd arranged to be together that Saturday?' She looks at me with a wounded expression. Before I can react, Mrs Williams says, 'Now he's got upper-class admirers he won't have any time for us.'

I feel shocked at such a shallow interpretation of events.

'I didn't say I'd go,' I protest. This is true, but it's also true that I feel excited by the prospect.

Mr Williams says, 'When you're a musician, you have to work when everyone else plays.' He turns to Elspeth. 'If you have a musician as a husband, don't expect him to be at home all the time.' His real message to Elspeth is, 'I told you so.' The three of them retreat into a self-satisfied cluster, reinforcing each other and excluding me.

I put the card into my inside pocket. It seems a signal for Mr and Mrs Williams to decide to return home, and I can think of no good reason why Elspeth should stay with me.

As Gerald and I walk back home, we discuss Mrs Gainsborough's invitation.

'I didn't like her much,' says Gerald. 'She gave me the impression she thinks she's superior to everyone else.'

'What do we need to wear do you think, if we go?' I say, too wrapped up in the excitement of it all to pay much heed to Gerald's opinion.

'I'm not sure, but I'll ask my mother,' Gerald replies.

Later that evening, when I'm at home lying in my bed, looking out over the Bolton roofs and chimneypots, I think of Mrs Gainsborough and Leyton Hall. I've never imagined that the day would come when I would find myself rubbing shoulders with people I considered upper class. I begin to feel apprehensive about the social pitfalls that are all but inevitable if we spend a weekend in such company. It will be an ordeal, but an interesting one, and for that reason an experience not to be missed.

A week later we're rehearsing together and discussing the looming concert weekend. I say, 'I'm sure we'll need a dinner jacket and black tie for dinner. That's what Elspeth recommends and we could hire the whole lot from Moss Bros.'

101

'Mother said white tie and tails.'

'Are you absolutely sure?'

'Well, mother said so and she should know.'

While Gerald's mother is an educated woman with considerably more knowledge of etiquette than me, I have a disturbing feeling she's wrong on this one. But without casting aspersions on her social savoir-faire it's impossible to continue any objection. I acquiesce, but the doubts linger.

12

Unhappy Families

The late evenings have become a sort of time-oasis for me, when I have silence and a room of my own for a brief period. It's impossible to play the piano because everyone in the house is sleeping, but there are other things to do, such as composition and reading. During these precious moments the silence becomes audible, and I sometimes pause between concentrated periods of work and daydream.

My dreams vary according to my mood. Sometimes I imagine that the spirit of a composer is hovering, looking on approvingly at my devotion to music. Whenever I write a particularly satisfying passage, I wonder if I have that spirit to thank for it. At other times I do my best to summon a spirit from the past, to invoke its help, to offer myself as a medium. Sometimes I even suspect I see a hand on the piano alongside my own, but I'm never sure because my imagination and my tiredness combine to make every experience dream-like. Sometimes when I'm daydreaming I hear music and am desperate to write it down quickly, but the sounds often lose their magic once on paper.

During one of my waking reveries I'm startled by a quiet knock on the front door. I walk to the door and nervously ask who it is, my heart beating rapidly.

'It's Stephen.'

He stands there with two suitcases. I can see that they're heavy.

'I'm on my way to Manchester to sell some of my books. I must raise some money.' The conspiratorial tone is back.

'But it's so late. You can't get there now. In any case, there's no point, the shops are all shut.'

It isn't only the time of night; my instinct instantly tells me that selling books is a way of exchanging treasured possessions for very little money. But I also sense that any such comments will indicate only that

I'm unworthy to be his friend. He's on the doorstep because I've been chosen to help carry out his plan.

We walk through the shop into the living-room, where the patch on the ceiling still shows plainly.

Stephen puts down his cases and sits in the armchair by the fireplace. The fire is still burning, and the effect of so much exertion followed by entering a warm room soon makes him perspire. He begins to dab his forehead and face with a very large navy handkerchief.

'Why do you need money so quickly?' I'm puzzled. Up to now I've thought of Stephen as having whatever he needs for books and music, certainly considerably more than I'm able to afford.

'It's a long story.' He pauses and looks enigmatic. He seems to be deliberating whether I can be trusted with the truth. Eventually:

'I wrote to Busoni's widow a year ago.' He pauses again, as if he's having further doubts about going on. He pulls out of his pocket a letter, takes the letter out of its envelope and reads it silently, carefully concealing the contents from me. He starts to read aloud, quietly and slowly.

'"My dear young friend Stephen..."' He stops, like an actor who has forgotten his lines, and shakes his head. 'I can't continue, I can't read it to you.'

He puts the letter back in his jacket and sits silently. I don't rise to the bait by pressing him for more of the secret letter.

'I thought I could fill in some of the silence his death must have created by playing the piano for her.'

Even by his standards the idea is breathtakingly audacious. Busoni has been dead for 25 years, so it's not a recent vacuum; but to suggest filling it himself is way beyond anything I would have dared think, let alone do. To me, the great figures of music are untouchable; mythical beings created by biography, anecdote, letters, and music. Knowing that Busoni's widow had lived her life with a genius, I wonder how Stephen can even suggest stepping into his shoes. However good his playing, it can't be compared with one of the legendary pianists of all time, who held audiences spellbound throughout his career, from wunderkind to international virtuoso. Busoni judged himself by Olympian standards. In a letter to his wife he wrote that he played the opening of the *Waldstein Sonata* the way he wanted to for the first time in his life after twenty years as a professional pianist. What an extraordinary performance it must have been, a holy performance, the performance of a god among pianists; and yet Stephen clearly has no difficulty putting himself into this category.

104

I'm unconcerned by Stephen's refusal to read any more of his letter because there is a predictability about it. I know his love of the melodramatic, and whenever anyone behaves in a predictable way it gives me a feeling of quiet satisfaction. I may be a spectator, but anticipating his enigmatic behaviour gives me a sense of control.

'His widow is living in Sweden and I want to go to see her before she dies.'

As he speaks I'm imagining the reaction of Stephen's parents when he explains he wants to sell his entire library of beautiful books; the books they have lovingly provided, even though they can hardly afford them. All to be thrown away so he can make a trip to Sweden.

Even though I hate the idea of his doing it, I can't be critical without implying that the visit isn't important.

'I'll come with you to the bookshop tomorrow morning,' I say, although I don't fancy the prospect.

'Thanks.' He speaks as if this is the least he expects.

There seems little else to do or say until morning, and even Stephen senses it's late. The staircase to the bedrooms is between the shop and the living-room. It's steep and narrow, with wooden treads and no carpet, so footsteps are always noisy. The doors to the two bedrooms on either side of the landing at the top of the stairs are always open: Mam and Dad in one, me and my two brothers in the other. The noise sounds deafening in the stillness of the night as we climb the stairs. I creep into the bedroom, doing my best to encourage Stephen to take the hint and keep quiet. Once we get into bed Stephen seems to adapt to the circumstances more easily than me and is asleep almost instantaneously.

The following morning, before either of my brothers is awake, we get up and dress. Mam and Dad both look surprised and resentful when they see Stephen come downstairs. I know that as soon as I'm on my own again I'll have to withstand a lot of moaning, which they're too inhibited to come out with in front of Stephen.

He's never stayed before and they've only seen him on the occasion of their early return from holiday, but they know he's a powerful influence on my thinking and are used to hearing me talk about him. Because of my strongly coloured descriptions of his behaviour, they have formed a view that he is eccentric. This view seems to elevate him above me. I desperately want them to regard me in the same way, yet when I behave like him it means nothing to them. Their ordinariness makes me ordinary.

I can only succeed in making Stephen, not me, special and different in their eyes. And it isn't even Stephen they see, but my description of him. Bourgeois parents of other friends are disdainful of Stephen's views and behaviour when they hear about him. Because I find qualities in him that I admire so much, I have difficulty accepting that other people can't see him in the same light. I naively believe that by imitating someone who inspires me, I'll have the same effect on other people.

As soon as he enters the living-room he sits at the table, confident in his mission and oblivious to the stir his sudden arrival is causing. He completely disregards Mam, whose instinctive hospitality dictates that he must be given a proper breakfast despite her having so much work to do. Stephen accepts this as if by right and is utterly engrossed in conversation with me, oblivious to everything else.

'How would you define music in the widest possible sense?' He asks the question as a fried egg is put in front of him. He doesn't look up as he picks up his knife and fork and begins to eat. I feel awkward about responding to his question, but my reputation as a dedicated musician is under his relentless gaze.

I eventually come up with an answer. 'I'd say it was the organised relationship of different timbres to create sensation in the listener.'

'That would mean that the beat of a single drum is music.' Stephen is eating the egg so fastidiously that he's dangerously close to conveying distaste for it.

'Yes, but the simplicity of music in its restricted range of sound creates a restricted range of emotion in the listener.'

Mam places an egg in front of me without saying anything.

Stephen continues poking at his food. 'It can't be assumed that the degree of complexity in music is directly related to the range of emotion it expresses.'

'I agree. I think complex modern music suffers from a restricted range of emotion, while a string quartet can express every emotion there is.'

I'm so intent on thinking and talking that I've neglected to start eating my egg. Suddenly Mam expresses all the pent-up fury she feels at being landed with an uninvited visitor.

'I might just as well not bother for all the appreciation I get!'

It isn't his presence that annoys her, it's the conversation, which is incomprehensible and excludes her. To her, it's posh talk and she hates it.

'We don't all want to listen to your kind of music and pretend to be better than everyone else. You both think you're so clever.' She isn't standing still as she speaks, but constantly moving back and forth through the living-room between bakehouse and shop. She looks hot and flustered. She never discusses anything. She erupts like a volcano when she can't contain her feelings any longer, and, having spoken, goes on her way.

Life is a serious, hard-working routine for Mam and Dad. They work long, stressful hours to pay their way and it grates on them that I do nothing except talk rubbish in front of them. It's the kind of conversation they associate with educated people who are well off, and we're not well off. Mam speaks angrily as she passes through again.

'Wait till you have to do some real work!' She now turns her anger on Dad. 'Make sure those pies are ready at dinner time. I don't want another day like yesterday. I didn't know where to put myself.'

The shop bell is pinging with increasing frequency and Mam is rushing faster and faster. I can hear Dad constantly fussing over the oven, stuffing more coke in and banging the oven doors as he looks anxiously to see how the bread is baking. For Mam and Dad, work is not something they do for pleasure. How can they understand that musicians are doing something they'd do for nothing if they could afford to? It's almost impossible for them to accept that someone can be working if they're enjoying themselves.

'Do you call that work?' Is the usual sarcastic comment. Or: 'Wait till you have to do some real work.'

The bitterness is always surfacing. One of hardest things to accept is Mam and Dad's corrosive resentment. Their life is a struggle and they take no pleasure in the thought that my life could be easier or better. They want me to suffer with them. They want my life to be as hard as theirs. My heartfelt ambitions are so joyous, the life I want to live so exciting, but the greater my happiness, the greater the animosity they feel towards me. We finish eating breakfast with threatening storm clouds around us, and even Stephen begins to sense them. As soon as we're able, we pick up Stephen's suitcases and make our getaway, passing a queue of customers waiting to be served.

Once outside and away from that claustrophobic room, our spirits begin to lift. My delight in being with Stephen, and my wish to be his helper, lead me to insist on picking up the heavier of the two suitcases, though I'm by no means as fit as Stephen. I change hands frequently as the load of books seems to get heavier and heavier. By the time we arrive at the bus station, both arms are at breaking point and the constant banging of the suitcase against my legs has rubbed the skin sore. Stephen has had an easier time of it with his lighter suitcase, but I note that he's made no offer to swap loads.

'Do you know anything about childbirth?' He makes no attempt to speak quietly, and other people waiting for the bus look round. He knows quite well that I'm unlikely to have any particular knowledge of or interest in childbirth. The memory comes back to me of being six and standing shivering in the cold backyard of Western Street with Dad while the midwife was with Mam. In a large family like Mam's, having babies is a secret concealed from children. It's probable that most people in the bus queue feel the same. Stephen continues with his blow-by-blow account of the birth process as we board the bus and climb to the top deck. He's loud enough to guarantee that half the bus hears everything he says. He is, I suspect, revelling in the knowledge that he can embarrass and annoy so many people at one go. I conceal my own embarrassment as much as I can, while he explains that everyone should know about childbirth in case of an emergency. His knowledge has been hastily gleaned from a textbook he's come across, and idle curiosity has been sublimated into evangelical zeal. He now sees it as his duty to help preserve the human race. I shudder at the thought of Stephen attempting to put any of his sketchy knowledge to the test.

When the conductor comes for the money, Stephen is too busy talking about the placenta to notice him and I pay for the tickets, handing over money I can't afford without a thought.

Once the bus arrives in Manchester it's another long walk to Moseley Street and my arms become yet further overstretched. It's only the thought of the imminent sale of the books that gives me any hope now. We enter the bookshop we both know so well, and where Stephen has bought many of the books we're carrying.

I recognise the normally effusively pleasant bookshop assistant, and see him quickly change character when he realises the purpose of the visit. He looks at the books with disdain.

'I'm afraid I can't give you much for this lot.'

Stephen seems untouched and unmoved by this affront and accepts without comment the three pounds he is offered for his beautiful collection of books. There is no obvious resentment or concern. It's as if he accepts that in the materialistic world, people do things which are right by their standards, and if he steps into this world he accepts the consequences. My thoughts are very different. I hate the sneering assistant. I want revenge for what I think is the exploitation of innocence. I can't forgive or forget such an experience easily.

Money in pocket, Stephen decides that we need to go back to his home to work on a particular project that is important to him. He doesn't make clear what he wants me to do, but my relationship with him is still such that it's impossible for me to question what he says without seeming to attack him. On the long bus ride to Blackburn the conversation is surprisingly mundane, in great contrast to our earlier journey. I begin to wonder if the disposal of his books has been a more salutary experience than I realised. As we walk from the bus station, I realise that the route is an unusual one.

'Why are we going this way?'

'Don't worry. I have somewhere to call.' He says nothing more.

We arrive at a street some distance from his home and I accompany Stephen to the door of a terrace house. He knocks and the door is opened by a pleasant, smiling woman. 'Come in, Stephen.' We follow her into the living-room, where I see an equally pleasant man and a boy of eight or so. They've obviously been preparing for some kind of outing. 'My friend called and there's some work we have to do.' Stephen lies with not a trace of apology.

'Oh. Can't you come then?' The woman speaks gently, no hint of criticism in her voice.

'Never mind, Stephen, it can't be helped.' The man speaks with good-natured disappointment. They're all obviously putting on a brave face. They've been preparing a picnic, and are sufficiently under Stephen's spell to feel it a real pleasure that he should be going with them. The boy suddenly realises that Stephen's arrival is not the beginning of his long-awaited treat but a disappointment, and he starts to cry. His parents try to comfort him and make the best of it, their touching simplicity making it all so much worse. Stephen stands and watches without a flicker of emotion.

As we leave I'm appalled at the unhappiness so casually and unnecessarily created, but Stephen is already turning his mind to the project he has in mind for our day's work. He makes no further reference to the consequence of his change of plans.

The work, I soon discover, is copying some out-of-print music of Busoni that Stephen has borrowed from Chester's Music Library. It's not work I enjoy doing, but I apply myself to it on Stephen's behalf. Each few minutes of music take hours to copy, and after an afternoon and evening's work I've managed to copy only half a movement of a work for piano and orchestra.

I've been so engrossed that I suddenly realise that my last bus will soon be going. Any regard for practicalities is unthinkable in Stephen's company, so I keep copying. By the time Stephen and I run to the bus station, I'm aware that the departure time of the last bus has already passed but I somehow imagine that the bus station will throw up a miracle. It doesn't: it looks deserted. I look around with a feeling of helplessness, gazing up at the night sky as if looking for inspiration.

'What shall I do?'

'That's simple, you can stay at our house.' We walk back and enter the living-room.

'Isn't it time he was going home?' Stephen's father, unaware that we've just tried that, sounds a little tetchy.

'He's missed his last bus.' Stephen sounds unconcerned.

'He's not the only one. Your mother's sick of it, and I'm not putting up with it!' His father's voice rises throughout the sentence in a crescendo of anger. I'm embarrassed by the sudden eruption of bad feeling that my return has caused, and try to excuse myself.

'I didn't notice the time.'

'That's not our fault. You can't stay here.' The anger is unabated. I'm plaintive and adopt an apologetic tone of voice.

'What can I do?'

'You can get a taxi.'

I'm stunned. I can't believe anyone can make such an outrageous suggestion to me. Hiring a taxi is utterly remote from my world, and the expense is out of the question.

'If anyone goes, I'll go,' retorts Stephen.

'Oh, don't let's have all this upset. It's no trouble to me.' Stephen's mother appears from nowhere and quickly tries to pour oil on troubled waters. I sense that I'm slipping from centre stage as Stephen and his parents take up their battle positions.

'I've told your mother, I've had enough of it and I'm having no more.'

'Let me make a bed up for him, it's nothing.' Stephen's mother looks pale and troubled. The rings under her eyes seem to darken.

'He's not sleeping here, and that's final.'

Stephen, in an almost comic way, makes as if to strike his father, whose heart I have heard is in poor shape. However, it's almost as if the mock blow has had the effect of propelling Stephen in the opposite direction, and with a dark and angry look he leaves the house, leaving me with his parents. Stephen's mother turns imploringly to me.

'Please follow him, make sure he doesn't do anything silly.'

I'm only too glad to have an excuse to leave.

110

It's a clear, cool summer evening and I hasten to catch up with Stephen, who is striding out in what I know is the direction of the moors. I have no doubt that for the time being, conversation is out of the question. Silently we walk on for a mile or two into the countryside.

Stephen suddenly breaks the silence with a quotation. 'No earthly parents I confess: I am doing my Father's business.'

'Which poet is that?' I ask. It's Blake and perhaps I should know or guess, but I don't. After a short silence Stephen says, 'There's a piece by James Joyce about a man and a woman enjoying each other's company, but in silence. The woman speaks and the man complains about the ugliness of noise.'

So he's telling me to shut up. Are all artists meant to be so cruel, I wonder?

'Are you going back home tonight?' I ask the question but somehow know what the answer will be.

'You can if you like. I'm not.'

Well, that's that. There seems nothing further to say, and all I can do is leave the next step to Stephen. It's in this uncomfortable state of mind that we continue walking for over an hour in silence.

It's now past midnight. We're still walking away from Stephen's home, and I'm becoming increasingly concerned about where we're going. It had been a pleasantly warm summer's day and I had dressed accordingly, though I notice that Stephen is rather better equipped for the cool night air. I turn up my collar and draw my jacket into me with both hands in the pockets. There seems no purpose in the direction we're walking. So far as Stephen is concerned, the momentum of the intense emotional recoil that propelled him out of the door is now pushing him as far away from home as possible.

Perhaps because I'm his audience, Stephen is out to prove a point and thus stubbornly reluctant to stop; but the need for sleep grows and compromise is inevitable at some point. It's impossible for me to forget that my and Gerald's Leyton Hall engagement is not many hours away, and my concern is intensified by an awareness of the need to sleep if I'm to acquit myself at all well.

Stephen at last breaks the silence again.

'We ought to be able to survive outside for one night. We should have some knowledge of gypsy life.'

It strikes me that this idea doesn't help us a lot, as we have only a romantic view of gypsies and certainly know none of their skills that might help us enjoy a night in the open air.

I say what has now become obvious.

'We'll need more than the clothes we're wearing to keep us warm.' The temperature is dropping by the minute, and a warm day is rapidly giving way to a very cold night.

'What about some newspapers?' Stephen asks.

'If we can't keep warm walking, I think we'd have a hard job sleeping with newspapers.' I'm beginning to feel irritable, but I'm surprised to discover that talking makes the cold more bearable. We're now in open countryside, and as the skies are clear of cloud it seems unbelievably light.

For anyone who takes the bright lights of town life for granted, the night seems a simple matter of complete blackness. This is the first time I've been away from urban illumination long enough to realise how remarkably clear and beautiful the night can be. The peace is softly punctuated by the hooting of owls and the tiny black shapes of bats flitting jaggedly across the sky. We pause on the narrow bridge over a small river to listen to the sound of gurgling water and to look at the patterns the current makes.

It's still cold, but I sense Stephen's attitude is becoming warmer and more friendly – enough to make the experience enjoyable instead of frustrating. I'm encouraged to express a thought I've often had.

'Do you ever think how this unending flow of water defies the imagination? It pushes your mind beyond its limits. If you had to supply it by thinking of water draining away from the hills and gathering into a stream, then a river, it would dry up on you a thousand times.'

Stephen says nothing. His silence is an answer. Again he is expressing his disapproval; I feel that my simple thought has been resented because it's striking out on a new path and is somehow in conflict with Stephen's state of mind. After a long pause he speaks.

'I think all aspirations, particularly in music, need the ruthless force of water. Water can force its way through solid stone and so whatever technical limitations you have can be overcome by the same relentless force.'

Stephen continues over the small bridge as he speaks, and I follow. My tiredness suddenly makes me resent Stephen's self-centeredness and I'm pricked into expressing it.

'Look, I've got to be back for a concert this weekend and I must get some sleep tonight.' Maybe I should have said this earlier, because Stephen responds with surprising initiative and consideration.

'We'll make our way to a small station I know. Perhaps we can sleep somewhere there.'

We walk on for another half hour or so, until we get to the station Stephen has in mind. It's deserted. We prowl around and find to our relief that the ladies' room is open. We decide very quickly that this is the best place we're likely to find to spend the night. After hours of anxiety and cold, this sudden successful discovery gives me a feeling of euphoric satisfaction.

'This is better than any gypsy's trick. We've got all mod cons here.' I give full credit to Stephen for finding this El Dorado.

'It's a wonder this place isn't full every night,' Stephen laughs.

Though unheated, the ladies' room seems so warm after the chill night air that I'm overcome with a temporary feeling of luxury. The only possible beds are hard wooden forms, so we select one each and lie down. But after half an hour I begin to shiver again. I try taking off my jacket and covering myself with it, but it's no better.

Eventually, tiredness overcomes the cold and discomfort, and I sleep fitfully, dreaming wildly and noticing with annoyance that Stephen is sleeping soundly. I begin to think of my concert, and feel furious with myself for not organising my life better. I begin to imagine what would have happened if Stephen had had a concert: he would make sure everyone was aware of its importance and had a part to play in ensuring its success. The more I think about it, the more I picture Stephen in the secure cocoon of his home life, pampered by his mother and careful to spend a comfortable and relaxed evening in preparation for his concert. But perhaps such uncharitable thoughts are a result of a bad night's sleep and a wooden form as a bed.

With huge relief I eventually detect the first light of dawn. The long vigil is over and another day is starting. I sit up and begin to stretch my cold, stiff limbs. Stephen looks across and smiles as if he's enjoyed a good night's sleep – which he probably has. In no time we're on our way again, this time back in the direction of Stephen's home. Minus the meanderings of last night, it's a surprisingly short walk. Stephen must have known this, but I suppress the thought without too much difficulty as it's a lovely morning, still fresh and cold but with a bright early sun to cheer us. A clock tower tells us it's just after five. The door of Stephen's house has been left open for us, and we slip noiselessly in. Stephen opens the bread tin and pulls out a brown loaf. He hacks off a piece or two as if for the first time in his life, and, after putting on butter and marmalade, gives me a piece. It tastes delicious, but all the while I'm listening apprehensively in case the sleeping parents descend and the drama of the previous night is revived. Stephen seems light-hearted and unconcerned. After eating faster than I really want to, I bid him farewell. I need to get home, but it's also a relief to leave the house before his mother and father appear, no matter how good a mood they might be in.

I wait at the bus stop with the early morning workers. The knowledge of how I've got through the night gives me a feeling of deep satisfaction. It was a trivial experience I know, yet it took me beyond the reach of the mundane lives led by my family and, for all I know, the people standing next to me now. I look forward to the Leyton Hall weekend, which I hope will take me even further from what I know as home.

13

Leyton Hall

I'm surprised to see that it isn't a chauffeur-driven limousine waiting outside the railway station. My impression of Mrs Gainsborough was of someone who would do everything in grand style, and I imagined something like an ancient Bentley waiting for us. Instead, it's a rather scruffy black taxi with a driver in his shirt-sleeves smoking a cigarette. As we're the only two passengers who emerge from the station, he has no difficulty identifying us. He gets out and opens the boot so we can put our cases in, but Gerald insists on clinging to his violin, stowing it between us in the back of the car. We sink back into the well-worn seats.

'Going to Leyton Hall, eh?' The taxi driver isn't remotely respectful. 'They're all toffs there, not like you and me.'

What he says is true, yet I resent it. I say nothing in reply. Gerald shows no sign that he feels bothered. I had hoped we'd be taken for musicians, a status that to me transcends social class, but to the driver of the taxi it's 'them and us' and he has no doubt which side of the fence we're on. He continues to talk, in no way discouraged by our silence.

Usually, conversation makes journeys shorter, but in this case it has the opposite effect. Every time he speaks, he takes his foot off the accelerator and slows down, and our silence only seems to spur him on to disclose more and more information of less and less interest. At long last the lanes become more private. As I sense that the end of the journey is imminent, I'm gripped with renewed force by feelings of nervousness and excitement.

'This is it,' the driver announces as he turns through an enormous gateway. Two large ornamental stone pillars topped by large urns support a pair of beautiful wrought iron gates. A pair of gatehouses stand at either side. The drive winds gently downhill through an avenue of large trees, and our view is obstructed by dense foliage until suddenly, rounding a corner, Leyton Hall can be seen, still at some distance, standing solitary and magnificent. No other building is visible in any direction, and behind it are woods and hills for as far as the eye can see.

When we get out of the taxi, my shoes crunch on the gravel drive in front of the hall. I look at the façade of the house, which has many gleaming, small-paned windows, castellated towers at each end, and an imposing central doorway. As I walk through the porch and enter the hall, I'm struck instantly by a strong feeling that I'm looking at something authentic. There's a quality I love in the flagged floor, the oak furniture, the walking sticks and canvas chairs stacked ready for the outdoors, the panelling, the antlers mounted on the walls, and a thousand other details I can't yet take in.

Because it's outside my experience I can't articulate what it is I find so compelling, but it's something I later realise can never be contrived. It's the quality a house acquires when allowed to mature with dignity over a long period of time; when things in the house are old because they've been there since they were new and have grown old with the house. Nothing has suffered the indignity of a sale room or an antique shop. I gaze round in awe at the hall, at the wrought iron balustrade and the white stone staircase curving round and on up to a landing. Oil paintings hang on every available surface, while oak-panelled doors, fine carpets and a multitude of ornaments all add to the visual impact.

As I look at the scene, I breathe in the atmosphere of a country house which up to then I have only read about in fiction or seen in films, and I relish the thought that I'm here as a guest. At eighteen I'm experiencing something that would have been unimaginable only a couple of years earlier. Gerald also stands and looks round, but I don't sense the same enthusiasm or excitement for what he sees.

Mrs Gainsborough enters the hall from one of the rooms leading off it.

'Oh good. I hope you had a pleasant journey. Do make yourselves absolutely at home. I'll show you where the music-room is. You can leave your cases here.'

Speaking quickly and concisely in her plummy accent, she strides off. We follow.

'By the way, this is the telephone.'

I notice to my astonishment that it's a public payphone. I can't decide whether it's meanness or simply a reflection of the number of guests they usually have in the house. We continue along passageways furnished with oak chairs, chests and tapestries, through a large, panelled oak door into the music-room. It's a magnificent room with tall, mullioned windows looking out over an exquisite park. At the far end of the room stands a magnificent, concert-size Steinway grand. Arranged to face it is a miscellany of luxurious leather chairs, small stools and tables.

'Do try the piano.'

Mrs Gainsborough turns a request into a graceful command and looks in my direction. I sit on the piano stool and tentatively finger the keys. It's the only thing in the whole house that reminds me of home. Mrs Gainsborough instantly picks up one or two songs from a large pile of music and opens them out in front of me on the already raised music stand.

'I'm sorry, but I need to warm up.'

I desperately want to demonstrate my value as a guest, so I begin to play the piano part of the first song. Without hesitation or shyness, Mrs Gainsborough begins to sing. She starts out quietly, as if she wants everyone to get used to the noise, but after only one or two lines she's in full flow. It's a cracked, strident voice, and whatever feeling she tries to put into it – superficially, a lot – she never gets further than a display of gestures and facial contortions. Unfortunately, when feeling is not synchronised with sight and sound, the effect can be quite alarming.

It's obvious that having lived for so many years with people who, despite their breeding, know little or nothing about music, she has developed an exaggerated opinion of her musical ability. I'm not brave enough to disabuse her. Someone ought to try, but as a guest who wants to have an enjoyable weekend, the last thing I can afford to be is honest.

Even though we've only just arrived, Mrs Gainsborough insists on going through a substantial proportion of her repertoire, and in particular the songs she intends singing at the concert. I revel in the opportunity to show off my skill in sight-reading, though Mrs Gainsborough clearly doesn't appreciate the skill needed to follow the erratic and capricious course she often charts. Her aim seems to be to shake me off, but I stick like a limpet to her vocal line, and despite every convolution and unexpected distortion of timekeeping I feel a great sense of achievement when I'm still with her at the end of each song.

After an hour or so she suggests we take our bags upstairs. We climb the back staircase, which is accessible from a passage just behind the music-room. We pass yet more portraits, landscapes and decorative furniture lining the corridors. I had assumed we'd be sharing a bedroom but Gerald is shown into one room and I'm led into another, a considerable distance away. When we're together some time later, Gerald comments, 'She intends to get her money's worth.'

His attitude isn't one I can easily share. I'm not a natural cynic and rarely assume that people have underlying motives. In any case, we're being treated in what I can only interpret as a very generous way. We've been given a bedroom each, which to me is a great luxury. The route between them is delightfully confusing, and I quickly memorise essential landmarks so I can find my way there and back.

As I lie soaking in an enormous bath of hot water some time later, I ponder on the fact that we've also both been given separate bathrooms, neither of which seems to play any significant part in the general life of the house. Used as I am to living in a house without a bathroom, this is quite remarkable. In fact it's so quiet in this part of the house that I feel as if I've been given a world of my own to scrub and wallow in.

We're told that the main party staying for the weekend will arrive on the Saturday in time for the concert, though we gather that various other members of the family are already in their own living quarters.

Mrs Gainsborough has asked us to be down for dinner at seven-thirty, so after my bath I began to dress in my white tie and tails. I'm still apprehensive about this but we have nothing else, and white tie and tails are after all the musician's uniform; we never wear anything else when we perform.

We make our way to the dining-room. It's large and yet intimate, with an oak dining table of great length filling most of it. As we enter, I see the look of consternation on the faces of the guests already waiting.

'I say, you should have said.' A male guest addresses Mrs Gainsborough in a half-apologetic, half-perplexed voice.

'No, no.' Just two words from her are enough to indicate that we're the ones out of step. In that instant I feel absurdly overdressed. It's impossible not to blush and perspire as the realisation of our faux pas sinks in. But there is no going back.

Mrs Gainsborough looks irritable as she introduces us to her friends and her fourteen-year-old son, Richard. Her friends all look elegantly informal, yet obviously appropriately dressed for a Friday-night dinner. Velvet jackets, flamboyant bow ties and suede shoes suggest style and opulence, two qualities we conspicuously lack.

After being introduced, Richard turns his back on us. He comments audibly to someone:

'Mummy asks some extraordinary people to stay. Only one of them ever turned out to be any use to me. He gave me a present of a very

118

good gun.' He exudes contempt as he glances in my direction. I shuffle uneasily in this chilling atmosphere, so far removed from the simple good nature of my own relatives. My skill in playing the piano seems to cut no ice in this company. I realise that Mrs Gainsborough is our only ally, and that probably only because she needs us to put her into the limelight.

'Do have a glass of sherry.' Mrs Gainsborough puts two glasses into our hands and turns to talk to her other guests. Usually Gerald and I have no difficulty in talking non-stop, but in this room our kind of conversation seems impossible. We stand nervously and silently while everyone else chats away. I sip my first ever glass of dry sherry and discover that I have no immediate liking for it.

Mrs Gainsborough sits us at the far end of the table, next to the estate manager and one of his assistants. The more important guests are clustered together, enjoying themselves greatly.

'How was the hunting today?'

'Very poor, we lost the scent on several occasions and ended up with nothing.'

'Did you see George's new horse?'

'Yes, a magnificent animal. I understand it's done a lot of eventing and done quite well.'

The talk of horses and hunting continues. Our neighbours show intelligent and lively interest in everything except us. We sit silently, feeling absurdly overdressed and ignored by everyone, even Mrs Gainsborough. It feels like a punishment. Nothing in our lives is relevant to these people, and as soon as we're able, we escape to our bedrooms.

Before returning to my own room, I visit Gerald and we hold a perfunctory post mortem.

'Hey, you were right about the tie and tails.'

There is no consolation in proving his mother wrong, so I say nothing. But I know it will be some time before I can think about the experience without squirming with embarrassment.

The following morning I wake with the sun streaming through the window and the promise of a beautiful day. I look out at the countryside, so different from my usual view of rows of chimneys. I can hear sounds of people moving round the house and I begin to dress. I imagine that Gerald might be ahead of me, but when I reach his room he's still in bed. He looks up with bleary eyes.

119

'What time is it?'

'I'm not sure.'

'You go on and I'll get up.'

I find my way to the dining-room again, not knowing what to expect. At the end of the room is a serving-table covered with various dishes on hotplates, and a large selection of cereals. Breakfast is obviously a meal one serves oneself. Four men are already tucking in. They clearly know each other well, and their confidence in each other's company induces a debilitating feeling of awkwardness in me.

They barely acknowledge me, and I try to carry on as if I've been breakfasting this way all my life, but the frugal meal I select would have given the game away to anyone who knows me. In any case my normal appetite seems suppressed, as though my stomach wants no unnecessary complications at a time like this.

My arrival at the table is scarcely noticed, and I have no sooner started to eat than a dark-haired young woman enters the room. Her well-proportioned figure, bronzed skin and plain but neat dress radiate a naturalness and healthiness which I find suddenly and extremely attractive. I'm disconcerted when my four male neighbours virtually stand to attention on her arrival. Although I haven't been accepted into their exclusive coterie, I decide that I too must stand.

As she spends quite a long time choosing what to take from the serving-table, I feel ridiculously conspicuous standing over my breakfast as the minutes tick by. I fidget and move quietly this way and that, but the truth is that I don't feel important enough to stand in the same entirely natural way as the others. I gradually adopt a posture that is neither standing nor sitting, and remain in this tortuous position until the others sit down. I then instantly sink back into my chair, covered in a mixture of embarrassment and self-loathing. I quickly resume eating, all the while watching anxiously in case another woman enters the room and the whole nerve-racking performance has to be repeated.

'Are you playing tennis today, Emma?' asks one of the men.

'I should think so, if the weather stays fine. Do you think it will be fine this afternoon?' I'm surprised by her voice, which makes her sound far less approachable than she looks. My confidence shrinks because I now seem even further outside this group of self-satisfied people. Fortunately, while they continue to ignore my existence, Gerald comes in. He too serves himself, but I'm annoyed to see that his more prosaic attitude to life rewards him with a much bigger and better breakfast. Inevitably he sits next to me, and his own discomfiture becomes evident when he starts speaking in whispers rather than trying to compete with the breezy conversation adjacent, still dominated by tennis and the weather.

'Shall we practise in the music-room after breakfast?' he murmurs.

'Yes, I'm sure Mrs Gainsborough said something about practising this morning.' It's a relief to think of getting to the piano again. After our hurried breakfast Gerald goes back to his room and I make my way to the music-room.

After the ordeal in the dining-room, the music-room is a sanctuary. It's been designed for musicians, and now that I feel more at home, my confidence begins to recover. Sitting in this beautiful room on a fine Saturday morning, playing a superb piano, is a far cry from the hot, oppressive bakehouse and the bustle and bad temper of a working Saturday in Haydock Street. But my pleasure is tinged with guilt as I think what Mam and Dad's reaction would be if they could see me enjoying such comfort while they sweated.

I begin to play through my solos for the concert. The touch of the keys and the sound of the piano make me feel like a real pianist. There is an intoxicating smell in the room, which I discover comes from a large vase of lilies on a table. I think of Stephen in the Whitworth Gallery, pausing to smell the flowers in such a theatrical way. As I practise, I feel my posture at the piano change somehow, as though the environment is elevating my importance. I'm lost in a world remote from my own, so beautiful that I never want to leave it.

'Oh good, I'm glad you had breakfast.' The strident voice peels away the cocoon from around me and the shock propels me like a rocket into the air. My heart pounds and I look round at Mrs Gainsborough.

'I didn't mean to startle you. Are you ready to do some practice?'

She pulls out all her songs once again and puts them on the music stand.

'I have a frightful headache. I get one every day.'

I'd noticed her heavily lined forehead, but this morning it's more obvious. She has a glass of water with her and pops a few pills into her mouth. As she lifts the glass I notice for the first time the dazzling array of rings and bangles round her wrist.

She selects her first song and I begin to play the accompaniment. I try to put everything into the piano part that the voice lacks. I'm caught up in the mood of each song, and my fingers tense with felt emotion, pressing the keys as if I were playing the violin. One song by Rachmaninov has a particularly appealing piano part. I'm captivated by its subtle harmonic progressions, and the pianism which gives the accompaniment the distinction of being like a piano solo with accompanying voice. It ends with eight bars of solo piano – to me, the most beautiful part of the song, providing a short, poignant postlude essential to the shape and feel of the composition. I'm puzzled to see that these eight bars have been scored out in pencil, but I ignore this and play them as the composer intended. I can't believe anyone could perform the song without them, but Mrs Gainsborough immediately stops me as I continue after her last note.

'No, no one plays those bars.'

I'm flabbergasted. I realise there is only one explanation: she can't bear the piano continuing after her last note, because she wants the applause to follow her singing. I have no choice but to submit to her artistic vandalism and omit the part of the song that would have given me most pleasure.

We continue after this for some time, until I happen to look round and see that Gerald has joined us and is comfortably seated in a leather armchair, reading a newspaper. He's obviously not in any way concerned about practising, and when Mrs Gainsborough comes to the end of her rehearsing he looks up as if to say, 'Do I really have to play?' He gets out his violin and starts to tune it. The sound of violin and piano is immediately so much more satisfying than voice and piano.

'I'd love to stay and listen but I'm afraid I have a lot of things to do.'

Mrs Gainsborough leaves us in no doubt that her performing is more important than ours.

After lunch, Gerald and I wander out of the house along the gravel drive. The house is flanked by walls with several doorways. Through one we enter a walled garden, and I gaze in wonder for the very first time on an immaculately cultivated vegetable and fruit garden. Up to now my knowledge of horticulture has been limited to moors and fields, daisies and buttercups, and small suburban gardens, but the composition of the vegetable garden easily outshines anything I've ever seen. Fruit trees are trained to grow horizontally along each wall. Along the gently sloping upper path are several ornamented glasshouses. I walk, look, stop and smell, and in every respect this is a vision of the Garden of Eden.

I've lived all my life in a town with tarmac as a lawn and nothing but the toughest dandelions growing in the cracks between the pavement flags. Flowers and vegetables are bought but never grown, while here the miracle of creation has suddenly unfolded before me. I'm captivated by what I see, and from that moment I have an irresistible fascination for all growing things. We walk round the garden for a long time, saying nothing, as speech seems superfluous. Eventually we walk towards a simple wooden form and sit down. This pause breaks the spell of silence.

'It's a beautiful place, isn't it?' Gerald's voice suddenly seems loud and I'm reminded of Stephen's cutting comment about the discord of noise amidst tranquillity.

'Yes, but it's a beauty that belongs to the past. This garden must have been created many years ago, perhaps when Bach was a child. I wonder why Bach's music seems so much older than this.' I'm speaking aloud what are really private thoughts.

'We've just passed a summer-house with "1669" carved on it. But what I mean is that although the garden is older than Bach, today it's as fresh and new as the day it was created. The stone's weathered but the same patch of earth stands under the same piece of sky growing things that are just as new each year.' I'm still in the Garden of Eden and reluctant to leave it.

'It must be a big job looking after this lot. I wonder how many gardeners they have?' Gerald is clearly not bewitched, and reduces everything to practicalities.

'Perhaps this is the Garden of Eden, and if we wait long enough we'll see the serpent gliding through the shrubs.'

This immediately sounds absurd even to me, and I'm embarrassed to have said it, particularly as it provokes a look of derision from Gerald.

At that moment, Emma walks briskly into the garden. She makes straight for us, and on reflex we both stand.

'It's all right. Don't let me disturb you. I'm just looking for a nice plant for my bedroom.' Away from her male companions she seems considerably more approachable.

'Do come and help me choose one.'

We over-eagerly accept the invitation and follow her into the tropical world of a hothouse, full of overpowering fragrance and vivid colours. There's a bewildering array of pots on all sides. In one corner is a stone waterfall with a small pool, the surrounding walls covered with green ferns.

'This is one of my favourite places. The Victorians loved growing ferns, so they created these small corners specially for them.' There's nothing condescending or patronising in the way she speaks. She begins to pick one plant after another, eyeing them critically, unable to make a clear decision.

To me, every plant in this tropical paradise is of equal interest and it's only my desire to show this interest that makes me point one out as my favourite. To my secret glee Emma selects it and stands it to one side.

'Yes, perhaps you're right.' She sounds uncertain, and I begin to feel as if my fate is in the balance and I'm being accepted or rejected. When I first saw her at breakfast I desperately wanted to be included in her circle, and now I feel as if I'm on the verge of being accepted. After more selecting and pondering, she comes to a decision.

'I'll take these two.' She picks my plant and another. It occurs to me that mine may have been chosen to spare my feelings, which have perhaps been too obvious. So instead of her decision pleasing me, it now fills me with new anguish as I convince myself that she has chosen out of compassion for my feelings and not a flattering regard for my opinion.

She loves me, she loves me not...

'What do you think of my aunt's singing?' She asks the question nonchalantly.

'Very good,' I answer, as straight-faced as possible.

'Everyone says she's frightfully good,' Emma replies with a slight note of reproof in her voice, as if to imply that my approval is lukewarm compared to everyone else's. Gerald has moved ahead while we're talking and opens the door for Emma. She steps through without a look or a thank you.

'I'm looking forward to the concert.'

'So are we,' says Gerald.

'Are you the violinist? I started to learn but I soon gave it up.' I try to walk alongside Gerald and Emma, but the path is too narrow for three and I reluctantly fall back to follow them out of the Garden of Eden.

As we head back towards the hall, we see a tennis court, where two matches are in progress. The players and spectators all seem so much at home, revelling in each other's company, all members of the same exclusive club that doesn't have room for us. The young women playing tennis are stunning in white, set off by lithe brown limbs. With them in it, it's a hugely seductive world.

Mrs Gainsborough sees us and walks over.

'I'm glad you're enjoying yourselves. Would you like another run-through before the concert? There'll be tea in the hall at four, we could do it after that.'

This time I notice rather a lot of vivid lipstick, not limited to the contours of her mouth. She smiles grotesquely in my direction. 'By the way, you can buy a very nice velvet jacket from Dunn's.' She says it artlessly but her meaning is clear. The previous evening's embarrassing encounter is not forgotten. She addresses her comment to me, out of earshot of Gerald, as if she senses that I'm more aware of the gaffe and more anxious to avoid it in future. She has no way of knowing that the prospect of buying such a jacket, even from a reasonably priced retailer like Dunn's, is remote. It's an unthinkable extravagance. But I try to look suitably grateful for the advice.

As four o'clock draws near, Gerald and I saunter over to the hall and find tea being served, along with the richest-looking chocolate cake I've ever seen. Everywhere else the austerity of the post-war years is evident, so afternoon tea at Leyton Hall seems like decadent luxury.

The tea is strong and hot and in a large cup, and the cake delicious. We return to the music room in a good mood.

14

Conquering Heroes

Mrs Gainsborough has instructed us to change and be down for an early dinner at 6.30, so we can be at the concert hall for eight. I have my second bath in two days, sparing another thought for my family as I lie and soak. With great care and pride I dress in my tails, confident that this time they're appropriate, and after making many adjustments to my appearance with the help of brush and comb I call on Gerald, who is also in the final stages of his preparations. When we're ready, we descend the main stone staircase and head for the drawing-room. We can hear a considerable hubbub of conversation. Mrs Gainsborough moves towards us as we stand reticently in the doorway.

'Good. Are you all ready?' She smiles, but the smile has an acid quality about it that does nothing to make me feel at ease. She is dressed in a flamboyant green silk evening dress, and when I look round the room I see that all the women are dressed to the nines.

'Do come and meet my husband.' We follow meekly. 'Darling, these are the young musicians I've told you about.' We shake hands with Colonel Gainsborough who, it turns out, is the lord lieutenant of the county. His face is ruddy; he has very little hair on his head but a considerable amount in the shape of a moustache, and the slightest touch of a squint.

'How do you do?' His smile is pleasant and warm, though how sincere I can't judge. 'Would you like a cocktail? I mix them myself.' We accept two orange-coloured drinks. Never having had a cocktail before, I'm not sure how appreciative to be.

'This is my sister.' Mrs Gainsborough introduces us to a sad-looking woman who has two dachshunds hovering around her feet, watching her every movement. A second later, Mrs Gainsborough has left us. I bend down to stroke one of the dogs. 'He's called Eins and his wife is called Zwei. Aren't you, my sweeties?' She stands back, unsure what to say to us next as we so obviously share none of the interests which fuel the enthusiastic conversation going on all around us. Just as the silence is becoming acutely embarrassing I blurt out, 'I like the vegetable garden very much.' But far from providing a topic of conversation, my comment is seized on as the perfect pretext for passing us on to someone else.

'You must speak to Mrs Simmonds about the garden.' She quickly seeks out Mrs Simmonds and brings her across to take over the unwelcome chore. Then she quickly walks off, followed by her devoted dachshunds.

'Are you keen gardeners?' Mrs Simmonds is the most natural person I've met since we arrived, and I'm immediately at ease with her. She doesn't wait for a reply, seeming to be instinctively aware that 'no' is the most likely answer from two gauche youths like us.

'I live here. Jimmy is my nephew.' From the direction of the glance I gather that Colonel Gainsborough is Jimmy. 'Most of my time I spend in the garden. I have a couple of gardeners to do the heavy work, but I'm usually with them. It's really not at its best now. You should come in spring when all the rhododendrons are out. It's quite beautiful.' She speaks with great feeling and I long to see the garden at its best.

'We only got as far as the vegetable garden.' I'm eager to make the position clear, to avoid getting her hopes up too high.

'Oh, did you see the globe artichokes growing?' Neither Gerald not I have any idea whether we did or not, but we try to show suitable interest in our expressions. 'I've grown them from seed and they've done frightfully well. I'm terribly pleased with them.' I'm getting to like this lady, whose passion for gardens I recognise as similar to ours for music. But our conversation is interrupted by a move toward the dining-room, so we're saved from having to express an opinion on globe artichokes.

The dining-room is completely changed in character from the informality of breakfast and lunch by a combination of dress, numbers, and servants. Colonel Gainsborough is at the head of the long table, his smile more benevolent and contented and his face ruddier than ever, perhaps after enjoying his own cocktail to the full.

Some distance along the table I see Emma.

'Did you hear about James getting the same room as Emma?' Mrs Gainsborough's singing voice cuts through the air. She laughs. 'Apparently, after James had left his things in the room, Emma had been given the room and was in the middle of changing when poor James walked back into it.'

Emma seems in no way put out by this disclosure, but James, whose experience doesn't seem at all pitiable to me, is covered with confusion and blushes to the roots of his red hair.

'Perhaps it was intended,' says the colonel, beaming at his own wit.

The conversation continues around the table, as if it's a kind of ball game with everyone throwing at random to everyone else, but the ball is maddeningly and consistently too high for me to intercept. Emma describes her new job in the City, working in public relations, but not to me. All I can do is listen and look on. In any case, I need to concentrate on the meal itself. I'm very unsure about the use of cutlery, and need to observe exactly what my neighbours are doing so I can copy them.

Once the meal is underway I become more confident, but then I notice that I've inadvertently picked up a wrong piece of cutlery. I do my best to conceal it and make a discreet change, but not without a feeling of anguish. When asked whether I want red or white wine I say white, then notice that all the other men say red and all the women white. I squirm inwardly, particularly as Gerald has chosen red. I feel sure everyone has noticed my choice and written me off as a fool. My throat dries and my face flushes at what I think must be another faux pas of the worst kind. So it is that my agonising lessons in social graces begin.

Gerald seems comparatively unperturbed. It's now the final lap and coffee is being served. I've developed some interest in health food, and on occasions have had Scotch moist sugar. It's therefore with some feeling of confidence that I pick up a silver bowl of what I think is this rather obscure sugar, and after both my neighbours decline it, put a heaped spoonful into my coffee with considerable aplomb. Unfortunately it doesn't dissolve like sugar, but makes a gooey mess on the spoon. I sip my coffee. It's vile. The horrible realisation dawns on me that my Scotch moist sugar is actually ginger provided for the melon. As I sit with a cup of undrinkable coffee in full view of the rest of the table, I feel sure everyone has noticed my inept and stupid behaviour.

To my immeasurable relief, dinner is eventually over and we prepare to leave for the concert.

It's a small village hall and it's packed to the door. After a sweeping entrance and a great deal of public show, the Gainsborough family and friends take their reserved seats at the front of the hall, while we retire to a small room with Mrs Gainsborough. As we sit and wait, my excitement grows.

Mrs Gainsborough says, 'I shall introduce you to the audience first and say one or two other things about the concert, then you play.' But before doing anything, she spends an inordinate amount of time titivating her appearance. Eventually she turns to us and asks, 'Do I look all right?' The question is embarrassing and unexpected. We mumble a half-hearted response, influenced not by any shortcoming in her appearance but by our own lack of savoir-faire. We quickly realise anyway that the question needed little or no answer and was asked out of habit rather then necessity.

'I've got the right order of programme, I think. You're definitely beginning with the Corelli, aren't you?'

After yet another look in the mirror and a final touch of powder to her face, Mrs Gainsborough walks out on to the platform to enthusiastic applause. I stand as near as I can to the stage without letting the audience catch sight of me, but I can't quite hear what she says. Her introduction lasts considerably longer than I would have thought reasonable, but eventually she returns and, looking delighted with herself, motions to us to go on quickly.

As we open the concert, we hit a perfect balance of tone and tempo. It inspires confidence in me. After my gaffes during dinner, fate seems ready to redress the balance. Our confident and passionate playing of the first piece is greeted by rapturous applause, and the seal is set on our success for the evening. It proves not to be in any way diminished by Mrs Gainsborough's rather extraordinary singing; in fact, it provides the perfect foil to our own performance. Our brilliant and ebullient playing contrasts even more vividly with the uninspired and inadequate technical level of her singing.

The vigorous applause at the end of the first half eventually tapers off into a buzz of voices as the audience resumes its various conversations. As we retire to the small ante-room, we're surrounded by helpers and admirers, among whom is Emma. 'That was marvellous!' she says, eyes shining. She is dressed in the most beautiful soft red dress and now looks extraordinarily pretty.

'It must be wonderful to be able to play like that. You're both so talented.' There is an earnestness in her face, which, combined with the fact that she is an aristocrat, makes her compliment the most welcome I've ever had. 'Do carry on with your cup of tea, don't let me interrupt you.' She turns to her aunt. 'You were absolutely wonderful, too.' Mrs Gainsborough is so busy organising the helpers, and generally busying herself with detail, that the compliment is accepted in a very casual way.

'Do tell me, is the lighting all right? Do you think the audience is enjoying it?' She fusses endlessly over herself and over everyone else in the room apart from us. We quietly sip our tea in a corner. I begin to see that she is attempting to restore a proper balance in the minds of her family and friends. Perhaps she fears that there is some danger of the supporting artists having too much of the limelight. Her friends and relations soon respond to her anxiety, and it isn't long before Mrs Gainsborough finds herself once more the adored centre of her circle, listening with increasing satisfaction to the ceaseless repetition of lavish compliments from all sides.

After the concert is over, we meet and talk with more members of the audience who come to our dressing-room. Mrs Gainsborough is showered with yet more flattering compliments, though it's now noticeable that they come only from people who know her very well. After most of the audience has gone, Mrs Gainsborough and her sister remain, discussing the evening's events.

'Everyone I spoke to loved it.'

'I think this has been the best concert we've had.'

The two dachshunds are being fed the biscuits left over from the interval refreshments.

As the exchanges continue, I'm astonished to realise that Mrs Gainsborough believes her singing is the principal reason the evening has been such a success. Our role is clearly regarded as incidental. I'm beginning to understand that the pleasure of success can be tainted by the realisation that someone else is unfairly getting the credit.

We return to Leyton Hall like unsung conquering heroes, and this time I feel more at ease among the upper classes. While my sense of self-preservation is too acute to allow me to relax completely, as I enter the entrance hall I almost feel as if I belong to the family.

After everyone has taken off their coats, they all make for the music-room. I've chosen to go to my bedroom for a few minutes, to fix any sartorial wear and tear before appearing in public again. As I walk back down the staircase alone, I momentarily feel the power and dignity of wealth and position, and as I feel it I walk with a subtly different gait. The feeling sparks a confidence that is in sharp contrast to so many years of shame and self-consciousness. It nourishes my growing certainty that the future is not constrained by what I inherited, but will be a consequence of what I can create. As I reach the foot of that grand staircase, I'm determined that I will change the boundaries of my destiny.

But perhaps not yet. The din of conversation reaches me from the music-room, yet I feel afraid to make the slightest noise as I creep along the passage. I draw a long breath, ready to plunge into the deep waters of a society that is becoming more familiar to me but in which compassion and feeling are hard to recognise, even when they exist. The dimly lit corridor contrasts with the lights of the music-room, which welcome me when I open the door. The many guests are now relaxing and enjoying a nightcap. Gerald is already there. Someone asks, 'Play for us?' That simple, affable request is all the encouragement we need. We sit down again and with the benefit of a better piano, return to the hallowed role of performers.

As I look around the room, I spot Emma and feel an acute need to gain her admiration. I feel a pang when I think of Elspeth. How can I reconcile my feelings for her with the urge to attract another woman? It's a betrayal, yet my guilt does nothing to reduce the powerful feelings I have. It's as if this upper-class world is unrelated to the one I've left behind. None of the people I know could live here. They would be out of place, awkward, an embarrassment. It's only through the magic of music that I've been able to enter it and be accepted, at least to a degree. Without music I would be irrelevant, just as Elspeth is at this moment irrelevant to me. All these thoughts go through my mind as I adjust the piano stool and play the A for Gerald.

As we begin to play the Fauré A Major Sonata, it's as if my playing of the opening rhapsodic romantic theme is pulsing with the feeling that now possesses me. I play as though for Emma alone, and as though I'm trying to seduce her. She probably isn't aware of it, but she has transformed my performance and given the music another dimension. And as I play, I realise that this is what life is all about: passion, feeling, intensity, beauty. From the comparative squalour of Haydock Street I have moved to a world of elegance and beauty, and I have secured a part of it.

At the end of the first movement Mrs Gainsborough comes over before we can continue with the second. 'That's absolutely beautiful.' She looks around her audience of friends and family, taking credit for providing them with such a musical treat. By now I'm far from convinced that she really understands music. Nor am I surprised when she picks up a few song scores lying on top of the piano, and with her best attempt at modesty looks through them. Inevitably someone says:

'Do sing for us.'

'Yes, do.'

'Oh, Aunt, you must sing something.'

The pleas increase from all sides. With a show of apparent reluctance she hands me the music and prepares to sing. I play the piano part with as much feeling as I can, but Mrs Gainsborough's corncrake voice overwhelms everything. Emma's enjoyment seems in no way diminished by the switch from my passionate serenading with Gerald to the abysmal tones of her aunt's voice. I'm reminded, but only fleetingly, of Elspeth's approval of Stephen's Blackburn concert but not his shirt. All that matters is Emma's face, full of interest, looking more beautiful and enticing than ever.

As the song ends I play the final chords with all the tenderness I can, still hoping to gain Emma's heart.

Gerald has taken the opportunity to sit back, and I can see he is drinking what looks like a whisky. I'm ready to carry on playing in the hope of gaining ground with Emma, but for some reason Mrs Gainsborough's singing seems to have sated the audience's appetite for music.

'Good concert, what?' The ever-beaming Colonel Gainsborough passes judgment.

'I'm glad you liked it,' I reply.

To my delight, Emma says, 'It was quite wonderful.' Her words touch me deeply. It's as if she is opening her heart to me, telling me that I'm appealing, attractive even. The urge to embrace her is immense, but I stand there transfixed, terrified of overstepping the mark. She couldn't possibly have any interest in me. It's absurd to imagine she would ever consider me seriously. As I stand frozen, Gerald joins us and immediately sits down next to Emma. His whole demeanour is uncomplicated by self-consciousness or the weight of feeling that is paralysing me.

'Did you enjoy the concert?' He asks the question nonchalantly, as if the answer is of little consequence.

'I loved it.' Emma's reply is full of warmth and sincerity. Mrs Gainsborough, overhearing, chimes in:

'Wasn't it wonderful?'

'Oh, Aunt, it was lovely and you were marvellous.' Mrs Gainsborough radiates utter contentment with the comment and utter agreement with the sentiment. But somehow she also signals to the gathering that the evening has ended, and one by one her guests begin to leave.

Almost everyone has left before Emma stands to say farewell.

'I so enjoyed your playing.' She looks at both of us but I'm convinced she's talking to me. She turns and leaves the room. I ache at what feels like a missed opportunity. With no one else left, Mrs Gainsborough turns to us.

'Thank you so much for playing. I'm sure we'll be able to arrange some more concerts.'

Gerald and I make our way to the grand staircase. I return to my room and lie on my bed for some time, my mind in turmoil. I feel a powerful, very powerful, desire to be a part of the elegant world to which I've now been introduced.

15

Twelve Studies in Independence

I'm feeling a growing uneasiness that my life is becoming too dependent on Stephen. Agreed, he has bolstered my sense of purpose and made the role of pianist-composer even more desirable and achievable. He knows exactly what he is doing, and that has given me greater confidence in my own career. But my increasing competence at the piano, in so many ways helped by Stephen, is encouraging me to assert my own personality and not be forever in his shadow.

In the early days of our relationship I felt privileged to be his close friend and was pleased, in fact anxious, to do whatever he wanted. But my instinct for self-preservation is now – and probably inevitably – detecting ways in which he is undermining me. On one occasion when I go to see him, he asks me to play him something I'm currently practising. Claude has given me a transcendental study by Liapounov called *Lezjinka*. When he first suggested it, I had misgivings because I knew it wasn't in the repertoire of virtuoso pianists. I somehow felt it was a second-rate piece. None the less, I felt I owed it to Claude to prepare it for him. I hadn't the heart to refuse, because he seemed so excited about the prospect of my playing it, saying, 'It will suit you.' When I got the music I discovered that my instinct had not led me astray. It wasn't a great piece, but it was pianistic and quite enjoyable to play. Indeed, I later included it in my programme on several occasions.

Somehow, playing it for Stephen became a declaration of independence. It was a way of showing him that I was developing in new directions outside his influence. We had never discussed or listened to it, and I was sure Stephen wouldn't even know the composer's name. I sat at his piano and started to play. Despite the shortcomings of the instrument, I had enough confidence to bring it off.

How different it was from the first time I ever played for Stephen! As the piece ended I sat at the piano for a minute or so, feeling awkward and not knowing what to say. Stephen broke the silence.

'Is that a piece Claude gave you to play?'

His question indicated his astuteness: he had realised it wasn't my choice. I nodded agreement, and began to feel that playing it for Stephen had been a mistake.

'There is a saying of Goethe's to the effect that the pupil can be ruthlessly exploited by the unscrupulous teacher and become in practice little more than a puppet.'

I felt my confidence reduced by his penetrating comment. In the beginning, my relationship with Stephen had resulted in growing confidence; now even that is beginning to change. I realise that there is growing danger in continuing the way we are.

A fundamental shift in our relationship is also hastened by my refusal to be exploited quite so readily in trivial ways. For example, on one of my last visits to his home he explains the growing complications resulting from a romantic involvement with his cousin.

'Her mother is trying to break it off. Every time we meet, she's obsessed with whether or not we're sleeping together. It's the only thing she can think about.'

I'm as much in the dark about the nature of their relationship as the mother. Stephen laughs about her concern, but doesn't convey any sense of whether or not it's justified.

'It all came to a head in a family row last weekend. I desperately need to speak to her before she sees her mother tonight. Would you meet her off the bus? I can tell you exactly where to meet her.'

'Why can't you meet her yourself?'

'I'm worried her mother will be waiting for her. If you go, you can think up some excuse to speak to her.' The request is so much in the spirit that has dominated our relationship that I feel a strong sense of guilt at resisting it.

'I'm not sure I can do it.' Inside, I'm much more against the idea. I'm just coming up to an important concert and have a lot of work to do, but I know it would be futile to mention this to Stephen. How can anything in my life be as important as the most minor event in his? He tries to press me to meet the bus, but in vain.

'I really can't, much as I'd like to help.' I can feel my determination growing, but I can also see his look of resentment.

It's ironic that Busoni proves to be the final straw in my disengagement from Stephen. I've loaned him a copy of the Busoni Piano Concerto, borrowed from the Henry Watson Music Library. Libraries of course expect their books back, but whenever I mention this to him he makes it clear that he is above worrying about such trivialities. It goes on so long that it becomes a serious worry to me. Finally I have to insist, to put an end to the ever-increasing fine. As he hands it back, I read in his face his feeling of irritation with my worldliness, which has come between him and the book. But I also sense that he understands my demand as a sign of my growing independence.

I go to see Stephen less and less frequently as my own work makes more demands on my time. In fact, I haven't seen him for several months when I'm astonished to see a poster in a music shop window advertising a series of masterclasses to be given by him. The masterclass had reached its summit with Stephen's beloved Busoni. His pupils were his disciples, and the masterclass was recognition by them and the world that Busoni was the master.

Stephen's presumption in proposing himself as a master is typical of what I have come to recognise as his incorrigible streak of arrogance, in this case combined with naivety. It's impossible to imagine that anyone will take the idea seriously. The venue he has chosen is a large lecture theatre in the centre of Manchester, and I can't believe it will be other than a disaster. My growing independence has replaced my previous veneration with something close to aversion. I'm ashamed to realise that I want him to fail.

Stephen's small poster appears in several shop windows. There is nothing particularly attractive in its design. It could just as easily be a poster for a whist drive or a union meeting. Yet it's the kind of idea that demands enormous confidence and drum-beating, particularly for a young man just out of college. Only Stephen among all the students would dare to attempt such a thing, but equally only Stephen would fail to appreciate what is painfully obvious to me – that few people will respond to it, and many more will relish his downfall. The truth is that he has no reason to be regarded by anyone as a master. He has established no reputation as a performer or composer outside the diminishing circle in which he moves; he hasn't been invited to give any recitals in major concert halls; he hasn't been invited to play with any orchestras. A few people recognise that his commitment is exceptional, but to the majority he's no more than a jumped-up student.

Although I've seen little of him for months, I can't resist asking for news of him. It seems he's immersed himself completely in the subject matter of his lectures. He has taken particular aspects of music which fascinate him – one is the Faust theme – and developed them into essays illustrated by music which he will perform. The masterclasses are to consist of four lectures on consecutive Tuesdays, timed to follow a popular series of weekly midday recitals in an adjacent hall. The idea is simple and theoretically sound. Of the comparatively large number attending the established Tuesday concerts, he believes there will surely be enough interested students to provide a smaller audience for his own lectures. But his prices are high, influenced no doubt by comments we've all heard from successful musicians about the beneficial effects of putting a high price on one's talent. In a materialistic society, so the argument goes, ability and money are often equated, and so an artist with a high price is an artist with high ability. In Stephen's case, I can't see any justification whatsoever for an inflated entrance fee.

Once, I would have been eager to attend; but over the past few months I've outgrown my role as devoted pupil. I see the masterclasses as a more glaring example of the lack of realism shown by the humiliating sale of his books. I decide to ignore them.

Some time later I'm on my way to college when I'm approached by a fellow music student: a young woman, whom I recognise but don't know. She knows me though, and is disarmingly blunt.

'I thought as a friend you'd be supporting Stephen and his masterclasses.' I immediately feel a twinge of guilt. She continues, 'I thought a lot would be there, particularly you.'

'What was it like?' I dread the answer.

'I bought a ticket for the whole series. When I arrived, no one else was there but Stephen. We waited for three quarters of an hour. He had tears in his eyes as he realised no one else was coming.'

Her declaration of faith in Stephen is so moving that I begin to feel somehow responsible, and to understand her bewilderment that I wasn't there. Her innocent trust in Stephen suddenly seems to be a wonderful and irresistible quality.

We cross the road to the Kardomah Café and order two coffees at a table near to a window. Now I can study her more closely. Her idealism lends a beautiful quality to her appearance, which seems to make conventional prettiness cheap and irrelevant.

'He told me he'd been obsessed by the idea of giving the classes and

138

had barely slept for months. I don't think he ever imagined that no one would be interested in coming.' As she talks, I notice her immaculate silk blouse. There is a fastidiousness in her appearance that has never struck me so forcibly in anyone before. Not Elspeth, not Emma. I sip my coffee, observing and listening intently all the time. She has the most wonderful hair, long and thick and coiled into two buns on either side of her head. She has no jewellery on her hands but wears a gold and pearl brooch. Her simple beige gaberdine suit highlights her neatness and cleanliness.

'I promised to try to find at least half a dozen people to attend the next lecture. I wonder if you'd come, and perhaps persuade anyone else you know.'

There is an innocence in her pleading which I find both moving and very attractive. I decide that I must support Stephen at his next masterclass, which is now to be held in a small practice room.

'Okay, I'll come.'

We finish our coffee and leave.

As we head back to the college I have a sudden idea.

'If you haven't seen the Blakes at the Whitworth and you haven't a class now, would you like to see them?'

'Yes, I would.'

I feel a surge of delight. It's like being Stephen with a disciple at my side.

We walk into the park, towards the gallery. The attendants as usual outnumber visitors at this time of day, and they look up with their now customary glance of annoyance.

The vase of flowers in the corridor gives me another opportunity to play Stephen, so I stop and smell them.

I lead her through the gallery confidently, showing her that I know exactly where to find Blake's *The Ancient of Days*. I stand looking at it, longing as always to penetrate to the depths of Blake's understanding. But however much I look, I can never achieve the frisson of inspiration that great music gives me. It's my head that tells me the Blake is a masterpiece, not my heart. We stand for some time together, then walk around the galleries looking at the Turners and anything else that takes our fancy. It's the first time I've been here with anyone other than Stephen.

'Have you read any Blake?' I ask the question hoping I can continue my role as teacher.

'No.'

'I'll lend you some.'

Her acceptance of my offer symbolises the acceptance of my friendship, and in this way the relationship between Ruth and me begins to develop. Motivated by innocent idealism, our mutual passion for music elevates our interest in each other above the usual boyfriend-and-girlfriend relationship. In those first few hours I find in her nobility, dignity, compassion, fastidiousness, loyalty, profundity and, more than anything else, exceptional sensitivity. Stephen has unwittingly and ironically played a major part in bringing us together. My bid to escape his influence is the catalyst that has drawn me to someone I might never have come to know.

Stephen's influence is also decisive in another event. His ambition to play the Twelve Studies Opus 10 has remained unfulfilled, and I have a wonderful opportunity to exploit it. It's the centenary of Chopin's death in 1849, and there is to be a concert dedicated to him in November. Claude now regards me as his best pupil, so when he first mentions the concert to me he adds:

'Perhaps you can play a group of pieces. A scherzo, nocturne and perhaps a polonaise.' I take a deep breath.

'I've been working on the Twelve Studies Opus 10.'

'Could you do them?' I hear an enormous question mark. No one has ever played them in their entirety at the college before.

'I think I can.' I'm not as sure as I sound, but I know I need to persuade him to let me do it. There is always a tendency to cut ambitions down to a size to fit the teacher's assessment rather than the pupil's aspirations.

'Perhaps you should choose half a dozen of them.'

'I really want to play them all.' I can sense Claude wavering.

'I've been working on them a lot and I already know most of them.' It isn't true, but I need to say it if I'm going to persuade him.

'Very well then.' He makes a quicker decision than usual, and I breathe a sigh of satisfaction. I'm committed to playing them. I have to play them. The date is set, the programmes must soon be printed – there is no escape. I'm desperate to get back to a piano in order to work towards the point I'm supposed to have reached already. And so begins the ascent of a mountain from which I believe I will see my future more clearly.

* * *

The piano in Haydock Street is feeble, but I hammer at the keys in a way that imprints the sensation of the fingers playing the passages of the studies. The difficulties demand repetition, and repetition makes the passages memorable. It's astonishing to discover that my commitment to play them is resulting in my ability to play them. The audacity of the idea has proved to be the catalyst that makes it happen. It seems as if the scale and outrageousness of the idea have elevated me above what I might have considered my limitations. I remember that when Stephen first mentioned the idea to me, it seemed so ambitious that even he hesitated to describe it as something he would actually do. I have now stolen the idea from him – not without a sense of guilt – and am about to realise it.

The morning of the concert dawns. As I get up, I look out of the window in the direction of the Municipal Secondary School and recall hearing Chopin for the first time while I was a pupil there. My dream of being a pianist-composer has always been inspired by his life and work, his poetry and fire, and to play at this concert in his memory is a moment of achievement I will always treasure.

I think for a few moments about Chopin dying in Paris a hundred years earlier. I know that his tomb is in the Père Lachaise Cemetery and I resolve to go there one day to pay homage. In a small way, this concert will link my name with Chopin forever.

As I go downstairs I make straight for the upright piano and begin to play. I've now spent hours practising each study. There is no danger of forgetting any part of them, because my fingers can recall the feel of every passage. I remember listening to two of the Opus 10 studies on my first visit to the college. They had sounded so brilliantly virtuoso, yet within two years I'm playing all twelve of them.

'Have some breakfast before you leave.' Mam is still concerned that I need breakfast more than any other meal. She brings a plate with a fried egg and half a tomato and puts it on the table.

Dad is drinking his usual morning coffee and eating a burnt cake from the previous day's mistakes.

I start to think about breakfast the following morning, when it will all be over. But just now, my breakfast is a reminder of how nervous I am and what an ordeal this concert might be. I eat a few mouthfuls, then give up.

I'm desperate to get to the college and into a music-room, because my own piano has such an inadequate touch: it's too light, and the studies will be a trial of strength on a heavier piano.

As I arrive at the bus station I meet Harry, waiting to catch the same bus.

'Are you all ready?' He's fully aware of the task I've set myself. I mutter a reply to the effect that I'm not complacent but modestly confident.

'Do you know Alfred Cortot's recordings?' The great French pianist had recorded the studies and I'd heard some, but I sense that this question is intended to unsettle me.

We board the bus and climb to the top deck. As the bus picks up speed towards Manchester we're both poring over the music of the studies.

'Interesting, isn't it?' Harry says. 'So many composers after Bach have written in twelves, it's as if they're paying homage to him.'

'Yes, but none of them has any direct relationship with the twelve semitones. The Chopin studies start as if he had some tonal scheme, but he abandons it in the middle.'

Just as I finish speaking, the bus swerves violently on a patch of ice and spins round, ending up facing backwards on the opposite pavement. One passenger has been thrown, and in protecting himself from falling has broken one of the windows and gashed his hand. It bleeds badly as he waits for an ambulance. Is this an omen for tonight's performance, I wonder? At least my hands are safe. As we finally disembark, I make a mental note never to travel on the top deck of a bus again.

Harry and I part company as I need to call in at the Henry Watson Library. I walk towards two small glass cases mounted on the library wall. One contains Chopin's death mask, the other a plaster-cast of his left hand. I gaze at the face, then the hand. I put my own hand alongside it. I want it to be identical, but I've done it often enough before to know that it's not; my thumb and little finger are both longer. I gaze at the hand, imagining his playing of the studies. I hope his spirit will be with me tonight. I want to play the music in a way that honours his name.

The college hall is buzzing with excitement as we try through our pieces in the afternoon. Albert, a piano professor, looks at me quizzically.

'Are you playing them in the order they're printed?'

I nod.

'That's difficult. The A Minor following the C Major is very hard. Most people switch the order to make them more playable.'

It has never occurred to me to do this. I've not noticed that the sequence of studies as written makes them more difficult. I begin to wonder if I've missed something, and don't know what to say to Albert, but I never consider changing the order of the pieces. I'm determined to play them in the order as written.

As the time of the concert approaches I can see all the college professors settling into their front two rows. Usually some don't attend, but the Chopin night is special. I see Gerald arriving at the last minute. By this time it's difficult to find a seat. My studies open the concert, and as I walk on, I recall my first attempts to walk naturally on stage at the talent-spotting competitions. I bow, then sit. As silence descends, my left hand strikes the C major octave and the triumphant arpeggio in the right hand begins to create those feelings of nobility and heroism which dominate the first study.

It feels good. It's going to be my night. Chopin is with me.

As I strike the final C major chord of the last study, the *Revolutionary*, I feel a wonderful sense of triumph. Stephen's idea has worked. It is a staging post in my life.

I sit at the back of the hall listening to the rest of the concert, just a few rows behind Ruth. As she turns round to look at me, we exchange a look of mutual pleasure.

After the concert is over, all my fellow students gather round chatting enthusiastically about the evening and the music. Gerald comes up to me.

'Well done.'

He speaks in an almost grudging tone of voice. When I first knew him, it would have been unthinkable for me to play these pieces. It seems as if I've caught a tide that is sweeping me forward, and perhaps Gerald fears I'll overtake him.

I leave with Ruth to go to our usual Kardomah coffee shop before setting out for home. As soon as we're sitting down, she opens her music case and pulls out a book.

'Thank you so much for lending it to me.'

I take it back with some surprise. When I had given it to her it was falling to pieces; now it's in almost new condition.

'This isn't the book I gave you, mine was much older.'

143

'No, it's yours. I must have damaged it so I got it rebound.'

I'm astonished. I didn't know it was possible to have books rebound.

'You shouldn't have done it. It was already in bad condition when I gave it to you.'

'No, I'm sure it was my fault.'

I accept the book, impressed and touched by her resourcefulness and generosity.

'By the way, I wonder if you could come to my birthday party. It's a few weeks away, on a Saturday. Mummy and Daddy are determined to have a party and I usually hate the people they invite. It would be wonderful to have someone there who I really want. It'll probably be boring, but I would appreciate it.'

'I'd love to come, and it won't be boring if you're there.'

We leave the Kardomah to walk towards the station, then continue our separate journeys home.

The following evening I've arranged to see Elspeth, and as I walk towards her house I wonder how I can explain my acceptance of Ruth's invitation. My relationship with Ruth, a fellow musician, has grown so strongly out of our mutual love of music that it has never seemed to be in conflict with my relationship with Elspeth. Why should I feel guilt? I've done nothing physically to betray Elspeth. Nevertheless, I feel growing uneasiness. I'm troubled by what I had originally decided was a matter of no consequence. I was swept away by the pleasure of the invitation and blinded to the realities of the corner I'm now in.

As I walk in, Mrs Williams sits relaxing by the fire, looking even more self-satisfied than usual.

'I've heard all about your weekend with the Gainsboroughs.' She turns to Elspeth. 'I've told you, he won't have any time for us now he's found new friends in high places.'

'I wouldn't describe them as friends, it's simply that Gerald and I have been playing for them and staying there.'

'I know, but once you get to know them better, you'll see.'

Elspeth shows no concern about me and the Gainsboroughs. In fact, she looks remarkably secure and comfortable. As I look at her, I wonder how I can possibly tell her about Ruth's birthday weekend. Why on earth didn't I think it through?

Mrs Williams goes out to make tea for us and we decide to go for a walk. There are very few people about as it's now twilight, and we stop by a bridge. There, I surprise myself by blurting out, 'I've been invited by a fellow student to a birthday party.' I feel awkward as I say it, knowing that I'm too afraid to be completely honest.

'That's all right, I have a lot of work to do at the moment.'

I struggle to continue my confession. 'I'll probably be away for the weekend.'

The words sound forced but Elspeth seems not to detect my difficulty. Then she asks, 'Oh. Who is it?'

I steel myself to drag it all into the open, but I can't say the words and instead make do with, 'It's a pianist I never mentioned, so you wouldn't know.' I've implied it's another man and she hasn't questioned it, but inside I feel an utter coward.

There are no further questions about my weekend. I feel less tense, and any misgivings I had dissolve.

It's the best way, I say to myself. If I'd told her the truth, she would have misconstrued the whole thing. It's better this way.

16

Bloomsday

I watch the trains pulling in and out of the station with interest, but without the excitement I used to feel. The first sighting of a new engine used to be as intoxicating as finding buried treasure, and every approaching train held the promise of a new delirious moment. To the uninitiated it must seem absurd, but once you become addicted the thrill is intense.

Today I can only remember the feeling; the passion is gone. I look at the slot machine on the platform and remember the many times I've tried to print out my name perfectly on a strip of aluminium. I never succeeded, but each new attempt started with utter conviction that it would be perfect this time. The memory of yearly childhood journeys to Blackpool is still sharp as I look around the station and recall waiting for the train. Wakes Week was the culmination of a whole year's dreaming and anticipation.

The excitement I feel today is very different. It's the day of Ruth's birthday party. I haven't met any of her family because she refused to allow them to attend any of the concerts at college, but I've gained the impression that her family are wealthy, despite her strenuous attempts to conceal the fact. When she invited me, I said I'd catch a bus once I got to the railway station, but Ruth was adamant that her mother would be upset if I didn't allow her to pick me up.

The sun is shining brilliantly as my train pulls into Southport station. Why is the weather in seaside towns always better? The Pennine mill towns so often attract rain clouds, as if in sympathy with the harsher lifestyle. Every time I travel to the seaside the weather seems to improve, and I feel my eyes readjusting to the greater light intensity. Beautiful weather on Saturday mornings is always particularly uplifting, and that combination now provides the perfect start for my visit.

When Ruth invited me, she explained the background. Despite her reluctance to socialise with her parents' friends or family, they've persuaded her to agree to this party. My invitation, I sense, is a way of her holding on to her values and counteracting those of her parents. I walk through the ticket barrier and Ruth's mother has no doubt who I am when she sees me.

Her appearance is a complete contrast to Ruth; I can see no similarities. She has an over-ripe but shapely figure and is dressed in a way that barely contains it. Her face is vivacious, but she's overdone the make-up. She extends her hand, which has long red nails and an excess of rings and bangles. She's wearing long, ornate earrings and an exotic brooch on her suit jacket.

'Ruth is busy at home and says she's sorry she couldn't come.' She takes command of me instantly. Her car, parked at the side of the station, is a smart, shiny, silver open-top tourer. 'Herbert bought it for me but now he says it's too fast.'

I look at it, fascinated by the novelty of a car without a top, and notice the smell of the red leather seats as we climb in. The dashboard has more dials than I've ever seen. The long bonnet has wind vents. Innumerable details strike me as unusual, but then I've never had much interest in cars as the prospect of owning one is so remote. I remember the contempt for materialism as Stephen and I passed the pebbles on Mrs Baumler's drive. That feeling of shared disdain was deeply satisfying. We were superior to people with possessions. We didn't want them, we rejected them. Our love of music gave us membership of the most exclusive club in the world; why should we want more?

But as I sit in the car, I feel the stirrings of different feelings, which I instantly recognise as a betrayal of the values that have shaped my life up to now. My relationship with Ruth has been built on the foundations Stephen helped me lay, but suddenly I feel insecure. I feel jealous of Ruth. She's learning to drive, and this car is a part of her life. I feel ashamed of my shallow feelings. I had believed that the profound spiritual experience of listening to and performing great music was a force that would always insulate me from a hunger for petty physical possessions. I imagine what Stephen would say if he could see me now, and be privy to my inner waverings. I'm surrendering to baser values and know I shouldn't, but I can't resist. I'm attracted to Ruth because of her purity and idealism, because of our shared love of music and the piano, and yet through her I'm being seduced by cars and possessions. Ruth has innocently opened the door to a world I know I should turn my back on, but which I find irresistible.

As the car moves smoothly forward, I glance at passers-by, who I imagine are looking on with envy.

'Ruth has told me about you and says what a wonderful pianist you are.'

'She's a very good pianist too.'

'She's so devoted to her music that I sometimes think it's bad for her. One needs balance in life. Too much of the same thing can be stifling.' She speaks in a pained, resigned way, as if she's had this conversation many times with Ruth.

The idea that music could matter too much seems impossible to imagine, let alone comment on. I wait, not knowing what to say.

'Herbert isn't the father to my children I would have wished.'

Alarm bells ring. This is embarrassingly more intimate than anything I expected.

'Then, of course, I was too naive to understand the signs when I met him.'

I wonder what on earth she can mean. I feel acutely uncomfortable hearing such confidences and have no idea what is expected of me. The car seems to swerve dangerously towards the middle of the road. I have no idea what to say about that either.

'Ruth has always been too intellectual. I do wish she could be a little more understanding and a little more human. She refuses to let me share her life. Of course she's quite wonderful, but I think she could bend a little and show me more consideration sometimes. Whenever I drive her anywhere, she insists on my parking the car a few roads away so no one will see her getting out of it. It's hard for me because I'm a very warm person and I feel everything so much.'

She appears temporarily overcome with emotion. I still don't know what to say but it clearly doesn't matter.

'We've introduced her to so many young men, but they all think she's too intellectual. She doesn't seem to want to be nice to them.'

As she speaks, I sense the coquettish, calculating way in which she's used to manipulating men, and the contrast with Ruth's more dignified approach.

We're now driving along the promenade and I look out at the sea, which had seemed such a distant and exciting luxury only a few years ago. I breathe in the refreshing air with pleasure. I didn't think it was that obvious, but Ruth's mother doesn't miss it. 'Fill your lungs, it's very good for you.' She takes a few dramatic breaths of her own, and this immediately inhibits any further energetic inhalation on my part. The open car certainly suits her flamboyant personality. She is constantly looking right and left, perhaps concerned not to miss an admiring glance from either side. Her confident, superior smile never relaxes.

The sandy beach stretches almost to the horizon, but in the distance the silver gleam of water reflecting sunlight is unmistakable. It shimmers with movement and its allure is still strong.

We turn away from the sea, apparently nearing our destination.

Growing up among rows and rows of uniform terraces, all at the bottom of the social scale, hasn't resulted in my being instantly seduced by more expensive houses. In fact, I've developed a dislike for modern semi-detached houses and much prefer Victorian terraces, which seem to have more integrity. The houses we're now passing are more individual and imposing, but the architecture is neither radical enough nor old enough to be distinctive.

As we park in front of Ruth's house, I look at its elevation. While large and impressive in its own way, its power is reduced simply because it's merely one among many similar houses in this residential area. Where I live, the houses denote that everyone is poor; where Ruth lives the houses denote that everyone has achieved a specific standard of wealth.

As I enter, I glance into a large room to the right and see a welcoming fire, large comfortable leather chairs, and pieces of antique furniture which all indicate quality and comfort. A trolley by the fireplace bears numerous bottles of spirits. There is a stale but luxurious smell of cigars. We walk on through the house and into the large back garden. On a well-tended lawn, several young people are sitting around in canvas chairs; two are playing badminton, all seem to be enjoying the weather and the occasion.

I instantly see Ruth. She contrasts strongly with her friends. Her enjoyment seems more genuine, she seems more alive. Her thick, fair hair is drawn back and her face shines with strength and character. She is playing badminton and frequently failing to connect with the shuttlecock, but that in no way diminishes her enjoyment. She runs about with great energy, but without the tenseness that competitive people usually display. She shows only good nature when she fails to score, which is often.

At one such moment, Ruth glances in my direction and smiles warmly. She hands the racquet to one of her friends and walks towards me.

'I'm so delighted you were able to come.' To my own pleasure, she looks genuinely happy to see me. Her mother is by this time at the centre of the cluster of teenagers. She's trying to cajole someone into playing badminton with her.

'Come, come, it's good exercise, darling.' She speaks with a distinct drawing in of air and thrusting out of her considerable chest. Although she's the only adult, she loses no opportunity to exhibit her enthusiasm for exercise. I'm surprised it's done so little to curtail the development of her figure. She's somewhat dismayed that her rallying cry is falling on deaf ears.

'I think everyone's played enough, Mummy, do let's have a rest now.' And to me, more confidentially: 'I do hope it's not going to be too boring for you, but Mummy and Daddy so wanted to meet you.'

I now feel distinctly insecure. Our relationship at college is uncomplicated by strangers. We've become close friends and I have no competitors, but now it's difficult. I can't be sure what other relationships mean to her. In our world of music I've established, by our sharing of similar tastes and ideals, that I'm her closest friend, but outside that world I have no idea what she feels and how important I am.

She introduces me to two brothers, John and Nicholas, who are old friends of hers. As if to assert his familiarity, John almost immediately turns to Ruth.

'Let's do something special tonight, there's a very good musical on, I think.'

'Thank you, but I hate slushy, sentimental musicals.' She adds a grimace to remove any doubt. I'm surprised by her frankness but it clearly causes no offence.

'Did I hear you suggesting a musical, John?' asks Ruth's mother, who has overheard despite being some distance away.

'Now, darling, that would be marvellous.'

'But I hate musicals, Mummy.'

'You must learn to be human, darling, too much intellectualising isn't always good for the spirit.' I sense that behind the remark is the disquiet she feels at her daughter's refusal to follow her own path, which led to early marriage and a comfortable middle-class life. It's evident that she doesn't think honesty is always the best policy in relationships between the sexes.

Just at that moment, Ruth's father comes into the garden. His roundish red face is beaming, his eyes twinkling. He has just arrived home from the golf club, in what I later see is a sleek Rolls Royce. He radiates utter contentment and happiness as he walks in with an almost beatific smile on his face, but instead of inspiring a similar sentiment in his wife, he has the opposite effect. The maternal and social organiser roles are abruptly cast aside, and in their place emerges a ferocious virago.

'Your father's pickled!' She spits out the words with an intensity that succeeds in conveying every nuance of human loathing. I see no obvious sign that she's right, but to the more experienced observer of drunkenness there is in this happy face just enough inanity to indicate that his normal senses have been left behind. Behind him troop several other men, who have obviously been invited to his daughter's birthday and are now dismayed by the far from cordial reception. Each step he takes seems less steady, and it becomes progressively clearer that this birthday party has indeed been an excuse to celebrate, a justification for buying his golfing friends several rounds of drinks. As he approaches Ruth the stagger is more pronounced, but he remains upright. Slowly but surely he reaches her, a cherubic grin distorting his features but indicating utter, oblivious contentment.

A human spring is about to release all its energy.

'Herbert! It's your daughter's birthday!' His wife screams the words, but his grin only becomes more inane.

'Herbert, you're an inebriated fool!' But screaming no longer affords her enough relief. She draws herself up in a regal pose and viciously pushes him in the chest. As it happens, he is standing in front of a large holly bush. His state of almost complete relaxation changes him into a human pendulum, swinging to and fro until his centre of gravity passes the point of no return. As he slowly sinks into the holly bush, the smile on his face is undisturbed.

The rest of the afternoon passes without ever regaining its earlier momentum. With some difficulty, Ruth's father fills a jug with milk and soda water, a mixture he obviously uses as an antidote to his drinking, and retires to his bedroom. Ruth's mother decides that the emotional trauma has been too much and retires to her own bedroom. Her soft centre, as she calls it, is finely tuned to her own feelings and completely overrides any consideration she might have for her daughter. She behaves as if it's her birthday that has been spoiled. She helps me discover how the most seemingly considerate and sensitive people can be the most selfish.

The crisis rapidly triggers a series of farewells, and before long only Ruth and I remain. For me it's a relief not to have to talk to the others, with whom I had little in common, and for the first time since I arrived I begin to relax.

'Would you like a walk in the park?' Ruth's suggestion is welcome, and I know from a conversation at college that the park is a very special place, a refuge whenever she's oppressed by her home life.

The sky is still cloudless, the sun shining. Ruth's birthday is the sixteenth of June, Bloomsday, the day in the life of Leopold Bloom immortalised by James Joyce in *Ulysses*. We walk to her park, talking non-stop.

'I apologise for Mummy's behaviour. I knew something would happen today. She can't bear not to be the focus of attention. Every birthday's the same, she has to manipulate it so that she's the principal character. Today she's the tragedy queen. I wouldn't mind, but she's so untrustworthy. I found that out very early on. I once told her a secret and made her promise never to tell a soul. Almost immediately, in front of me, she told some friends of hers. I've never trusted her since. Everyone thinks she's so wonderful.' She says it with bitterness.

'She does seem to share confidences easily.' I disclose the one-sided conversation on the way from the station.

'She has no shame. Mummy and Daddy have always been swinging from sick-making sentimentality to vicious antagonism. She can be so weak.' She loads the last word with distaste.

We walk through the park entrance and up an incline between banks of pine trees. I breathe in the strong aroma of pine needles and can easily imagine how this place could cleanse the mind of its worries and concerns.

'Listen to the warblers and finches.' I can't distinguish any difference in the jumble of bird sounds, but it continues as we walk through the wooded part of the park and I too feel soothed.

I'm beginning to sense a growing intimacy in my relationship with Ruth. Through our mutual feeling for music, and now my growing awareness of her exceptional qualities as a human being, I'm being drawn into something I've never had before. She's more complex than Elspeth, but I sense she feels more deeply about all the things that are important to me. Her fastidiousness isn't simply a physical attribute, but a quality she applies to everything she does and thinks. In being accepted as a confidant, I know I'm being accorded an exceptional privilege.

I'm not yet aware that her father is constantly attacking her for her unworldliness, and has repeatedly told her she'll end up an old maid. Her devotion to music has become more than a career. It insulates her against the world her father and mother inhabit, and for which she has so much contempt.

It seems to me that her mother's worldliness has nurtured in her a strength to be the person she wants to be, to the exclusion of all else – including, if need be, marriage. She has a deep emotional need for

153

independence. But now, as I sense the change in our relationship, I begin to wonder if Ruth senses it too, and feels under threat from what is to her an alien emotion.

We come to a clearing with a pool. We sit on a wooden bench and contemplate the view.

'I think this is the nicest birthday I've ever had.'

I suddenly realise I've forgotten to give her my birthday present.

I pull a small book out of my inside jacket pocket – a volume of Keats's letters.

Ruth takes the book, looks at it, and fights to hold back tears. I've never known anyone who feels everything so deeply. She leafs through the book with care and tenderness.

I say, awkwardly, 'The letters to Fanny Brawne are particularly wonderful. Even though I hated school, I still felt a glimmering of inspiration when we were made to read Keats's poetry. Since I started at college, my love of Keats has grown. I hope you like the letters as much as I do.'

'Thank you, I'm sure I'll love them.'

We resume our saunter round the park, which is now reflecting the magic of early evening sun. We're walking side by side and I feel a longing to touch her hand. Up to then our relationship has been purely spiritual. After several hesitant minutes my hand touches hers, and we clasp hands. It's a deeply moving moment that needs nothing further to cement our new relationship. But then serenity is shattered.

'I thought you already had a girlfriend.'

I'm stunned that Ruth knows. I hadn't realised my relationship with Elspeth is common knowledge. It's true she's attended a few concerts at the college when I've been playing, but otherwise there has been no obvious contact between us in public. I've never thought of my two relationships as deception. They seem to be in different worlds: one earthbound, the other spiritual.

Ruth's question conveys so much about her. I instantly realise that integrity is more important to her than personal happiness. I've been carried away by the beauty of the experience, but Ruth is ready to destroy it in her demand for honesty. My touching of her hand demands a resolution.

'I've decided to finish with her.' I don't think of the consequences. I've been pretending to myself that the two relationships are compatible, but this moment of hand-holding signals the inevitable shattering of another relationship with someone who, I soon discover, is deeply dependent on me.

My dream of being a musician has never fitted comfortably with Elspeth's parents, but from the moment I meet Ruth's mother and father I sense a very different world. It encompasses a more broad-minded, liberal view of human behaviour in which bigger issues dominate and the artist can flourish. For all their faults, the respect Ruth's mother and father have for her views, even when they conflict with their own, impresses me.

We continue to walk through the park, now symbolically and physically joined by our hands. It's exquisitely innocent and beautiful. We slowly walk back, knowing that everything in both our lives is irrevocably changed.

'You know I come from a poor background.' I don't know why I feel it necessary to bring up my family. 'Perhaps you'd like to come and meet my parents?'

'If you'd like me to.'

'Of course I would.'

But I feel far from sure as I say it. What will the consequence be other than embarrassment, I wonder.

By this time the sun is setting and the first stars are visible in the luminous blue sky. I know that our relationship will have a profound impact on my life. As we return to her house we're still holding hands, and just as we approach the front door it opens and her younger sister greets us.

'I wondered where you'd gone. You seemed to disappear so quickly.'

It seems extraordinarily simple: one minute I'm an outsider attending a birthday party; the next, I feel like an insider, accepted into the family.

Ruth's mother has heard us return and is evidently back from her retreat. She has put on even more make-up.

'Let me get you some food, I'm sure you're starving.' She addresses me in the warmest maternal tone.

'No, really, I'm fine.'

'Mummy, we're just going to listen to some music upstairs. We'll come down a bit later.'

'Are you sure you don't want something now, darling?'

'Positive.'

I follow Ruth up the stairs. I'm fascinated by the evident tolerance and understanding of a family which doesn't demand conformity. As we reach the first landing, I can hear a radio in a bedroom at full volume. Ruth creeps in and turns it down. I can now hear that what I'd thought were atmospheric noises are Ruth's father snoring and wheezing. Yet, within seconds he regains momentary consciousness and turns the volume back up. He realises Ruth is there.

'Are you all right, lamb?' The voice and words are gentle, but he sinks back into sleep without waiting for any response.

We walk up a further flight of stairs and enter Ruth's own sanctum. It's a spacious attic room with a low ceiling that gives it a feeling of intimacy and charm rather than grandeur. It's also securely private, because any approaching visitor can be clearly heard. Ruth explains that no one ever intrudes without invitation, and I find it difficult to believe that a child can override a parent's wishes or rights in this way. But Ruth exerts an extraordinary strength in even the simplest things.

I soon begin to understand the contrast between her strength and her mother's weakness. Only through deception can Ruth's mother assert any counter will against the embargoes and refusals. A visit to the top floor will be justified on the grounds of bringing a coffee, or the mail, or a piece of news that might pass as important. But Ruth never relents or softens her stance. No apparent act of kindness is seen as anything other than a ploy to gain unauthorised and unwanted entry. I'm aware even then that Ruth's inability to compromise will come to dominate both our lives. But on that first evening together, left in peace listening to Alban Berg's *Wozzek*, it's enough to savour the moment and listen to music that depicts prophetically the heaven and hell of our life together, but in a way that makes it irresistible.

17

Cabbage Salad

It's Tuesday evening and Mam is having her weekly meeting with the Jehovah's Witnesses. Her simple approach to religion won't allow her to turn anyone away when they come preaching the Bible. There are three of them, a man and two women. They've been turning up for several weeks and spend the evening in a little cluster with the Bible and Mam in the centre.

Despite the inconvenience, there's a general acceptance by Mam and Dad that everyone is entitled to do whatever they want. When one room is shared by everyone, it would be unfair to allow one person to dominate all the activity. My brothers are allowed to play, someone can listen to the radio, and I can practise the piano. The Witnesses have come to accept that this is the only basis on which they can hold a meeting in our house. On this occasion they're visibly disconcerted when they find me practising a particularly loud and percussive piece: the fugue from Beethoven's Opus 101, which Stephen played to such great effect on his first visit, and which I'm playing as one of my examination pieces. As they sit down, they flash a smile in my direction that conveys anything but pleasure.

As usual, they start with a prayer. The man intones, 'Let us pray to the dear Lord to keep our beloved sister in her journey on the path of righteousness. The dear Lord who gave his blood so that we might have everlasting life. The dear Lord who died on the cross so that we might live.' As I play, I ponder the words. Far from conveying a powerful sense of everlasting life, they suggest something life-threatening. Bach had transformed this same message into wonderful, life-affirming music which will live as long as humanity, but I know instinctively that neither the Witnesses nor Mam could ever enter Bach's holy world. They can only reduce the words to mumbo jumbo that makes a mockery of real spiritual feeling. It's as far away as anything can be from the glorious inspiration of great music.

157

If I could enter Bach's world of religion, it would be glorious: a church service with the most wonderful music ever written. Instead, Mam's religion is supported by the most doleful, sanctimonious hymns, which is all they seem able to enjoy.

I feel the gap between me and Mam and Dad widen. They'll never understand the world music has opened up to me. We'll always be divided, joined only by blood. I abandon my attempt to play Opus 101 and begin to play some of the Bach 48 preludes and fugues. I thrill to the purity and nobility of the music as I play.

But now, the prayer meeting is in danger of disintegrating. My two younger brothers are quarrelling, Dad has the radio on, and my piano playing, far from setting the scene for Mam's conversion, is causing considerable irritation. Mam is oblivious to the hints dropped by the Witnesses. It's difficult to concentrate on my playing as I listen in on the unfolding events.

I'm sure that when they first called, they underestimated the work involved in making Mam one of them. Usually Jehovah's Witnesses are rebuffed, and when they meet someone welcoming it must seem too good to be true, but they're clearly having difficulty in making progress with Mam.

'Mary, we are here to help save you from eternal damnation. Only those who follow the Lord's path can be saved.'

I know from experience that Mam is invulnerable to words like these. She believes them completely, but without ever feeling under threat. She has no doubt that she is following the Lord. Her strength is that she hasn't got a defence. She believes everything they say, but their frustration is growing because they can't manipulate her into feeling saved by them. She enjoys their visits and prayers, but she doesn't respond in a way that satisfies them. They're on a mission, and Mam is too simple to understand it.

'You obviously have a lot on your mind at the moment. It's perhaps better if we leave you now and see you next time.'

I'm sure this remark is aimed at me and my piano playing, which they clearly hate. Mam is so used to ignoring the sound of my playing that she can't understand that anyone else might be bothered by it.

'If you want to come again, you can do,' she answers good-naturedly.

'Let us pray.' They bow their heads and hold a prayerful farewell amid piano playing, quarrelling and radio.

They then leave with obvious alacrity, and Mam returns to her knitting.

'I don't know what you see in them coming.' Dad always resents people visiting us, particularly men.

'You never want anyone to come. If you had your way we'd see nobody. I've never known such a jealous nature as yours. Just because I like to see my family, you have a face as long as a fiddle whenever they come.'

'All you ever want is to be with them.'

'I don't know what's the matter with you. Every time anybody comes, you sit sulking in the corner. I feel ashamed of you sometimes.'

'I'm happy as we are.'

'Well, I like some company.'

Dad grunts with frustrated resentment, unable to resolve a conflict that has been present ever since they've been together. No argument ever results in anything but the further entrenchment of opposing views.

I begin to practise again with fresh vigour, but while playing, troubled thoughts disturb my concentration. How can I tell Elspeth that I've decided it's better for us if we part? What possible reason can I give to justify my claim that it's better for her? Better for me, yes, because it suits me. It's going to be impossible to do it humanely. The unvarnished truth is that I've found someone I think is better. Ruth is a musician and her parents are not middle-class, small-minded people constantly constraining and limiting my life. I've been able to breathe culturally in Ruth's house in a totally different way from Elspeth's. There's no doubt I have to make the break, but I'm deeply worried about how.

The following morning the sun is shining as I settle at the piano to work. Mam and Dad are bickering as usual.

'I hope that oven's hot today.'

'I lit it at five thirty, so it should be.'

'How many pies are you making?'

'Five dozen.'

'I thought I told you to make six dozen today! There's a special order from the mill. That's why I said six dozen.'

'You're imagining things, you never told me.'

'The number of times you forget what I tell you! Your memory's going.'

Their incessant wrangling doesn't distract me from my work. Nor is the music I play ever a problem for them. But what does continually grate on them is the fact that I'm not working. Their idea of work is very clear: it's something you'd prefer not to do if you had the option. It's monotonous, tedious, hard. My practising can sound monotonous and tedious and hard, but it fails to qualify as work because it's my reason for living. This is what is incomprehensible to them.

'Now you've got a new girlfriend, what are you doing about Elspeth?'

I'm astonished that Mam has understood without my saying a word. 'She's a nice girl. I don't know why you couldn't be satisfied with her.'

It's utterly impossible to explain the complexity of something I barely understand myself.

'I am satisfied with her.'

'It's a funny way of being satisfied when you spend the weekend with someone else and come back looking star-struck.'

How sordid everything becomes in their minds. My relationships with Elspeth and Ruth have both been so beautiful and yet so different. Mam can't begin to understand what I feel, but I decide to carry on playing, leaving her with the last word.

I feel very nervous at the thought of Ruth's forthcoming visit. It was unnecessary in a sense, yet I've gone out of my way to insist on it. The mere thought makes me blush, so why am I doing it? Perhaps I want to brave it out in the open; perhaps I'm attracted to the situation, like a moth to a flame. Of course, I can rationalise and tell myself a thousand times that no one of any consequence can seriously think worse of me because of my family. My parents are decent, honest people and I'm proud of that, but after the temporary anaesthetic of rationalising has worn off, I'm still left with the uncomfortable ache of fear. With my family I feel warm and secure, but when people from a different class visit I feel vulnerable.

'What's that you're doing?' Mam snaps.

I'm in the middle of washing a cabbage in the only sink in the house – not easy, because of piles of dirty tins and pots waiting for the next big wash-up. I'm rinsing the chopped cabbage in a colander because I've decided a cabbage salad is the only sort of lunch I can offer without going through the agony of Ruth judging Mam's cooking. In any case, my interest in health foods is shared by Ruth and I feel I need to make a meal I can be proud of. It's not a particularly fresh cabbage and it's limp except for the heart. I begin to slice it into a mountain of crinkled pieces.

'What's that supposed to be?' Dad grimaces.

'As if we haven't enough to do.' Mam is less benevolent. 'Move away from that sink. I want some cake tins.'

The heat from the big coke oven is intense in this small, overcrowded, untidy, back kitchen bakehouse.

My anxiety about Ruth's visit is obvious to everyone, but instead of sympathy, all I'm managing to provoke is uneasiness and antagonism.

160

I find a lemon and begin to mix a French dressing. Jack has sidled in to look at the unusual sight of a pile of raw cabbage. He's picked up that this is for my new girlfriend.

'Ooh, what a horrible-looking dinner.'

I pretend to ignore him and find a glass dish to put the cabbage in and pour on the salad dressing. I mix it around and taste it. It isn't too bad, but it's a bit watery and limp. It's seemed an enormous effort under the circumstances. But now it's done, my success recedes little by little as I taste it and look at it. I turn to Mam.

'Would you like to try it?'

'I wouldn't eat such stuff. I'd sooner eat cabbage cooked.'

I can tell that her reply is an expression of aversion to what she feels are alien ways, and her feeling that I'm growing away from them. This confirms what she's always feared would be the case when I became educated and mixed with different social classes.

'Can we get to the sink now? Your father wants to get washed up.'

I put the bowl of cabbage on the side of the sink and walk back to my piano. I begin to practise, and the normal business of Mam answering the shop and walking backwards and forwards through the living-room continues as I concentrate on the keyboard, all the while listening out for Ruth. I would have been happier meeting a bus or train than waiting nervously and tensely at home, but it wasn't possible to arrange a precise time. I try as always to overcome my feelings by working hard and pretending the outside world doesn't exist, but it's difficult.

Mam speaks up. 'Come on Dad, you get your dinner while you can.' Eating is always informal and the opportunity is snatched when it arises. Dad brings in a plate with two of his own meat-and-potato pies on it, and begins to eat. I pray that Ruth won't arrive just now. The heat seems to increase in the room as I work at the difficult passages of a sonata.

'I don't know. All this fuss over someone coming, anyone would think you're ashamed of your own family,' Mam says.

'It's nothing to do with that.' I try to continue playing.

'Well, what is it then? You've been like a cat on hot bricks all morning.'

I have no reasonable answer to offer, but my discomfort increases and so does my concern about the wisdom of arranging the meeting at all.

'I don't know what's wrong with girls of your own kind. You can be carried away by a pretty dress you know, and it's only money that buys that. You think you're too clever for us, I know. All we count for is nothing. We've slaved to bring you up and this is the thanks we get.'

161

'Mam, it's not that.' I feel the pressure of Mam's unhappiness and suffer at the thought of it. What I'm doing is so right to me, but I know I can never communicate that to Mam.

Someone comes into the shop and our conversation comes to an end. Mam is used to having public and private conversations punctuated by the arbitrary ring of the shop bell. Dad continues eating his pies, but after a few minutes I decide to retreat to the bedroom rather than face another emotional outburst.

I creep stealthily but quickly, as if I'm being chased up the bare wooden stairs. I lie on my bed while my mind whirls in a mixture of despair and optimism. I look but don't see; sounds come from all directions but I'm deaf to them. I look up at the old cracks in the ceiling and try desperately to see the prowling tiger, the malignant dwarf, the serene old man, figures I can usually see so clearly but which now mysteriously defy all attempts to find them. My conflicting emotions are sapping my strength and I feel the urge to retreat into sleep. Street sounds – voices, dogs, bicycle bells, the shop bell – float at random in a haze of ordinariness, soothe me and act as a kind of lullaby.

I'm floating away gently and happily, when suddenly one sound strikes me like a blunt knife on a raw nerve. It's Ruth, in the shop talking to Mam. I'm instantaneously overcome by anxiety and nerves, excitement and pleasure as I go downstairs to meet her. She's already in the living-room, talking easily and naturally to my family. Introductions are fortunately unnecessary, as the relationships are all obvious.

'I hope I'm no bother,' Ruth is saying to Mam.

'Of course you're not,' I reply abruptly, thinking of the minimal effort my family has made for her.

'Oh, but I'm sure I've put your mother out. She has enough to do without worrying about someone arriving in the middle of the day.' There's a perfectly calculated reproving tone in her voice as she speaks to me. She has a sureness of touch that enables her instinctively to say and do the right thing. I feel overcome with pride as I look at her in my own living-room. Every aspect of her gives me a feeling of confidence and rightness. This environment has never to my knowledge produced a human being of this kind. I've had no reason to suppose they even exist, and yet I've responded to Ruth as one would to a lifelong friend. The joy is deep, because in finding Ruth I've found a dream.

Mam says, 'You'll have to excuse us being in such a mess.'.

'Please don't worry about me. Can I do anything to help you?'

'Of course not,' I leap in before Mam can say anything. I feel almost indignant that such sincerity should be lavished on my family. I have no feeling of tenderness for them. I move an old newspaper and some washing and mending from the most comfortable chair in the cramped living-room to make room for Ruth. David stands aimlessly about, afraid to miss any part of this remarkable event.

'You're David, aren't you?' He blushes without replying.

Dad has only just finished his pies. He smiles without speaking as he gets up, plate in hand, ready to return to his work. They all behave like shy animals, normally garrulous but silent in the company of strangers. I begin to feel as I'd feared I would – uncomfortable and awkward. I try to think of Stephen in the same circumstances, aware of Art and Being, blissfully unaware of social shortcomings. I am, however, very conscious of Ruth's utter lack of awkwardness or embarrassment, and while this is solace, it does nothing to allay my misgivings.

'I'm sure I could do something to help your mother.'

'No.'

This insistence on help is becoming disconcerting.

I pick a manuscript from the top of the piano and show it to Ruth. 'This is what I'm working on now.' She picks it up reluctantly. I insist, by sitting at the piano and playing from it. The noise, so normal to me and the family, seems unpleasantly incongruous to Ruth.

'Doesn't your mother mind so much noise?'

The question is so complete a surprise that I can think of no answer. My noise is me, it's my work. It's liberation, success, career, important, sacred. Why should I consider the effect it has on someone else? I bridle a little at the suggestion, and am disturbed even to imagine the shattering consequences such extreme consideration would have in my circumstances. I'm not accustomed to anyone showing consideration to my family, and I once more divert attention to music.

'Have you seen this composition of Stephen's before?'

'No. He's too egotistical for me, even in his music.'

'But artists must be egotistical in order to survive.'

'That's typical of self-centred people without any humility, and I absolutely disagree with it.'

'But surely you need to be able to disregard anything that could distract you from your goal?' I cling tenaciously to my point. I hate disagreement, particularly over such an important tenet, and I want desperately to have Ruth's admiration.

'I think it's more important to show consideration.' There is in this sentiment a strength of personality that outdoes Stephen. I recognise and admire it, but it's beyond me. It demands the sacrifice of my ego, and I've fought too hard for my ego and depend on it too much to be able to jettison it at a moment's notice. In any case, my family demand little consideration of that sort, so I'm unused to showing it. I try to steer us on to less controversial ground.

'I thought we could go for a walk this afternoon. I want to show you some of the beautiful country on the edge of the moors.'

I desperately feel the need to be alone with Ruth, to communicate directly by touch and not run the risk of argument. In front of my family I exhibit no obvious sign of the close feeling of intimacy we have developed. Certainly Ruth encourages none, and I begin to feel as if I'm disliked or hated rather than loved.

'I'd like to come, but I can't be too late. There's a train I need to catch at five o'clock.'

Once more the hard, practical sentiment stings me. I want an utter disregard for time and place. I think of my night on the railway station with Stephen and that seems to me the approach to life I need. But I also need Ruth in a more dependent way and I have somehow to compromise my dreams and desires. I decide to take the initiative.

'Well, let's get a move on before it's too late. Will you have something to eat?'

'Nothing for me.'

I'm again unused to politeness and don't know how to cope with it. I'm so close to Ruth, and yet in so many ways unable to approach her honesty and simplicity.

'You ought to have something.'

'No, really, I don't want to trouble your mother.'

Ruth leaves little room for argument and in front of my family I'm unable to make any reference to the effort I put into making a salad. Then I remember how pathetic a meal I'd judged it to be, and her refusal gives me a feeling of relief. I brighten as I rise.

'Let's go then, while we have time.' I'm all ready to leave, right now.

'Are you sure you won't have something to eat?' says Mam.

'No, really.' Ruth is standing now.

'You've not been here five minutes,' Mam persists. She now seems dissatisfied by the transient visitor.

'Don't worry, Mother, Ruth will be here again.' I can't make the break without softening it.

'I'm sure she ought to have something before she goes.'

164

The shop bell rings and cuts short any further discussion. As Mam goes through to the shop, we follow her and gesture a goodbye as she serves a customer.

18

A Parting of Ways

Everything seems so different when I'm with Ruth. Her parents welcome the prospect of me becoming their son-in-law and seem proud of my piano playing. The thought of leaving Haydock Street and moving into Ruth's flat is constantly in my mind, but I still have to broach the subject at home. Although I'm only a few months away from my twenty-first birthday, I need my parents' permission to get married before then.

Before I have the courage to raise the subject, they seem to sense that my growing dissatisfaction with life in Haydock Street might lead to something they don't want.

Dad approaches me.

'Look. I know it's been difficult for you, but we can make a room for you in your grandad's house so you can have some privacy.'

'It doesn't matter.'

'You could move your piano in.'

'I'm all right as I am.'

'You could do what you want.'

'Thanks, but leave it for now.'

I don't want to encourage them, because I know it's only a matter of time before I'll be leaving Bolton altogether.

Their unexpected consideration couldn't be worse timed. I feel guilt and remorse. As if he instinctively knows and wants to add more coals to the fire, Dad pulls out a brown box and gives it to me.

'We bought you this for your twenty-first. You may as well have it now.'

I open it. It's a gramophone I'd noticed for sale at a reduced price in Horrocks' shop window. I feel a pang of pain, which I conceal. They're reduced because they're redundant. A few months before, I'd heard of a new technology which meant a symphony could be played on one record by reducing the speed from seventy-eight to thirty-three and a third revolutions per minute. In place of a heavy head and a needle that quickly wore out and damaged the record, they'd developed a lightweight head and a needle that rarely needed replacing. The present seems to symbolise everything about them: their generosity, their frugality, their hopeless unworldliness. They've been duped. They want to give me something that matters to me, but all they've managed is something that means I'll never think of my twenty-first birthday without pain.

Later that afternoon I lie on my bed, listening to Beethoven's C Sharp Minor Quartet on the new gramophone, but desperate for something even great music can't provide. There is no contentment gained by lying and listening; I'm suffering an exquisite form of discontent. I need to see Ruth. I know her well enough now to know that she will never be vulnerable to this kind of irrationality and emotion. How can I be a musician if I can't focus single-mindedly on myself and my career? I try, but I know it's only a matter of time before I'll give in. What's the point of trying to resist the irresistible? I can hear the shop bell ringing still, but with less frequency as the afternoon draws to a close. There is no way I can say anything to Mam. She can never understand and will be indignant that I'm so pathetically weak-willed. The music which normally inspires me has lost its power and is now an intrusion.

I can hear David climbing the stairs. I'm still lying on the bed as he comes in.

'What you doing?'

'Nothing. I'm just listening to this music.'

He looks at me with displeasure. I was just six years old when he was born, and it was the most wonderful moment; I felt emotions beyond my years. But from the beginning his life seems to have been full of unhappiness and discontent. He cried a lot and it was impossible for Mam to give him the attention he needed, particularly when we moved to Farnworth and the cookshop.

I'd tried to comfort him as he grew older, but his unhappiness was utterly different from mine. Physical contact was repugnant to him when he was upset. A hug would provoke a violent kick. It was very hard for me to witness his suffering and feel powerless, knowing that only by ignoring it could he be helped.

'D'you want to come and play cricket?'

It's a rare invitation. Our games on the tarmac at the side of the shop with a tennis ball usually end disastrously. If he's caught or bowled out, he'll sulk and leave the match immediately.

'Not just now.'

'Oh come on, I've nothing else to do.'

He never shows any consideration for me, but I feel the contradictions welling up inside me. I have to refuse, yet I know my refusal is selfish. I know I can't walk away without leaving a trail of guilt behind me. But even the pain of letting him down can't overwhelm my desperate need to see Ruth.

'Look, I really can't now, but I promise I'll play tomorrow.'

'No, I want to play now.'

It's the kind of confrontation I couldn't have withstood normally. The need to practise or study would have been swept away like a feather in a gale. My own needs seem to have such a low priority that they count for nothing, even in my own eyes, when I'm put under the pressure of other people's needs. But today is different: a power beyond my control enables me to refuse, but not without feeling guilty. I must see Ruth, but at the cost of further damaging a relationship with David that is already decaying. How can things stand so badly between us after all the love I felt when he was born? I'm discovering that love is no guarantee that a relationship will be trouble-free.

'I'm sorry, I can't. I've got something I must do.'

'What?'

'I promised to meet someone.'

'Who?'

'It doesn't matter.'

The determination in my refusal surprises David and it surprises me. I get up and turn the gramophone off. David is still looking defiantly at me. I go downstairs.

'Mam, I'm just going out to see Harry.'

'Don't keep your Dad up late!'

Dad still insists on waiting for me to get home, but moans continually the following morning if I'm later than half-past ten.

I leave through the shop door and start to half-run in the direction of Trinity Street station. I have no idea what time the trains are and I don't even know if Ruth will be there. It's a mad idea, but some powerful force is dragging me there as if my life depends on it. The station is eerily deserted, in contrast to Wakes Week.

I have to wait half an hour for the Southport train, so I pull out the volume of Blake's poetry I carry with me. I want to elevate my emotions and feelings on to the higher plane which I'm sure is the world of the artists I desperately want to emulate. I want to escape from my earthbound environment. The love I feel holds the promise of some new world in which I can live, but not without causing pain to those I have to leave behind.

As soon as the train arrives at Southport I find a telephone box to call Ruth. What a wild goose chase this could prove to be if she isn't at home. I can hardly believe it when she answers.

'Look, I need to see you.'

'Where are you?'

'I'm here. I just arrived at the station.'

'There's no one here to pick you up.'

'Don't worry, I'll get the bus.'

'I'll meet you at the bus stop outside the park.'

I rush to the bus stop and manage to jump on a bus just as it leaves. As it trundles in the direction of Ruth's park, I begin to feel embarrassed by my rashness. What on earth will her family think of someone who is so volatile? Someone who can so easily be distracted from his work? Someone whose emotions are so uncontrollable? What makes it worse is that I know Ruth would never have given way to the same feelings. I'm the vulnerable one, not her.

As I get off the bus, I see Ruth waiting. We walk slowly together along the road bordering the park, in the direction of the sea. The evening is still and warm, and brought to that perfection of temperature and atmosphere by the onset of darkness. The air is tinged with the acrid smell of an autumnal bonfire and we look up at a breathtaking array of stars. In that moment I see my love for Ruth clearly and brilliantly, and no petty considerations can stand in the way. I'm in love with Ruth and I can't turn away from it. It's a beautiful, unfolding experience which has permeated my soul as ink soaks into blotting paper. I never doubt that the love I feel has been created by a spontaneous union of our spirits, and I seek and clasp Ruth's hand as we walk side by side.

When I return to Haydock Street, the impossibility of working under such difficult conditions, the joy of thinking of a life with Ruth, the comfort of her flat – all conspire to give me the strength to broach the question of marriage. I've never even hinted at it, but I know their reaction will be hostile. It's always been the same. Whenever a school friend invited me to stay with him at his aunt's by the seaside, they would bristle and snarl with indignation.

170

'All you ever want to do is to get away from here!'

'We have to do all this work and you're enjoying yourself.'

'It's a pity you don't know what work is!'

Consent to desert is rare and grudging. Any pleasure is diminished by their resentment. There's no way something that promises to give me so much happiness will be acceptable to them.

Surely they can't object to Ruth, part of me reasons. Life with her might mean I can do more for them. This time they must be able to see that a happy marriage will be something they can enjoy. Why should they object? None the less, it takes a lot of courage to raise the question.

'Can I speak to you, Mam?'

Before I've said a word about Ruth, I see her stiffen ready for battle.

'What is it now?'

'I want to talk about Ruth.'

'What about her?' Hostility is growing.

'We want to be together. We're in love.'

Mam looks at me with animosity.

'What are you trying to say?'

'I'm trying to tell you that we want to spend our lives together.'

'Ugh. She can afford to do what she wants. They're not like us, we have to work for what we want.'

The yawning gap between their understanding of their lives and purpose, and Ruth's family, suddenly seems unbridgeable. They don't want to bridge it. The difference between their taste in music and mine is already a deep enough chasm. The Leyton Hall experience has been impossible to discuss with them. For me now to leave their world and enter one of luxury and taste is, to them, a pretension much too far. It's the stuff of fiction.

'I don't know why you couldn't be satisfied with Elspeth.'

'Mam, it's nothing to do with that.'

'It's everything to do with it. You just want what you want.'

'I want to be happy and I think Ruth will make me happy.'

'You can buy nice clothes with money. Don't be fooled with appearances.'

'I'm not fooled by them or interested in them. We both love the same kind of music and the same kind of things, that's why we want to get married.'

Mam reacts with genuine shock. She looks suddenly upset and angry at the same time.

'That's just about it isn't it, after sweating all our lives that's the thanks we get.'

'It's no good worrying. You'll only upset yourself,' Dad cuts in.

'But Mam, I can't help it. We want to get married,' I appeal.

'*Marriage*,' she says with disgust. 'All these years you've brought nothing in and now you just want to get *married!*'

'Is that all you had children for, to get something out of them?' I'm angry now.

'Mam, can I get a bottle of pop?' my younger brother chimes in. Ignored, he hovers, out of range but not out of earshot.

'No, but you can expect a bit of gratitude after all the sacrifices we've made.' She looks upset as she speaks.

'I am grateful, but I'm entitled to live my own life,' I still fight.

'Yes, that's what you say. Wait till you've children of your own. You'll know then.' She almost sneers.

'I hope I'll consider them,' I say.

'You're too selfish to consider anybody. All you want to consider is yourself. That's why you're getting married.'

'But I want to consider you, and you won't let me.'

'No, what you want is your own way.'

'So do you.'

'Don't you think we're entitled to something more after sweating here all these years? More than two minutes' notice from you that you want to get married? That's what hurts me.' She sits down and starts to sob. 'After all this, you're just going to clear off and leave us in the lurch. Look after yourself, don't bother about us. Go on, get out!' She begins to scream.

'But Mam, don't you want to know when it is...?' I'm upset now.

'Mam, can I have a bottle of pop?' my brother persists.

'No, I don't want to know when it is and I don't want to see you! Clear out and don't bother me again!' She collapses in a wave of hysterical sobs.

I feel torn but helpless. After looking impotently at my mother for a few painful seconds, I leave the room and our house, never to return.

19

Herbert and Sophia

It's seductive to be adopted by a family with none of the financial pressures that had reduced life with Mam and Dad to the crudest essentials. As a small child I never complained; they'd explained patiently that I couldn't have what I wanted because Dad was out of work and they had no money. There seemed no point in crying for something that was impossible.

But now I'm enjoying a new experience. Suddenly I'm being treated like the son of rich parents. Wherever we go and whatever we do, Herbert accepts that I don't have money, just as I'd accepted that Mam and Dad didn't have money. I'd never complained then and it doesn't occur to me to argue now. I feel no loss of dignity. I have no hang-ups about preserving some kind of financial independence. Herbert clearly enjoys playing the host. When the bill comes, he always assumes he'll be paying it and I sit back and enjoy living in luxury for the first time in my life.

We're all going to the opera house, to see a new play by Peter Ustinov. We're travelling in a flashy American car, given to Herbert by some Canadian friends who had been staying with him. They'd been so impressed by his hospitality that they'd sent a brand-new Chrysler at a time when new cars were a rarity in postwar Britain.

We all climb into the car, and Herbert has his usual chauffeur, Peter, at the wheel. Sophia can only ever travel in the front of the car because of her inclination to feel unwell. Conveniently, there is a sound-proof glass screen between driver and back-seat passengers, and I'm soon to discover how effectively this terminates any arguments Herbert decides have gone on long enough. The road is at sea level all the way and the Chrysler is quieter, smoother and swifter than any car I've known. Trees and buildings streak past us, but the smoothness of the ride makes it all seem unnaturally safe. The brightly shining sun contributes to the relaxed mood in the car. It's difficult to imagine what could spoil such an idyll.

'Peter, stop at my usual place.' Herbert speaks in his most imperious manner.

Sophia reacts instantly, with intense irritation in her voice, and looks at all of us as if we're collectively responsible.

'Oh Herbert, all you ever want to do is meet up with your drinking pals. We'll be late.'

'We won't be late.' His face expresses defiant annoyance.

'You say that every time.'

'I'll just have one drink. The landlord would be upset if he thought I'd driven past and not called in.'

'All he's interested in is your money!'

'He is not interested in my money.'

'Daddy, don't spoil our evening.' Ruth appeals to him, concerned that despite all the favourable omens the usual conflict between her parents is about to erupt.

'I wouldn't dream of spoiling your evening, lamb. All I want is one drink. I won't be more than five minutes.'

At this point he decides to take no more chances and presses the button which raises the glass screen, silencing but not necessarily stopping further criticism from his wife. As if to restore the good mood, he pulls out an enormous cigar from inside his sock. As he begins to light it, he looks at me conspiratorially, tapping the side of his nose. 'If you want to carry a cigar without damaging it, that's where you put it.' He shares his secret with me perhaps only because I'm his son-in-law.

Peter dutifully drives into the car park of the pub where, Herbert insists, the landlord regards a visit from him as one of the highlights of his life. Our stop is for the publican's sake, and is certainly not an act of self-indulgence.

Sophia stays in the car, still fuming. I have no option but to follow Ruth, who seems more indulgent of her father's drinking. Herbert is now smoking his cigar in great style and beaming with pleasure as he enters the pub. The landlord doesn't react as I'd imagined he would. His face reflects indifference, not delight, but Herbert isn't in any way perturbed.

'A large whisky and water.' He sits on a bar stool, very much at home despite what strikes me as a distinctly frosty reception. He taps off an inch of cigar ash and takes a gulp of whisky. He turns to Ruth and me.

'What will you have to drink?'

'Nothing, thank you.' I really don't feel thirsty. Herbert looks at me.

'You must never let these women get between you and a drink.' He

174

imagines I'm being influenced by his wife's hostility, but she's still in the car. 'I'll have a beer,' I say.

Ruth looks at me with annoyance. I don't want it, but would feel too much of a killjoy to have nothing. The landlord looks at me. 'Pint?'

'Er, no, half a pint.' I sense contempt from all the drinkers at the bar, who are no doubt into their second and third pints. Herbert drinks contentedly, his whisky nearly gone.

'Put another in.' The publican takes his glass and puts two more slugs of whisky in. I sip my beer with little pleasure. Herbert holds his glass and sniffs the whisky aroma in a state of near-ecstasy.

'Whenever I take Mummy on a cruise, we're always invited to the captain's table. The captain soon knows I'm on board. The last time we sailed to New York, the captain invited me to see him. "We all know about you, Herbert," he said.'

Herbert imitates the captain's knowing look, suggesting a secret world where anyone who is anyone knows Herbert.

'They made sure I had a bottle of whisky in my cabin every day. I've crossed the Atlantic many times. I have friends all over the world and they all love to see me. Do you know how I got the car outside?' I didn't, or at least not the full story.

'My friend Quentin in Toronto. He'd do anything for me. He and his wife came to stay with us for a few weeks. We went touring in the Chrysler and continued together to Monte Carlo and stayed in Cannes and Nice for a few days, at all the top hotels. Peter drove us.'

It's a dream world to me. It belongs to Hollywood, and Cary Grant, and people with wealth I can only imagine. But Herbert puzzles me. He doesn't fit into that mould. He has an element of the fraudulent about him. He's clearly boastful, and yet the chauffeur, the cigar, the whisky and the lifestyle are all real.

'When Quentin discovered it was impossible to buy new cars in England, he said, "Leave it to me." The next thing I heard was that a car was waiting for me in Liverpool Docks. When Peter went to collect it, it was in a wooden packing case. The silly buggers had nailed the packing case on to the top of the car.' Herbert gives a hollow laugh. I imagine the brand-new, shiny black car pierced with nails.

'Daddy, we've heard enough of all this. Let's get going.'

'All right, lamb. I'm coming now. I just wanted me drink.' The whisky seems to have mellowed him.

We return to the car and find Sophia still seething.

'You're back, are you?' She shoves her chin out defiantly and indicates

175

with a toss of the head that she won't be resuming harmonious relations for some time.

Herbert puts on his best unperturbed smile. The whisky has weakened him and he is less and less concerned about everyone else. Peter opens the rear door for him, and Herbert settles deep into the leather seat. The aura of whisky and cigar envelops him in luxurious contentment.

Peter straightens his chauffeur's cap. I notice for the first time that he's rather small for the job. His face adopts a pugnacious defiance, as if to protect himself from Sophia on his left and his employer in the back. He obviously has a great deal of experience of being sandwiched between these two opposing forces, and is clearly able to recognise the fine line that he'll cross only at his peril.

The opera house is a quite grand building and the bar in the foyer gives Herbert an opportunity to resume drinking. He turns to Sophia diplomatically. 'What are you having to drink, Mummy?' The appeal isn't to the mother of his children but to a matriarch, plaintively.

Sophia is still behaving like the offended heroine, but is sufficiently a woman of the world to answer: 'I'll have a Martini.' Herbert is aware that the frost is melting. When I'm asked the same question, I'm momentarily stumped. Ruth has no difficulty in declining to drink anything, but that somehow makes it imperative that I join in. More beer is not only the last thing I want, it also doesn't seem right. I panic inside as I try to come up with a drink that will reflect well on me.

'Er, a shandy.'

Herbert looks at me with a question mark on his face, but he orders it. The bar is filling up rapidly as the performance draws nearer.

Herbert has selected a bar stool and sits with his legs apart; he looks into his glass of whisky, seeming bored and ill at ease in this arty gathering. He taps his glass absent-mindedly.

Just as the air is hanging very heavy, Peter comes into the bar followed by a prosperous-looking man in a smart blazer.

'Sir, this is the mayor of Thornton. He asked me to introduce you.'

Peter then turns round and leaves the mayor with us, but stands patiently at the rear of the room.

Herbert picks up immediately.

176

'What will you have to drink?'

It's a question Herbert clearly loves to ask. The mayor has no difficulty in answering.

'A whisky.'

Herbert is well pleased. The mayor pulls up a stool and sits confidently next to Herbert.

'What's your line of business?' says Herbert, evidently delighted to be back in the world he loves.

'I have a few radio shops.'

'I made a cat's whisker radio when I was a boy.' Herbert is in no hurry to know why the mayor has asked to be introduced to him. He seems to make it more rather than less difficult for the mayor to tell him. He points to his glass as the barman passes in front of him. The barman brings over the whisky bottle.

'Another?' he looks at the mayor.

'Thank you.' The mayor continues, 'Is that your car outside?'

'It is.'

'I think it's the first Chrysler I've ever seen round here.'

Herbert looks over to Peter, who has anticipated this moment and quickly strides over.

'Peter, take the mayor for a ride.'

'Yes, sir.'

Herbert turns to the mayor.

'I'll see you back in the bar at the interval. If you like the car, you can buy it.'

I'm astonished at the unspoken understanding Herbert displays. I'm also taken aback that an extraordinarily generous gift has no moral obligation attached to it in Herbert's mind. The present is now his and he can do whatever he wants with it.

Sophia, however, has other ideas.

'You're not seriously thinking you can sell that car, are you?' She looks at him with a mixture of disbelief and derision.

I sip my shandy, looking from one to the other. Herbert seems unperturbed and is about to reply when the bell rings signalling the start of the performance. We head for the nearest usher and are quickly directed to our seats.

Neither Ruth nor I have been excited at the prospect of the play, and already the drinking episodes have persuaded us that we've made a mistake. Sophia's behaviour is progressively more appropriate to the stage than the auditorium, with the result that we're becoming a focus of

177

unwelcome attention as we take our seats. This is anathema to Ruth, who always seeks a dignified anonymity.

'Mummy, please don't make such a spectacle of yourself.' She whispers the words with undisguised distaste.

'Darling, if people can't take me as I am...' Sophia's tone gives the sentence the emphatic ending it doesn't technically have. The embarrassment we feel is more acute because her extensive cleavage, barely noticeable when we set out, becomes glaringly provocative as our private altercation heats up. Sophia has no intention of letting go of the audience she has gained.

We cause maximum disturbance along the row. As people stand to let us pass, Sophia says, 'Thank you,' as if she's really saying, 'I should think so too.'

I begin to realise that Herbert and Sophia have no intention of behaving like respectable theatre-goers. Their bickering continues, to Ruth's acute discomfort.

'Herbert, have you got a coin for the opera glasses?'

'No, I haven't.'

'I can't possibly see without them.'

'Well, I'm not getting change now.'

I feel in my trousers with a sense of desperation. Thank goodness! I pass the coin along, relieved to solve what is threatening to become a major impasse. She puts the coin in and takes out the glasses.

'These aren't very good. Let me try yours, Herbert.'

It's clear she's determined to create as much annoyance as she can.

The theatre darkens and the play begins. Usually in the theatre I can leave the real world and live in my imagination, barely breathing. But the real world holds me in its grip. I can't take my mind off Sophia and what might happen next. I can't concentrate on the play. I continually try to focus on Peter Ustinov.

I become aware of the discontent of people nearby, irritated by Sophia's constant and intrusive use of the opera glasses. I try to focus on the play, without success. My senses are so highly tuned that every slight move and noise around me seems to be amplified to an unbearable level. I long to withdraw into oblivion. The play is in full swing, but I have no idea what it's about. It's too late to get a foothold now; the dialogue is meaningless. All I can do is look forward to the interval, and wonder what pretext I might use to excuse myself from coming back. Worse, Ruth implicates me in her parents' public behaviour. Ever since the pub en route, Ruth has exuded hostility towards me. I feel totally isolated

178

and exposed. Time drags, my legs twitch. I try to get some relief by moving my legs and twisting in my seat, but nothing helps. I stare at the head in front of me, looking for something to hold my interest. The action on stage is now an irritating irrelevance. The twitching gets worse; I cross and re-cross my legs. I have an itch on my face, on my head, on my face again. I'm in a state of continuous movement, trying to appease the twitching and itching in a way that hopefully conceals my agony from my neighbours.

Suddenly, Herbert stands up and makes it clear he's had enough. We all seize the opportunity to leave, and to a boiling ferment of annoyance and inconvenience we shuffle along the row, treading on toes and obstructing views.

It's a relief to return to the serenity of the bar, and the cooler air soon assuages my embarrassment. Sophia is still bristling with indignation, but the more private setting makes everything easier to cope with.

'Herbert, you're a selfish, self-centred, inconsiderate, drunken oaf.' She spits the words at him, knowing they'll have little impact. The level of alcohol is enough to insulate him against petty insults, but not enough to turn him into an unpleasant, aggressive drunk.

He grins benevolently at all of us, as if he is the Pope and impervious to the views of lesser mortals.

'A large whisky,' he orders, much more comfortable here than in a theatre seat. The barman pours a generous double. Peter, lurking in the corridor outside the bar, follows us in. Herbert ignores us and turns to him.

'What did he think of it?'

'Guess what? He thinks it's wonderful,' says Peter.

Herbert sits smiling complacently, as if he's achieved what he wants. Sophia suddenly asserts herself.

'Herbert, I'll have a gin and Italian.'

'Of course, darling.' Herbert is suddenly in a more benevolent mood.

'What would you like, lamb?' He turns to Ruth.

'I'll have a glass of white wine.'

He looks in my direction.

'Red wine please.' My experience in Leyton Hall has left its mark.

We all settle into the cosy chairs of the bar, for different reasons pleased to be out of the theatre. Just as we're settling back and enjoying the quiet, the doors to the stalls open and the audience swarms in for the interval.

In a few minutes the mayor has joined us and is drinking a large whisky, with Herbert in full flow.

179

'I can do business all over the world. My friends always tell me, "Herbert, we can trust you and we like you," that's what's kept my business going through the difficult times.'

I'm surprised to see that the mayor seems impressed. I'm curious about the total absence of any reference to the Chrysler. With Herbert holding court, no other public conversation seems possible and Ruth engages in the odd whispered comment: 'I wish we could get back home,' and 'I can't believe anyone can be taken in by him.'

Herbert's monologue rolls on. 'I've always collected antiques. I bought a magnificent pair of oriental vases from a shop in Salford. They're museum pieces. One day a fellow called to see me. He told me he was from the V&A. "We know all about you, Herbert," he said. "We're keeping an eye on you." I've collected all over the world and if I see something I like, I buy it. The one rule I make is never to ignore my first instinct. If I like it when I see it, that's it. If I don't like it, no amount of persuasion will change my mind. That first instinct is the one to trust.'

I begin to wonder if this is pushing in the direction of the car.

'Have another whisky.' Herbert gestures to the barman to pour the mayor another double. 'My chauffeur has been all over the Continent with me. We've been over the Alps a few times on our way to the South of France.'

Sophia suddenly shows some interest. 'Ah, yes, we've had some wonderful evenings at the Grand Hotel in Cannes.' She speaks theatrically, as if addressing more than her family and the mayor.

'She's so disgusting at times,' Ruth whispers to me.

'I always like to stay in one of the suites looking out over the Mediterranean.'

Sophia is now using her cleavage to advantage and the mayor is clearly attracted. He says, 'Look, would you like a glass of champagne?' Sophia's eyes sparkle. 'Bring a bottle of champagne.' The barman quickly supplies the champagne and some glasses.

'Not for us, thank you.' Ruth speaks on our behalf without reference to me. We're clearly not part of the South of France tour and the mayor makes no attempt to persuade us to join them in drinking the champagne.

By now the theatre-goers are returning to the play, but the mayor shows no inclination to leave this little party. The champagne sparkles and flows. Herbert has no difficulty in combining the whisky with champagne. The barman is evidently familiar with the mayor, and is attentive to the point of fussiness.

180

'Herbert, you're not considering selling the car, are you?' Sophia suddenly focuses on the subject everyone is avoiding.

'Don't you worry about what I'm going to do.'

'But that car involved Quentin in a lot of trouble and he only did it for you.'

'Just leave it to me. I shall decide what's right to do. No one has ever complained about what Herbert has done. Herbert always keeps his nose clean.'

The mayor looks rather uncomfortable at this turn of events.

'Look, I only asked if it was for sale. I quite understand the position.'

Herbert immediately asserts control.

'John,' – the mayoral formalities have been dropped – 'if I say I can sell it to you, you can take it from me that I know what I'm doing. Herbert has never broken his word in forty years of doing business. I'm the only one who knows all the facts and Sophia doesn't understand business.'

'But I only expressed interest. I didn't say I wanted to buy it.' The mayor is obviously uncomfortable.

'If you like it, you can have it. There isn't another one in the country and it's done less than eight thousand miles. Whatever price I put on it, I'd be underselling it.'

The mayor is clearly attracted by the idea of having a unique car. The champagne has disappeared by now, and Herbert switches straight back to the whisky bottle. The quick succession of drinks seems to be getting to the mayor.

'Have another ride if you like. Once we've done the deal, Peter will take you home. What do you think it's worth? You can decide what to pay.' After a short pause he adds, 'It's the kind of car that needs an important man.'

Herbert offers the mayor a large Havana cigar and lights one himself. Soon the air is thick with the now familiar smell of cigars and whisky.

'I have a friend in Havana who sends me half a dozen boxes of Monte Cristo at a time. Customs always argue, but in the end they accept that I only get them for my own use. And a few friends,' he chuckles mischievously. 'Take a couple.' He produces another two from his sock and insists the mayor take them. By this time the mayor is too fuddled to resist.

'Daddy, I think it's time we were going, I'm sure the mayor wants to go.' Ruth's impatience is evident. She isn't as intrigued as I am by the unfolding plot.

181

'We won't be long, lamb, but I've got business to do first.'

I'm amazed that an outing to the theatre has mysteriously metamorphosed into an episode in the life of a businessman. The mayor, responding to the plea from Ruth, suddenly moves centre stage.

'Tell me what you want for it. I'll say yes or no.'

'I can tell you want it, but I don't know whether you can pay what it's worth.'

'How much do you want?' The mayor's voice develops an edge of impatience. Herbert suddenly looks grave, the bonhomie disappears, and he looks intently into the mayor's eyes. 'When I set out tonight, I had no intention of selling the car. I've already turned down seven thousand because I didn't like the man. The money doesn't matter to me. I'm not interested in money. I only do business with people I like.'

'Look, I want to be straight, I wouldn't pay seven thousand.'

'Did I ask you for seven thousand? I know you can't pay seven thousand, I knew that when I met you, but I want it to go to a good home.' The good nature and bonhomie suddenly returns in abundance. 'Look, give me a cheque for five thousand five hundred and it's yours.'

It suddenly seems remarkably cheap.

'I can't give you a cheque now, but I could pay you in a couple of days.'

'Pay me when you like.' Herbert is disarmingly charming. I can't understand how he can be so indifferent to getting the money. He deliberately and ostentatiously grasps the mayor's hand and shakes it.

'Your mayor knows how to do a good deal.' He addresses the barman and everyone else in earshot.

'Can we go now, Daddy?'

'After we've had one to seal the bargain, and one for the road.' He smiles contentedly.

The barman pours the drinks, and after more back-slapping and good-natured comments we all return to the car, and, having dropped off the mayor, drive home.

'What an extraordinary man your father is!' I say to Ruth later. 'He must be attached to nothing. Everything is for sale.'

'He'll use anything to get his own way.' Ruth is bitter. 'He's a very twisted man where money's involved. He boasts to all his business friends about his money and flaunts his wealth when he can, but in private there's nothing he won't do to avoid or delay paying. Every term at

182

school, the headmistress would call me into her study and tell me that Daddy hadn't paid the fees. It was humiliating. He leaves bills unpaid and loves causing everyone embarrassment and worry. When he's done a particularly good deal, he'll give Mummy a thick pile of pound notes. A few weeks later, when they're back fighting, Mummy will taunt Daddy with the unpaid bills and tell him the gas and electricity will be turned off. Daddy will then say he gave her the money to pay the bills a few weeks earlier. But every time Mummy gets money, she pays it into her private bank account.'

I contrast this complex situation with the total trust between Mam and Dad. It was Mam who controlled all the finances and gave Dad pocket money. I know that whatever success I have, I can never attach so much value to money that I behave like Herbert.

As I lie in bed, I reflect on the profound difference between my attitude to success and Herbert's. Does this difference mean that I couldn't succeed in business? I float into sleep with this question turning over and over in my mind.

The following morning, Herbert calls me down to meet a friend of his who has just arrived.

'This is Sydney.'

He is bald, with a thin face and pointed features. He is not over-friendly.

'Sydney is an accountant who fiddles the books.'

Herbert roars with laughter. Sydney seems not to appreciate the humour, and I get the impression that if he did do anything illegal, the last person he'd share it with is Herbert.

'Sit down.' Herbert points me to a vacant armchair. He and Sydney are comfortably ensconced in the leather chairs with what look like whiskies, and Herbert is sucking his ever-present cigar. I sit awkwardly, feeling so far away from the world that unites them. I have such a deep reverence for great pianists that it's hard to grasp that successful people can be as indifferent to them as Mam and Dad. My ambition to be a pianist is obviously of little interest to Sydney and he makes no effort to include me in the conversation. I feel determined to say something. Eventually, I find a gap and start speaking before I know what I'm saying.

'Do you help businesses keep their books?' It's the nearest point of reference to my own experience on Haydock Street. I used to write up the weekly takings, very amateurishly, in a printed format aimed at small businesses. Mam and Dad paid all the bills out of the takings, so the takings varied as the purchases varied. The figures I entered were all a rough guess, and I decided it was safer to stick to a similar figure every week.

Sydney smiles at me indulgently. He knows he's dealing with an innocent. He takes a drink of his whisky.

'My main job is to help people avoid paying tax – legally, of course.'

Herbert sniggers. 'Why do you think he's here?'

At that moment the phone rings. Herbert listens for what seems a long time, then speaks brusquely.

'We made an agreement.'

A pause.

'I have witnesses.'

Another pause.

'Don't worry, I'll take it in part exchange. I'll expect you within the hour. Bring cash and we'll settle the deal here.'

I don't know what impression he's made on the caller, but he's intimidated me.

'What's all that about?' Sydney asks.

'I sold him the Chrysler and now he says his wife doesn't want it.' He grins, knowing he's bullied the mayor of Thornton into submission. 'He said he already has a Rolls, so I told him I'd take it in part exchange.'

'You'd better let me look at the tax implications in the sale.'

'Don't worry. That's why I told him to bring cash. You tell me what I can sell it for without any tax problems. That's all I need.'

I listen with little understanding but lots of unease. I decide to make a getaway and return to the purity of my music.

'I'm sorry, I must go because I'm preparing for a concert. It's nice to meet you. I hope to see you again soon.' I shake Sydney by the hand, little realising that he will prove to be a major stepping-stone in my career.

20

Love Hurts

I romanticise the idea of two pianists sharing their lives and dreams. I can't imagine anything more perfect, but the reality is different. From almost the beginning, it's a relationship marred by the sensitivity that superficially makes it so perfect. I begin to realise that Ruth is easily hurt by things so subtle that the hurt can't easily be anticipated. What makes it difficult is that she blames me for not foreseeing or preventing the injury, so each hurt is compounded by an argument. Perhaps if I were more secure I'd be able to resist the temptation to defend myself, but it's hard to be accused of being hurtful when one feels nothing but love.

The sun is still high, but cooler as it moves towards the horizon. I look at it through the lead-patterned window of my music-room. It seems a million miles from Haydock Street, with its bakehouse heat and smell. For the first time in my life I have what I've always imagined to be the perfect working environment, but my experience of it is progressively the opposite of what I expected. In the quiet stillness of the room, I feel an emptiness. After working for so many hours, all I sense is my own sterile talent. I look back at the Steinway piano and the manuscript paper strewn over it. The few notes I've forced on to paper seem worthless.

It's the end of what I had hoped would be a fulfilling day's playing and composition. I have the perfect piano, I have peace, quiet, solitude, a spacious room with a view towards the sea; yet, instead of affirming my self-belief, all these things are conspiring to make me feel painfully inadequate. It's true I started the day playing well, but after an hour or two I began to feel restless. I turned to composition, hoping to rediscover the innocent, unselfconscious freedom I'd felt in the earliest days. But instead, everything seems contrived, imitative, stilted, commonplace, inferior. I struggle to continue, listening to my ideas as I play them and hoping to experience the kind of excitement I'd felt when Stephen played me his compositions. I remember listening to the first, haunting sounds

185

of great pianists on records. I imagine performing, my audience captivated, as I once was, by that bell-like quality of notes repeated and varied, stirring feelings of poignancy, heroism and nobility. Instead, here I am feeling a failure, looking for something in life that my playing and composition are not giving me.

I hear Ruth coming up the stairs. As I open the door, I see the pain in her face. She has just got back from a lesson with Gordon, her piano tutor at the college.

'How was it?'

'All right.'

'You don't sound as if you had a very good day.'

'I think Gordon's attitude to me has changed. I don't think he has the same interest in me since we got married.'

'When you played the Schubert, what did he say about it?'

'He was lukewarm.'

'I'll make some tea. You look tired.'

Ruth sits dejectedly in the chair we've had re-covered.

'I feel as if I'm losing confidence in my playing.'

'But your playing is improving so much.'

'Gordon doesn't seem to think so.'

From the moment I sense her unhappiness, my own despondency begins to disappear. I realise that whatever may prey on my mind, deep down I'm secure. Ruth is not, and perhaps never will be.

I return with the tea. We sit down together.

'The cake's one I baked today. I hope you like it.'

I'm very proud of it. I'd followed the recipe to the letter. I want to demonstrate that I'm serious about sharing our lives and not leaving the usual domestic jobs to 'the wife'. We've decided to share everything so that my career isn't in any way advantaged over hers.

After we finish our tea we return to our music-rooms to practise. I'm ashamed that Ruth's self-doubt has renewed my own sense of purpose. After some particularly satisfying practice, I pause and notice that Ruth's piano is silent. I think nothing of it and carry on, but when I stop again I still hear nothing.

I enter Ruth's room and find her holding her head in her hands, sobbing uncontrollably.

'Darling, what's the matter?' I'm shocked to witness the depth of her suffering.

She shakes her head, unable to talk.

'Please tell me what's upsetting you.'

After some minutes, she struggles to regain her composure.

'I don't know what's wrong. I've never felt like this before. When I hear you playing, I can't continue. You sound so confident, and I feel my own confidence slipping away.'

'But I'm not confident. I'm no more confident than you.'

'You don't know what it's like to be a woman.'

I feel so much love and sympathy for her, but it does little to help. In fact, her unhappiness is developing an edge of resentment towards me and I can feel my stomach tightening at the injustice of it. I put my arm round her, to soothe my own agitation and her misery.

At that moment we hear Ruth's mother coming. Ruth desperately wipes her face and eyes and glares at me, indicating that her unhappiness is private.

Sophia knocks and enters, her face a picture of innocence.

'Darling, I'm just going to the shops, can I bring you something?'

'No thank you, Mummy.'

'Are you sure you don't need something?'

'I'm sure.'

All the while, Sophia is scrutinising her daughter's features as if fully aware she's uncovered a secret. I can imagine her relishing the thought that something is wrong. Her own marriage is clearly deeply flawed, while ours looked set to be an idyllic union: two pianists playing and listening to beautiful music, in a life of perfect harmony. And now, in just a short time, she detects a fault line. She looks intently at her daughter, but Ruth is beginning to bristle with indignation at her mother's persistence.

'Would you mind leaving us?'

I'm chilled by the rudeness and effrontery. I can't imagine being able to speak to Mam like that, however wretched I might feel. I'm torn between love and concern for Ruth, and a genuine desire to be reasonable and considerate to her mother. Sophia puts on a pained expression, as if wounded once more by her daughter, then simply turns to leave. As she goes, she looks at me. 'Oh, I've got a message for you. Gerald rang and said he wants to speak to you urgently.'

'Thanks.'

Ruth gets up from the piano stool, makes her way to a comfortable chair and sinks into it.

'Look,' I begin again. 'Try to tell me what's wrong. What are you feeling?'

I still can't believe that anything of any consequence can spoil what seems such a perfect life.

'It's something to do with our marriage. Since the wedding, Gordon has changed. He doesn't have the same interest in me. He was the first man I met who gave me reassurance. I wanted more than anything to be a pianist, and he made me feel it was possible.'

I listen, wondering what I can say or do.

'Now, he seems more interested in you than me. From the moment he knew of our marriage, he started talking about the difference Daddy's money could make to your career. He's never talked about the difference it could make to mine.'

Gordon's attitude is thoughtless, but his implicit approval of my career is unexpectedly reassuring. To my shame, I'm momentarily distracted and have to remind myself that Ruth is in torment.

'Look, maybe you've misinterpreted him. Why not talk to him about it? Explain your feelings so that he's aware.'

Ruth looks angrily hurt.

'I wouldn't expose myself to anyone like that. He wouldn't understand. He'd decide I was a paranoid female.'

Further useful suggestions are in short supply, but I make the effort.

'Would it be better if I didn't play for an hour or two? Try practising again, and I'll do some reading.'

'I'll try it, but I'm not sure I feel like it now.'

I leave her and walk downstairs. There's something else I'm more anxious to do than read. I didn't dare mention this to Ruth, but I know Gerald wouldn't call without reason, so maybe there's the prospect of an engagement.

In the sitting-room, Sophia is arranging flowers.

'Do you mind if I use the phone?'

'Not at all,' she trills. I ring Gerald.

'Clifford Curzon has cancelled a concert at Kendal at short notice. They've asked me to step in. I don't know whether you're free, but can you do it with me?'

'Of course I can!'

'It's next Thursday, is that all right?'

'Definitely.'

'I've already given them the programme. They're all pieces we've done. I've put Beethoven Opus 96 in, and the Fauré A Major, and some solos.'

'That's brilliant.'

'Don't you want to know how much you're getting?'

'Anything will do.' The money seems totally irrelevant. Living with Ruth has taken away any sense of realism about money.

'Can we meet to practise on Saturday?'

'Yes, where?'

'I could come to you, because I'm in Preston the night before.'

'Great, come any time in the morning.'

I put the phone down, hardly able to contain my excitement. Replacing Clifford Curzon! This is a real opportunity for me. I can't wait to get back to a piano. But as I leave the phone I remember Ruth.

I still can't hear any piano playing, and my anxiety returns. But before I can get to Ruth, Herbert and some friends return noisily from the golf club. They invade the sitting-room and Herbert sits down in his favourite chair. He smiles benevolently at his friends.

'Just find yourselves some seats, lads. Don't stand about, Bill, get yourself a drink.' Eventually, he says, 'This is my son-in-law, Ernest.'

I feel embarrassed. I'm not sure whether to leave or stay, so as a compromise I stand awkwardly. Bill, helping himself to a whisky, comes to my rescue.

'I understand you're a pianist.' His two companions quickly follow his lead and pour themselves two generous whiskies.

'Yes, I'm studying in Manchester.'

'Ruth's a wonderful pianist, isn't she?'

Before I can answer, Herbert says, 'They're both marvellous pianists.' He then decides that he wants to prove the point.

'Come on, we'll go upstairs to your flat and you can both play for us.' He begins to galvanise everyone into action. I stand helplessly, thinking of Ruth's desperate unhappiness upstairs and wondering how I can avert a catastrophe. I do my best.

'Ruth's got a bad headache.'

Sophia, who has been standing by and looking with frank irritation at Herbert's cronies as they pour their own whiskies, suddenly moves to centre stage.

'She never said anything to me.'

Herbert switches on his cherubic smile. 'I'm sure she'd like to meet my friends.'

'I don't think she would.' Sophia spits the words out ferociously.

'If she's got a headache we won't disturb her,' says the diplomatic Bill.

'Nonsense, I know my daughter.'

Herbert is imperturbably confident, and determined to have his own way, especially now that Sophia has objected.

'The only thing you know is what the whisky tells you,' retorts Sophia venomously.

'What's wrong with me having a drink?' Herbert continues to be tolerant, as a father might be with a child. 'Anyway, leave us alone.' He waves his hand, as if brushing off a fly. 'This is man's talk.'

This insult is more than she can bear. She sweeps out of the room with the most contemptuous flourish she can command. Herbert looks sheepishly triumphant as she leaves.

'Just have your drink and we'll go upstairs.'

They all select a comfortable chair each and sink into it. One points to an ornate desk.

'That's a nice piece of furniture.'

'Fred, it's yours if you want it.'

Everyone looks at the desk with greater interest.

Something tells me that Herbert has started to circle for the kill.

'I paid five hundred for it. It was a good buy, but I've no room for it and it doesn't really go in here. You can have it for what it cost me. It's probably worth nearer a thousand.'

Fred shuffles uneasily. He doesn't really want to buy it. His hand trembles as he lights his cigarette.

'I'm not sure I have enough spare money at the moment.'

'Don't worry about that. I'm not in a hurry for the money. Pay me when you can. I know you want to buy it. It's probably the best deal you've ever had.'

Herbert smiles. I can see that Fred is losing ground, and Herbert knows it. Fred doesn't want to buy the desk, but he can't say no without appearing either ungrateful or stupid. The moment when he could have positively refused passes, and his awkward silence becomes his tacit, witnessed agreement.

'Have another drink.' Herbert pours another generous measure into Fred's glass. This gesture seems to clinch the deal publicly. Fred looks distinctly unhappy, but helpless in the contest of wills with Herbert.

'Come on, we'll go upstairs and see my daughter.' The entourage gathers around Herbert like a pack of obedient hounds.

'Look, I'd better go and make sure everything's all right.' In my mounting panic I mumble the only thing I can think of to gain some time. I make a quick exit from the room to alert Ruth to the imminent invasion of her privacy. I sprint up the steps and rush into our sitting-room. Ruth isn't there, or in any other part of the flat. My panic subsides. She must have gone out, probably to the park. I go down the stairs even more rapidly than I went up, and meet the entourage halfway up the first flight.

'Ruth's gone out.'

Herbert looks totally unconcerned.

'Never mind, you can play for us.'

They continue and enter our sanctuary, to my colossal concern. I know only too well that Ruth would have prevented them from entering, and will bitterly resent my allowing them in. But it's so much against my nature to be hostile and confrontational, and in any case I'm in Herbert's debt and it would seem churlish to be difficult without good reason.

The piano is open and the white keys gleam invitingly. The group settles into the available chairs.

'What would you like me to play?'

There is a distinct silence and awkwardness. Herbert clearly expects one of his friends to supply an inspired answer. He's in the most comfortable chair in the room, the ash from his cigar growing perilously longer. The tension in the silence grows, until finally someone says, 'Play something from *Dream of Olwen*.' This is a trite, popular tune of the day. The request tells me how little they understand my kind of music, but it doesn't tell me how to play *Dream of Olwen*. I'm at a loss to know what to do. Then Bill comes to my rescue again.

'Play something by Liszt.'

I begin to feel the ivory keys without depressing them, unsure what to play. What do I know that I can play without running into a difficult passage? I look inside the piano at the strings and at the gold 'Steinway' lettering under the lid, hoping for some sudden inspiration. But I don't need it. Instead I hear Ruth's footsteps on the stairs. She bursts into the room, eyes flashing, her whole body pulsating with resentment.

'Daddy, how dare you come barging in!'

Herbert goes immediately on to the defence.

'We wanted to hear you play, lamb.'

'Well, I have no intention of playing for you.'

The group's mutual alcohol-inspired bonhomie crumbles into awkwardness and embarrassment. They all rise to make an exit. I feel more awkward than anyone, still sitting on the piano stool. Their contrition somehow demands forgiveness, but Ruth shows no sign of relenting. At that moment, Sophia appears in the doorway. The look on her face tells me that she's tipped Ruth off, knowing that no one can more effectively turn the tables. She smirks at Herbert's humiliation. The room empties, except for an odour of whisky and cigars.

Sophia turns to her daughter, intent on capitalising on her moment of triumph. 'Would you like some of the lunch I'm making, darling? I've got some soup and it's full of goodness.'

'No thank you, Mummy.' Ruth is still in a disgruntled, defiant mood, anxious not to give up the ground she has just retaken. Sophia turns towards the door in the wake of Herbert and his friends. A last, wounded glance provokes no response from Ruth, and she leaves. Ruth turns on me.

'Why didn't you stop them coming here?'

'I couldn't. I didn't know how I could stop your father.'

'You can be so feeble!'

'It's his house.'

'That's nothing to do with it.'

In my world, ownership and power have a lot to do with it. My parents are powerless, and I've grown up with a strong feeling of respect for those who have it. And how can one have power without wealth? Even Ruth's own exceptional self-determination is underpinned by her father's business success. My life has been overshadowed by the knowledge that I'm powerless. My love of music has done nothing to enhance my personal power in the world. I'm still someone of no importance, and will remain so unless my piano playing elevates me from obscurity and I become successful.

'I just didn't feel I could say no to your father.'

'I've had to learn to say no to him, otherwise he would have dominated my life.'

I sense the enormous strength she must have gained from winning such a battle.

From my earliest discovery of music I've had a purpose, a feeling of destiny, but my relationship with Ruth seems to be blurring the clear focus I once had. Our common passion for music ought to strengthen us, but it seems to be creating unprecedented problems for Ruth, and those problems are beginning to sap my own energy. Is it possible that the very thing that unites us could divide us?

I suddenly remember I'm playing with Gerald next Thursday and haven't told Ruth yet. I'm in turmoil as I struggle to balance my personal ambition with my love for Ruth. My ambition seems selfish compared with her suffering. Could it be that loving her will lead me to abandon the thing that brought us together?

During my years at college, I was nourished by dreams of a wonderful life as a pianist, but as the four years came to an end I realised that a job as a teacher was the most likely outcome – perhaps the only outcome.

It's one thing to love playing, but to be engaged to play and be paid a reasonable fee for playing now seems unrealistic. Could it be that Ruth's insecurity is providing me with something I'm looking for: a justifiable way out of a career which may in the end result in me being no more than a second-rate musician?

Moreover, my life with Ruth is giving me a taste for a life which could only be sustained by a highly successful career. Thursday's concert with Gerald will be the most important professional engagement I've had, but even then I'm being carried by Gerald's career, not my own. Could it be that I'm losing the determination and optimism I once had?

A few days later I'm forced to tell Ruth about the coming concert.

'Gerald invited me to play for him.'

'When?'

'Next week. It's a midday concert in Kendal. Would you like to come?'

'I don't think so.'

'Why not? We can walk around Kendal afterwards and find somewhere to have tea.'

'We'd be with Gerald and I don't like him all that much.'

Any hope of turning the concert into a pleasure Ruth can share drains away.

'He's coming to practise tomorrow.'

'That's so typical of you! You can't be straight about anything. Why didn't you tell me before?'

'I'd forgotten until now.'

'How could you forget, when the concert's on in a few days?'

'I hadn't forgotten about it. I'd forgotten to tell you.'

Ruth looks at me with contempt.

I'd imagined that my life with Ruth would be in the tradition of nineteenth-century virtuosi. I'd even dared to ask her whether she could regard me as a Paderewski. She'd said yes, but I'm now realising that the reality is no. Far from turning her into the self-sacrificing wife supporting me in my career – an attitude to cringe at now, but commonplace in the early 1950s – marriage has released in Ruth a corrosive mixture of resentment, hostility and insecurity which jeopardizes the prospect of my becoming a professional pianist-composer. I haven't the strength to disregard her unhappiness. I'm vulnerable to her feelings, and my career can't withstand the pressure of her emotions.

I recall that Mozart wrote one of his most sublime string quartets while his wife was in the next room in the throes of a particularly difficult childbirth. That's the quality a musician needs: the ability to shut off from everything else and focus only on oneself. In that context, my sympathy and love for Ruth suddenly stand out as weaknesses. I'm more concerned about her than about my own career. I'd imagined that marriage would augment my ambition and reinforce my sense of purpose, but instead it's weakening both.

I've always suspected that beneath my passion were the seeds of failure, and now marriage is fertilizing them. They have begun their insidious development, and my dream of a life of music is being covered by their barely visible fine tendrils, stretching further and further and growing in strength day by day.

21

A Life-changing Decision

Almost before I'm awake, the comforting smell of coffee alerts me to the fact that Ruth is already up. I can hear her in the kitchen and the additional smell of toast tells me she is making breakfast. I sit up and look out of the window on to a grey and windy day. As I enter the kitchen I see that she is already dressed.

'Why are you up so early?'

'I'm going to Gordon's for a lesson.'

'You never mentioned it.'

'I did, but you obviously weren't listening.'

She's immaculately dressed and groomed, and I'm sure she has arranged to be out of the house when I'm practising with Gerald.

'What time will you be back?'

'I don't know, but late I should think, knowing Gordon.'

'You say it as if you're enjoying the thought of being away from me.'

'You'll be busy practising, won't you?'

Her jealousy and resentment of my engagement with Gerald is palpable. I want my happiness but I want her happiness as well, and it seems I can't have both. We sit down to a joyless breakfast, silently hostile toward each other and afraid to risk any further exchanges.

I had thought that marriage to Ruth would reinforce my career as a pianist, nurture me, encourage me, strengthen me. But instead it has exposed my weakness. Her personality is strong, but so too are her feelings of inadequacy, and the combined force has begun to undermine my certainty. I'm too vulnerable to her feelings to be sure of my own. I can feel her unhappiness acutely and I want to comfort her, but the only way I can do this is by sacrificing my own interest. We finish breakfast in this state of warring emotions and Ruth leaves the house, barely saying goodbye.

Only moments later I hear footsteps on the stairs and a gentle knock on the music-room door. Sophia stands in the doorway, her makeup so heavy it feels threatening. Her dress is too tight and her nails, too long to be natural, are painted a deep maroon.

'Will Ruth be back soon?'

'She's gone for a piano lesson, and I'm waiting for Gerald. We'll be rehearsing for our concert.'

'I just wanted to make sure you're all right. Do let me know if you need coffee or anything.'

She leaves, knowing with her uncanny instinct that she has uncovered some rift between Ruth and me. I'm sure she's enjoying the thought that all is not well.

I start practising but find it difficult to concentrate. After half an hour or so I feel relief when Sophia's voice, full of fake *joie de vivre*, rings out from downstairs. 'Gerald's here!'

As soon as Gerald walks in, all the emotion that has been rendering me helpless seems to disappear and I feel energy surging through my body.

'I don't have a lot of time because I'm playing on the radio tonight and I need to get to the BBC for a rehearsal.'

I feel a pang of jealousy. 'Who's playing for you?'

'Katherine Jones. She's used a lot by the BBC. I've played a few times with her before and her technique is shit hot.' My heart sinks at the obvious implication.

'What are you playing?'

'Some potboilers: *Ronde des Lutins*, Paganini *Caprices* and *The Devil's Trill.* It's the sort of programme they love.'

I'm full of admiration that he can rehearse our programme and only hours later play completely different pieces on the radio. But as we start to play the first piece, Gerald stops after a few pages.

'That's all right. We'll just top and tail them. I don't know about you, but I think that's enough.'

'Are you sure we don't need to do any more?'

'I don't need to. I'm sure it'll be all right.'

Even though I feel anxious that we haven't done enough, I silently acquiesce. What I had hoped would be an intensive practice session is in the end a cursory run-through of excerpts from each piece.

'Can I make you something to eat before you go?'

'I wouldn't mind a cheese sandwich.'

As he stands in the kitchen watching me make it, I can no longer contain the uncertainty about my future that is gnawing away at me. 'Gerald, I'm really wondering whether I'm going to make it.'

As soon as I say it, I realise I'm expecting him to reassure me. I want him to say, 'Of course you'll make it, you're too good to give it up, it would be absurd, you're one of the best pianists I've ever worked with.'

But instead he says, with painful bluntness, 'Do you want me to tell you you're good?' He makes me feel that all the question has done is undermine my relationship with him. I'm astonished that he's so aggressive.

'No, I'm wondering whether I should do something else.'

'What else do you want to do?'

I can't continue the conversation without digging a deeper hole. To my relief he obviously has no interest in pursuing it.

'Can you get a train to Preston to meet my train and we can travel together?'

'I'm sure I can, it's easy to get a train to Preston from here.'

As he goes, I'm left feeling that I've made a fool of myself.

The rehearsal has one good consequence: it revives my feeling of excitement about the concert. On the day, I wake quite early. Ruth wakes as soon as I get out of bed; she half sits up and says, 'If it's all right, I've decided to come with you.'

'Of course it's all right.'

I should feel nothing but pleasure as it's what I originally wanted, but instead her change of mind makes me uneasy. As I shave I try to analyse why.

There's no doubt I'd be happier on my own. Ruth's presence will expose all the difficulties we have in sharing happiness in public. Concern about Ruth's attitude to people and whether she'll like them or not is bound to make everything more complicated. On my own it's so simple, but with Ruth nothing is simple. As we sit down to toast and coffee I ask, 'Are you sure you want to come?'

'Yes. You asked me to come, didn't you?'

'I did, but you refused and I wonder why you've changed your mind.'

'I decided I might enjoy the trip.'

'I hope you won't feel I'm ignoring you when we're there.'

'I'm not expecting you to ignore me.'

'I won't deliberately ignore you but I'll be thinking of the performance and focusing on that.'

'I won't come if you prefer me not to.'

'No, of course I want you to come.'

Far from making matters better, this conversation only dampens our spirits, and we board the train to Preston in this subdued state. We sit on opposite sides of the compartment, reading and looking out of the window. Anything to avoid talking.

Ruth is wearing the gabardine suit I love so much. Her silk blouse, as always, is immaculate, and her shoes are shining with that special lustre that comes from care and quality. I look at her and recall our first meetings, when she looked so similar. Only one thing is noticeably different – her face. It seems as if marriage has taken away the serenity it once had. The strain of her unhappiness is clearly visible to me now.

I begin to feel apprehensive that the rift between us will be evident to Gerald. We leave the train at Preston and make our way to the platform for the through train to Kendal. In a short time it arrives. Gerald has opened a window and is looking for us. He's brought a girlfriend, Elizabeth. I recognise her from college but have never spoken to her. We all exchange greetings and settle down in the compartment.

Suddenly the strain between Ruth and me is relieved, as we're no longer preoccupied with each other. My happiness in the occasion begins to return.

'We should have a big audience,' says Gerald. 'The hall seats a thousand and it was a sellout for Curzon. They have the option of a refund but I think most will come to the concert.'

The sun has struggled through and is sending shafts of bright light across the fields. To my relief, Ruth and Elizabeth know each other from college and appear to get on well. Her decision to come with me isn't turning out as badly as I'd feared. As Ruth and Elizabeth talk, Gerald and I are able to sit back, gathering our thoughts and emotions in preparation for the concert.

After a while, Gerald pulls down his violin case, takes out his violin and, after quickly tuning it, begins to play with his usual verve, totally unconcerned about disturbing people in other compartments.

'When we play the Beethoven, can you make sure you don't let the tempo sag?'

'Why, was I slowing down?'

'No, but there's always a tendency to make a bit too much of the melodies. We all do it.' He adds the last comment, I'm sure, to take the sting out of his observation. I bristle a bit because I'm sure I don't slow down.

He then plays some unaccompanied Bach, perched on the edge of the seat. The sun is shining continuously now and I feel on top of the world.

* * *

We walk the short distance from Kendal railway station to the concert hall, which is larger than I expected. As we approach it, the excitement of the occasion really begins to grip me and I'm conscious that the palms of my hands are damp with perspiration. I see a board outside the hall advertising the change of performers. Despite Gerald's optimism, I wonder how many people will be disappointed and decide not to come.

As we enter the hall, I see the grand piano which had been provided for Curzon. Gerald takes immediate charge.

'We'll have to try a few bars to get the balance.' He turns to Elizabeth. 'Will you go to the back and listen?'

I try the piano. The tone is beautifully rich. As we play through the opening of Opus 96, I feel a tremor down my spine. Yes, this is the life I've dreamt of having. Yes, this is the world I want to live in.

Gerald calls to Elizabeth and Ruth, standing at the back of the Hall. 'Is the piano too loud for the violin?'

'Perhaps a little,' Elizabeth replies.

'I thought it might be. Do you mind if we put the lid of the piano down?'

Gerald puts the lid down without waiting for any response from me. I'm dismayed how much effect it has on the sound of the piano and the feel of playing it. With the lid down, all that richness has been reduced. I can do nothing but make the best of it.

As the hall fills up, we retire to a room just off the platform. Elizabeth and Ruth stay in the hall.

The time for the performance arrives. We walk on to the platform and bow. The applause is stirring and I feel particularly excited that Ruth and Elizabeth are witnessing the occasion.

I've never experienced a greater sense of being inspired by music as I play it. This undoubtedly has a lot to do with Gerald's beautiful, strong playing. His confidence gives me confidence and I feel tremors of excitement as the music unfolds, and with it the certainty that the audience is sharing the same experience. Their enthusiastic applause means that we play two encores, even though the concert has already overrun.

Afterwards, we both look at each other with satisfaction. The dressing room gradually fills with people connected with the concert – and, to my surprise, Mrs Gainsborough. As usual she makes her presence felt immediately, with an elaborate, eye-catching hat and a manner that seems to sweep everyone else aside.

'That was a marvellous concert!'

I notice the large amount of mascara on her eyelashes, which complements the over-supply of lipstick.

'I've been wanting to get in touch with you again. How would you like to play at the French Embassy in London? My husband is a great friend of the Ambassador and they're frightfully keen on the idea. You'd have a very distinguished audience.' The importance of what she's saying makes it difficult to turn away and greet Ruth and Elizabeth, who have now joined us.

To my embarrassment, Gerald breaks away easily to speak to someone I don't know and leaves me to deal with the situation. I blush as I interrupt the flow of conversation and beckon to Ruth and Elizabeth. Mrs Gainsborough hardly looks at them, and I stand awkwardly, aware that I'm making a mess of introducing my wife.

'Mrs Gainsborough, er, this is a friend from college, Elizabeth, and my wife, Ruth.' She gives them a cold, unsmiling 'How do you do?' and immediately directs all her attention back to me.

'I'll arrange the concert as soon as possible. It will be delightful to do another concert with you. I so much enjoyed singing when you accompanied me at Leyton.'

'I enjoyed it too,' I say, trying not to recall the unpleasant noises which masqueraded as her singing.

'By the way, Emma was so sorry she couldn't come. Unfortunately something cropped up at the last minute. She asked me to be sure to give you her love.' I feel excruciatingly embarrassed, and Ruth's loathing is palpable. It's a world I'd intended to keep secret, and Mrs Gainsborough has casually taken the lid off it.

It seems inevitable that just when things are getting better, something happens to give Ruth a reason to feel resentful. Once we say goodbye to Gerald and Elizabeth, we revert to our earlier silent, hostile and deeply unhappy selves all the way back home.

The weeks that follow are repeats of the same cycle of unease, hostility, argument and reconciliation. It seems to me that our marriage is being progressively tainted by Ruth's jaundiced relationship with her father. However much I try to be her ideal man, her view of me is always through a lens distorted by her experience of Herbert. Despite my own behaviour being the complete antithesis of his, the hostility she feels towards him is progressively turning on me.

We had decided that Ruth should keep her own name despite marriage, and our routine of making all work sexless, shared on an equal basis, does little to ameliorate the general view she has of men. I try to earn her approval, and my efforts occasionally earn a temporary respite, but something always triggers a reversion to antagonism.

Through Ruth's unhappiness I begin to appreciate the fortunate beginning of my own life. Despite the hardship, I had the security that Mam and Dad's unqualified love gave me. Their ignorance of middle-class values left me free to enjoy a life without criticism and parental ambition. Whatever I did was good enough; however I looked, however I spoke, what time I went to bed – it was all good enough. A hint of not feeling well enough to go to school kept me at home. To the people who mattered most, I was more than good enough. Their exaggerated good opinion insulated me from the withering cold wind of reality long enough for me to develop. It was only by degrees that I became aware that I'd been living in a false world, imagining myself to be something I wasn't. But my playing was improving as reality slowly dawned, and it seemed as if my defects were disappearing just in time to escape being exposed by its cruel light. The good opinion of my parents is now being strengthened by the good opinion of Mrs Gainsborough.

Then, something happens that will eventually change my life completely. I am required to do two years' national service. It has been deferred while I'm a student, so I'm 23 by the time duty calls.

I am hardly natural material for military service. In my mind, then and now, anyone committed to music ought also to be committed to spreading peace and reconciliation, and to me this is incompatible with bearing arms. Many of my musical heroes have been staunch pacifists, so I decide to follow their example and register as a conscientious objector. I know it's imperative to register while still a civilian. Once in the army and subject to military law, the penalties for refusing to bear arms are much more serious.

Events move quickly. A letter orders me to go to Liverpool for a medical examination that will also put an end to my civilian status. I therefore duly turn up at Liverpool but refuse to take the medical. I am summoned before a tribunal, where I argue my case. The tribunal is a deeply disturbing experience; its evident purpose not to put a genuinely held belief to the test but to dispense ritual humiliation, which it does with sadistic ease. The eventual compromise, if it can be called that, is not to exempt me from service but to assign me to the Non-Combatant

Corps. I will be subject to military law but with no obligation to carry weapons.

On joining the NCC I enrol on a typing course, not then thinking far beyond the need to keep my fingers active. My nascent typewriting abilities get me assigned to office work – and what a revelation it is! I spend most of my national service preparing legal and official documents, and soon find that office work isn't the anathema I had expected. It's surprisingly satisfying and I have an aptitude for it. Up till now, the only work I have known, apart from peeling potatoes, is music. A big problem with music as work is that it is very difficult to gauge how much real progress, if any at all, I am making. And the more I do of it, the more there is to do and the harder it gets. Office work, by contrast, is easily measurable. It's obvious to me when a task is complete, and equally obvious that I have done it either well or badly. Throughout my national service I seize every opportunity to develop my new skills.

I also discover that the army isn't completely without pianos, nor is the NCC completely without other musicians. Given my experience of working with Gerald I gravitate towards a violinist, and we hold occasional practice sessions.

Word soon spreads upwards that we can put on respectable musical performances, and the ingredients come together for the most pivotal incident of my adult life. We're asked to perform in lieu of a cricket match that, it is assumed, will have to be cancelled because the weather forecast is bad. In the event, the weather clears up and the cricket goes ahead, making our concert redundant. We are ordered instead to perform *during* the post-match officers' dinner. It's made clear that our role is simply to provide suitably refined background noise while the cricketing fellowship eats and drinks, and drinks some more.

Something in me snaps. I am outraged, not so much at the affront to the two of us but to the music we had planned to present. So I refuse to perform. And I know, from my immersion in legal casework, that I'm in the right: the *Manual of Military Law* states explicitly, if bizarrely, that *no one can be ordered to play a musical instrument*.

The next day, all hell breaks loose. My commanding officer is in a white fury about my wilful disobedience and makes all sorts of threats – none of which come to anything because the retribution he has in mind would be unlawful. He is clean bowled, and has to acknowledge it.

Army life soon regains its equilibrium but the incident brings home to me a harsh realisation: if I try to pursue a career as a musician, this fight for musical integrity will have been only the first of many. I'll

202

probably lose most of them, and be forced to make compromise after compromise to earn a living. At the level of music I idealise, there is just too little work to go round.

I decide that a complete re-think is needed. My love of music might have to be protected by abandoning music as a career and keeping it, somehow, as a private passion. I know my creative energy won't diminish; I'll just have to find new ways to channel it. I know also that I now have an affinity for administrative work, and that he who can administrate has perhaps boundless possibilities – certainly far more than I'll have as a struggling professional musician. I resolve that it must be possible to further my musical ambitions by a non-musical route. It's an enormously powerful and liberating moment. I don't yet know what that route will be, but I do know that this is a decision made not from weakness but from strength.

I thus leave the army not crushed by pessimism but buoyed up by a new optimism. But Ruth is distinctly unchanged, and my optimism starts to waver as all the constituents of our awkward relationship start to fall back into place.

It's Herbert who seems to notice something different in me. My growing enthusiasm for office skills registers with him, and he's shrewd enough to recognise the signs of someone restless for change. One evening, he calls me into the room he uses as his office.

'Look, I've been meaning to talk to you. Sit down.' He motions to a chair that normally belongs in the hall. 'I've no son, as you know.' This isn't true. He has a son by his first wife, who died in childbirth, but I let it go. 'Sophia and I have both built the business we have. It was Sophia who started it. When I first met her I was working for a very successful millionaire, doing deals and travelling a lot. She was a dynamic young seventeen year-old working in the office of a rainwear manufacturer in Salford. He was in some property we owned and I had to go in periodically to sort a few things out. From the first moment I could see that Sophia was ambitious as well as attractive. Over the months, I got to know her and I was impressed by her drive. Eventually she asked me if I'd lend her the money to start her own business. I did, and it wasn't long before I could see it was going to be very successful. When it was, I gave up my job and we got married. I ran the business and made it even more successful. But now there's no one to take it on. Ruth and her sister don't want to know.'

He proposes, in short, that I become his business heir. Remarkably, he seems to take it completely for granted that I can do whatever it is that needs doing.

Is that all there is to being a businessman? Can I just turn up some morning and become one instantly? His confidence in me is so flattering that I'm speechless. One moment I'm a musician without a job, and the next...

It now dawns on me that my enthusiasm for office and administrative chores may have loomed large in his decision to offer me entrée into the world of business. My new skills are worth money, even if not much, and Herbert can get them for virtually nothing. Is this an unworthy thought, I wonder? I decide that where Herbert is concerned, it isn't.

A few weeks later I'm in college and I call in to see Claude. He enthuses, 'I've got a remarkable new pupil called John Ogdon. He plays octaves faster than Horowitz.' On the records I'd heard, Horowitz played octaves extremely fast. Faster than that! It's hard to comprehend.

'He's playing the Chopin and Liszt B Minor Sonatas and the *Hammerklavier* at a concert here.'

My own achievement of playing the Twelve Studies Opus 10 of Chopin suddenly shrinks. Never before has a concert been given over to one student.

The arrival on the scene of the genius John Ogdon is another nail in the coffin of my musical ambitions. The emotional turmoil of my marriage compounds the growing feeling of uncertainty. Now, since talking to Herbert, a new factor has to be considered. Becoming a successful businessman suddenly seems considerably more achievable than becoming a virtuoso pianist.

I leave Claude determined to change the direction of my life. My career as a pianist seems to have gone as far as it can. I have the occasional concert, but little realistic hope of succeeding enough to get even close to a virtuoso lifestyle.

A few days later, I make a firm decision to become a businessman.

There is something perversely satisfying about turning my back on my dreams of being a musician. It's as if my passion for music has given me a deep feeling of insecurity, and in abandoning my career I'm removing that feeling. I've no doubt my friends will be shocked at the change, but this only reinforces my determination to burn my bridges.

That evening I'm sitting in our music-room, reflecting on all this, when Ruth walks over to the piano and picks up a volume of Schubert sonatas. She flicks through the pages, looking for the one she wants to play. I realise I'm tapping my fingers on the arm of the chair, as if the lure of the piano is still strong. I may be succumbing to the temptation of a life in business, but music still has a hold over me.

As Ruth begins to play the opening of the posthumous B Flat Sonata, it strikes me how much the serenity of the music reflects the shining clear conscience of the composer. That's the world I've wanted to be a part of since my first discovery of beautiful music. Now I'm considering sacrificing all of that, because I want more than the life of an unsuccessful musician. I stand and walk over to the piano, looking at the music over Ruth's shoulder. I long to sit down and play the same passages. It's as if the complex, conflicting emotions I'm feeling are giving me a greater range of expression than I've ever experienced. It's as if the purity of the music demands an awareness of corruption to better express the beauty of purity. As the music pauses I start to speak.

'I've been talking to your father. He's suggesting that I join him in the business. He seems to want me working with him, and it's really made me think. I've decided I'm going to do it. But it's all happened so quickly. Do you think it's the right thing for me to do?'

Ruth looks at me, and I know immediately that I'll get no sympathy or help.

'Don't do it if you don't want to.'

'It's almost as if I have no say in the matter. I feel as though something beyond my control is deciding my fate for me.'

'Of *course* you can decide what you want to do.' She has such strength that the idea of not knowing exactly what she should do is unthinkable.

It was naive of me to think I'd get any advice from Ruth. I'm on my own. I'm afraid and apprehensive, but I know that music is no longer a viable option.

'Yes, I can decide, and I've decided already. I just wanted to be sure it's what you want me to do.'

'You must decide what you want to do and do it.' Ruth is plainly irritated by our conversation and determined to make it clear that any decision I make has nothing to do with her.

Later that evening I get a phone call from Gerald.

'I've just come back from the Edinburgh Festival. Did you know John Ogdon was playing all the Bartok piano concertos?'

'I didn't know.'

Even though Claude had said John is exceptional, I'm amazed to hear of this extraordinary achievement.

'Have you ever played the Bartoks?'

'No, I've got the music, but I never got round to trying any of the concertos.'

'You know how fiendishly difficult they are, particularly Number Two.'

'They seem very difficult.'

'Well, John's performance was a triumph. The audience went mad. The critics rate his playing as one of the highlights of the Festival.'

'I wish I'd been there. Thanks for letting me know.'

As I put the phone down, I'm overcome once more by a feeling of inadequacy. John Ogdon may now be the only pianist exceptional enough to have any prospect of living the kind of life I want.

Yet I still feel reluctant to accept that my career as a pianist is at an end. I wonder whether the Bartok concertos really are as difficult as I once thought. I find the music and begin to play through parts at random. As I struggle to master the notes, I realise that if anything they're more difficult than I remembered. Any hope that they might give me a lifeline is gone. With a sense of hopeless inevitability I put the music away, and with it my dream of being a pianist.

22

A Passion for Business

The black stone mill stands exposed on the skyline, starkly utilitarian and dour, the surrounding fields and cottages all sloping away from it. Perimeter walls, where they exist, are broken, pieces of stone scattered everywhere. The grass and weeds look dirty and miserable, struggling to survive. Any trees and shrubs still standing have been stunted and deformed by the incessant wind and cold. Even when the sun shines, the gloom of the mill and its surroundings persists. It's hard to believe anyone would choose to live or work here if they had an alternative.

When I first fell under the spell of the piano, I imagined a life far away from the mills my family worked in. Music was to be my deliverance from a life of drudgery. Instead, my path has now led me back to a textile mill grimmer than any I've ever seen. But what's even more extraordinary is the excitement I feel as I look at this desperately ugly building. The moment I began to study the crafts of spinning and weaving, I was captivated by the prospect of immersing myself in textile manufacturing. Now, I feel a powerful sense of anticipation and complete certainty that a career in textiles is the way forward.

The office block is in a small square at the side of the large weaving shed. The shining brass plate at the side of the main door has been polished so much over the years that the company name is barely legible. The warmth of the air in the office makes me realise how cold it is outside. As I gaze around the room, the smell of textiles is reassuringly familiar, but everything I see is different from anything I've imagined. The desks and chairs are all well worn; every flat surface is littered with cones and spools of yarn; the walls are almost invisible behind various pieces of textile testing equipment and glass cases containing balances.

Joe Webster, the mill manager, comes in. He's generously offered to put me up temporarily because Ruth has decided it's impractical to stay with me, with no piano and nowhere to keep her beloved dog. Joe is a stocky man with a firm handshake and a strong, bulldog-like face. He wears a brown overall and his hands show signs that he's already been working with oily machinery. His eyes twinkle as he looks at me. 'I hope you'll be comfortable enough, but don't expect the Ritz.'

'I'm sure I'll be fine.'

'My wife's worried to death that it won't be good enough for you.'

He takes me to his little house just round the corner from the mill, and I meet his wife. The house is clean and neat, and I feel a sense of comfort and hospitality which makes any physical shortcomings irrelevant. I've never known such an ordered existence. It's as if they're both playing parts in which the rules are understood and observed, leaving no room for disagreements. I soon realise that all aspects of their lives are reassuringly predictable. The menu is always the same on each day of the week. If there's a meal you particularly enjoy, you can look forward to it the following week on exactly the same day.

Joe has suggested to me that I learn to weave, and the best way is to work with one of the weavers. The next morning after breakfast, Joe and I walk into the weaving shed. I'm overwhelmed by the violent noise of the looms and the percussive force of the shuttle banging from one side of the loom to the other. Speech is impossible and I notice all the weavers mouthing words to each other.

Lily is a delightful, gentle woman, but so impressively deft that I begin to adjust my idea of cleverness. Joe has told me she's the best weaver in the shed. Her main job is changing the shuttle with new yarn when the old one is empty. She shows me what to do, and my total inability to understand how to do what she does with such facility only provokes a good-natured smile, never exasperation. She's an aristocrat among millworkers. Everyone respects her, yet the fact that she does everything so expertly gives her no air of self-importance. As the pirn which carries the weft is emptying, more and more of the brown pirn can be seen. She judges the time to replace it so exactly that when she takes out the old pirn and pulls off the remaining yarn, there is almost none left.

The feel of the yarn is soothing, and the smell of the oil which permeates everything is strangely satisfying. It's exciting to see the shuttle fly from one end of the loom to the other, but difficult to grasp the rhythm that governs where the shuttle comes to rest when I stop it. It often ends up stranded halfway across, and has to be pushed through the warp yarn little by little to the end of the loom. If the yarn runs out before the shuttle has been changed, the thread has to be taken out and a shuttle with a full pirn thrown through.

Everything you do is either right or wrong; there is no fudging. I soon discover that any mistakes the weaver makes are found out when the cloth comes off the loom and is inspected. Every piece of cloth is chalked with the number of the loom, and the weaver is called up to the inspection room by the manager if the quality is below standard. Anything wrong can be put right by one of the menders, but this is an expensive process.

All the cloth we're weaving is white. Once ready, it's sent to the dyers' finishers to be dyed the colour ordered by the customer.

The weaving shed has around a hundred looms. The personal pride that results in such large differences among apparently identical houses in a working-class district is also apparent in the weaving shed. Some looms look clean and tidy, the metal back-roller shining brightly because the weaver takes the trouble to hold emery paper against the roller as the loom is running. Others look uncared for and dirty. During the course of the day I meet more and more of the weavers and soon begin to feel one of them. My first day is exhausting and exciting, and at the end of it I go back to Joe's house.

Joe enjoys reminiscing about his life in the mill. He tells me about 'Mr Paul', whose family built the mill and owned it for several generations.

'Mr Paul wouldn't spend a penny if a ha'penny would do. There was nothing he wouldn't try to save money. All the coffins for the family were made in the mill workshop, and he always delivered his Bradford post by horse and cart.'

He chuckles at the memory of Mr Paul's frugal ways.

'The only water tap in the village was in the mill yard, and it depended how he felt whether he locked the mill gates or left them open. He were a right old devil, Mr Paul.'

Joe needs little encouragement to talk about the past. After all, the past is where the glory has been, and what exists now is, to him, a pale shadow of the better days. 'You've probably never heard of the Great Strike. Every mill in Bradford was involved because the overlookers' union had decided to strike for more money. It was hard for everyone, but we were all determined to get what we thought was a fair wage. After the strike had been going for a week or two, Mr Paul called me into his office. "I need the production," he'd moan. "I'm letting all my customers down and there'll be no business left by the time this strike's finished. I'll tell you what I'll do, I'll give the overlookers a rise providing they don't tell anybody." I looked him in the eye and said, "You can't do that. If you give them a rise it'll have to be made public." I thought he was going to have a thrombosis, he was so furious. "Get out of the bloody office!" he shouts, "You're no bloody good to me!" Anyway, the strike went on another two months and in the end the mill masters had to give way. We all went back to work and on Friday, pay day, I went into Mr Paul's to get the wages. He always did the wages himself, and as usual he put them in an open wooden tray. I pulled one of the wages out and looked at it. I couldn't believe it. It was the same wage he'd been paying before the strike started. I said, "Mr Paul, you haven't given them the rise." He looked at me with such anger, I thought he'd burst a blood-vessel, and in a fit of temper he threw the tray and all the wages into the air. He yells, "If you hadn't said anything they wouldn't have noticed!" No bloody chance of that, but that's just what he was like. After he'd sold out I used to see him in the town in an old mac with a shopping basket, looking like an old tramp.' Joe laughs. 'Anyone who saw him wouldn't think he had a penny to his name. He only died a few years ago and he left a fortune. It all went to some relatives he hardly knew.'

I've already found out that while no one will ever replace Mr Paul in Joe's hall of notoriety, Herbert comes a close second. When back from an over-indulgent lunch, inebriated and smoking a large cigar, Herbert thinks nothing of accosting someone having a five-minute tea break, accusing them of being bloody idle and doing no work. But Joe's experience of unreasonable authority is so deeply ingrained that he's come to regard it as an essential component of being a successful employer.

'Before the war, business was terrible and we were struggling to survive. Once war broke out, there was such a shortage that whatever we could produce was guaranteed to be sold. I've often thought that every manufacturer should put a statue to Adolf Hitler in the mill yard.'

'What went wrong?'

'Once the war was over and rationing finished, demand dropped and every mill was struggling again to stay in business. That's when this business was taken over by a large group. They bought the business just to get the order book so they could keep their own looms going. Within a month or two the mill closed down. It was only reopened less than a year ago.'

Up to now I'd imagined Herbert would be well thought of by everyone in the mill. But now I realise he's regarded as second division compared with his predecessors.

Herbert has been a successful trader, but without any understanding of manufacturing. His main skill has been bargaining to buy cloth cheaply, then selling it for a profit. I've never understood exactly how and why Herbert acquired this loss-making mill. I get the impression it was an accidental consequence of some complicated deal. He's spent little or no time running it, and seems powerless to stem the continuing losses.

Herbert's interest in the mill is erratic in every way. He'll visit on impulse, cause chaos by refusing to sign cheques, and be impervious to any kind of reason. Any discussion goes no further than the end point of the previous visit. He is emotional about any subject involving money, and as his approval is needed for any spending, the morning is a constant tirade of abuse from him. However, relief comes as lunch approaches. He will eye the clock, desperate to get to the pub and enjoy a good drink and good lunch. There's usually a visiting spinner or dyer or a business colleague he's dragged along to see his mill, and despite their protests they're usually persuaded to join him.

He always insists on me joining them too, though I try to persuade him to let me carry on working. The more Herbert obstructs my determination to work, the more determined I become. I'm hungry to know everyone's job, and without meaning to be I become indispensable in a very short time. I enjoy the variety of the work: doing the wages for the weavers, calculating the weight of yarn in the warp and weft of different qualities of cloth, adding up the purchase and sales invoices in the day books. I soon begin to understand how all the different components come together to create a trading account. Why was maths at school never so fascinating, I wonder?

I learn some elementary accountancy and the principles of a balance sheet. I'm fascinated by the way assets and liabilities balance. I grapple with the concept that a company owns itself and its assets and liabilities, but owning the shares in the company doesn't legally give direct access to its assets. I also realise that all the physical complexity of a weaving mill can be simplified if it's related to the balance sheet. Every stick of furniture, every shuttle, tool, loom, every electric light bulb, all collectively become the *fixed* assets in the balance sheet. All the yarn and cloth, all the money owing from customers, all the money in the bank – these become the *current* assets. The total of fixed and current assets in money is one side of the balance sheet. The other side is the money owing to suppliers and banks, and the total of this taken away from the total of the assets gives the financial net worth of the company, represented by share capital and reserves. This difference is continually changing, either positively or negatively, according to whether the company is profit-making or loss-making.

This insight into the nature of companies makes everything so much easier to understand. It hits me with great force that the mill which overshadowed the house I was born in, and which sacked Dad, is subject to the same principles. I also realise that a building and machinery give little indication of the actual worth of the company. It might all seem impressive, but only a balance sheet can reveal whether it's as good as it looks.

I'm increasingly absorbed by the costings because of my anxiety to make the mill profitable. We're weaving about 80 pieces of cloth a week, each piece approximately 65 yards long when finished. There's the calculated cost of buying the yarn and finishing the cloth, which can be easily identified and is predictable. The rest is subject to variation, some of it unpredictable, and that part of the costing determines success or failure. If the total of the wage bill and the electricity, rates, repairs and all the other variable costs can be accurately forecast, then all we need do is sell the cloth at a price which will recover that cost over the 4,000 or so pieces made during the year.

The purpose is to make a profit, but that only happens if the costs of production are accurately forecast. Competition means that pressure is always on to reduce prices, otherwise it's impossible to sell anything. However, I discover that it's all too easy to be optimistic about both costs and production. Optimism creates sales, but it can also easily create losses. We employ no salesmen, just agents who get commission on sales, so they're happy to sell at almost any price.

Every evening I play with the costings, fascinated by the speculative nature of textiles. There's no obvious way of telling whether we're making profits. We never take an order without believing we'll make a profit from it, but there are so many ways we can be wrong. When we're running short of money we can always find reasons why, yet we never imagine it could be that we're *losing* money. It could be because the stock has increased, or more money than usual is owing to us, or we've spent more money on fixed assets.

Other factors, which we never anticipate, can cause us to lose money. Customers will complain that a fault in our cloth has made their garments unsaleable and will claim compensation. If weavers are away ill, production will fall and the cost rise. Production can also be affected by the quality of the yarn.

Because there are too few customers we're always afraid to lose them, even when they do things which result in us losing money. For example, orders can be cancelled even though theoretically they're legally binding.

A cancelled order means cloth without a customer, and this in turn usually means selling it at a loss.

Some customers are so personally intimidating that it seems impossible to withstand their demands. Increasingly I'm talking to customers on the phone about deliveries and about money, and I begin to understand the difficulties in making a profit. It's easy to make a sale, but will it be profitable? This is the culture of business, and I find myself drawn completely into it.

One day, Herbert brings over a customer from Manchester who is interested in buying cloth. He's meticulously dressed and fastidious in appearance, with manicured hands. His face is lean and tanned, his eyes large and restless, his thinning hair well brushed back. He is remarkably similar in appearance to the pianist Claudio Arrau. As he enters the office his eyes flick round the room, registering every detail.

Herbert introduces him to me as Gus. Gus doesn't smile. As I find out later, he rarely smiles.

'I'm only a small buyer.' Gus seems at pains to lower expectations.

'I know how much you buy. You're a big buyer,' Herbert retorts good-naturedly.

'And I've no money,' Gus presses on.

Herbert looks at me, intent on getting down to business.

'Show him the cloth patterns.'

I pull out some samples and hand them to Gus. He fingers them without interest.

'I'm not in the market at the moment, but just in case, how much is this one?' I mention a price that's more competitive than usual.

'I'm buying a better quality than that cheaper now.'

'We can make any quality you like. I'll send you a pattern,' Herbert says, determined not to be put off, but I feel my confidence draining away.

Gus doesn't seem put off by the disparity between what we're asking and the price he says he's already paying.

'When you quote me, don't forget I want five per cent discount for seven-day payment.'

I'm excited at the prospect of selling to a customer I've just met. Although it seems impossible to make a profit even at the price he says he's already getting, I want to sell so badly that I begin to persuade myself it might be possible to do it.

'Herbert, you said you'd have me driven back when we'd finished our business.'

'Stay and have some lunch.'

'No, I'm too busy, I've got work to do.' Gus is fiercely adamant.

'Have a drink before you go.'

'I don't drink.'

Herbert looks at him in disbelief. 'Just have a small one.'

Gus shakes his head.

'What's the matter with you, are you a bloody Methodist?'

'No, I'm a Jew and I need to get back to work.' His answer is a clear rebuke, and so uncompromisingly resolute that Herbert has to give way. I soon discover just how effective that attitude is in conducting negotiations. Herbert has met his match and Peter is summoned to drive Gus back to Manchester.

As Gus is leaving, he turns to me and says, 'Always remember there are only two kinds of customer – the ones who don't let you sleep and the ones who don't let you eat.'

Before too long, I'll understand the full meaning of this enigmatic remark.

A week later we receive the pattern from Gus and Harold the manager has the job of analysing it. He cuts out a square inch with a template and counts the threads in the warp and weft. He then weighs the square inch and calculates the weight of a yard of cloth 58 inches wide. The sheer impossibility of getting an accurate answer is no deterrent to Harold. He's naively confident that his method works, but when I think about it, it's obvious that the smallest discrepancy is magnified 36 by 58 times. In any case, I soon discover that all customers exaggerate the value they expect. They describe their cloth as 14 ounces per yard when in practice it might be much closer to 12. I'm never sure whether this is because they've been hoodwinked by their supplier or whether they're trying to improve the quality without increasing the price. Another garment-maker tells me, 'When the retailer gives us a price for a garment we work it backwards. If there's anything left for the cloth, we know we've made a mistake somewhere in the costing.' He laughs as he says it but the message is clear: making a profit out of clothing manufacturers is going to be very difficult.

Nevertheless, we're desperate to get orders, and I sense that Gus will give me an order if we can get the right price. Not everyone is prepared to try a new supplier; many people feel safer with what they know. I realise that only by cutting the price can we get the chance of supplying a new customer. I scrutinise the costing and work the figures out again and again. It's astonishing how the price of cloth falls when you look at the figures optimistically. Optimism can always reduce the costs of manufacturing.

However, there is one element in the costing that can sometimes be reduced without using optimism, and that's the cost of the yarn. The most important yarn supplier locally is Harry W. I regularly phone Harry for prices and he comes across as helpful, competitive and very efficient. In a short time he becomes our principal supplier. I begin to visit him regularly to discuss prices, but also to gain his confidence. We need credit from him as we're always short of money, and I know the only reason he gives us credit is that he trusts me. He's extremely wary of Herbert, and I know he wouldn't have been happy but for my involvement. The growth of our business with him leads to an increasing mutual dependence.

Harry's office is in one of his spinning mills. It's a modest affair with a fire burning in the grate only when autumn gives way to winter. He always wears a long cotton coat with a small blue and white check, which seems to be the spinners' uniform. He's a genial but authoritative man who has built a substantial business. Moreover, he has a sizeable balance of money on deposit so he has no financial worries. This is in complete contrast to our position. We're constantly straining to pay overdue debts and always in danger of going over the bank overdraft. Although I have no shares in the company and am not a director, I feel as if my whole life and career are under threat when I'm dealing with overdue bills. Without any training, I develop the ability to reassure people that they'll be paid and by degrees bring a sense of stability to what is in reality a business in crisis. Herbert seems oblivious to the situation and is unconcerned about creditors or payments. As I become more expert at handling both customers and suppliers, Herbert has even less reason to worry and I realise that he is coming to depend on me.

Every time we have an enquiry for cloth, I get a quote from Harry for the yarn and only then quote for the cloth. If we're successful I place an order for the yarn. Being in business seems so much simpler than I've imagined. Harold is still officially the managing director, but only a few months after I start I sense that I'm displacing him, because customers, suppliers and employees increasingly ask for me and not him. It's perhaps not surprising, as Harold always sounds so miserable and negative and I can't be anything but enthusiastic and positive. This transfer of power is not formally ordained by Herbert; it simply reflects the reality of our positions. If customers regard me as the MD, it's inevitable that I come to regard myself as MD and Harold as my second-in-command. It's a painless transition for everyone, including Harold.

Despite my inexperience, I quickly grasp the language and methods of business. As I'm working as both a salesman and a buyer, I use my experience in one role to improve my ability in the other. If a supplier is late delivering, I reflect on what happens when I'm late delivering to a customer. There might be several phone calls from customers, all anxious about delivery and pressing me for priority. I analyse what it is that one customer says that makes me give him priority over the rest: why am I more concerned about not letting him down? How has he made me afraid and why do other urgent enquiries seem less worrying? If a customer makes me respond dynamically and I think through what he says and how he says it, I discover that, by using the same phrases in the same way, I can influence my suppliers to react just as positively as I've been made to react. I'm astonished how well it works, and I rapidly become more and more confident in my ability to handle any situation.

Even though Harry W is so successful and so experienced, I find that he is just as vulnerable to the techniques I use, and despite the difference in our years I can tell he's treating me with increasing respect.

'I hope my son is as good as you when he joins the business.'

I feel profoundly flattered when he says it.

23

A Green Patch of Land

Things are slowly looking up. The business is expanding, turnover and production increasing, and we're using more and more yarn from Harry. But profitability is still a huge problem that shows no sign of going away. Because we're selling to many customers who are good payers, we're under the illusion that we're very profitable. Only months later, when we look at the accounts, do we see that we are in fact making very little money. Herbert has never involved himself in the costings, nor has he ever stressed the importance of gross profit. My natural optimism doesn't help. It's a powerful aid when dealing with customers and suppliers, but very dangerous when applied to costings. It's no good believing that production will be higher than it is, and costs consequently lower.

One day, I'm over at Harry W's.

'It's been a very good week for me,' he says. 'I'd built up a big holding in wool futures and I decided to sell the lot yesterday. Look at this.' He hands me the *Financial Times* and points out a section I've never noticed before. It's devoted to wool futures and the news item he clearly enjoys reading is beneath rows of prices which are meaningless to me. It says, 'Prices went lower in the afternoon trading session as a consequence of a very large selling order.' He smiles with pride as he reads it. 'I netted a tidy amount. Well into six figures.'

I'm intrigued by what he says, but don't understand it.

'What are futures?'

'Well, you can buy a £5,000 lot of wool for delivery in any month up to 18 months ahead. I thought wool was cheap six months ago and I started buying. As the price went up I bought more, and yesterday I sold it all.'

'You mean you sold it and didn't take any delivery of wool?'

'No, I bought it all to sell.'

I struggle to understand this bewildering idea.

'Who did you sell it to?'

'I've no idea. It would have been sold to a lot of different people.'

'But why would they buy it?'

'Because they thought the price was going up.'

'Why did you sell it then?'

'Because I wanted to take a profit and I thought the price might go down.'

'But what happens to all the wool?'

'There may be no wool in the end. For every buyer there's a seller. Before the final date attaching to the contract, if every buyer sells and every seller buys, they all cancel each other out.'

'So you can sell before you buy?' I'm increasingly intrigued by futures.

'Certainly. If you think the price might go down, then you sell, and if you're right, buy it at a cheaper price later on.'

It all sounds so simple, and Harry has made a lot of money doing it. He can see how interested I am.

'I'll give you the number of my wool broker and you can try if you like, but be careful. Every penny I make, somebody else lost.'

That same day I ring the broker and introduce myself.

'I'm interested in buying.'

'Which month?'

'About twelve months ahead. What's the trading price now?'

'I think we could buy at about 130 pence per pound. By the way, you understand that if this price goes against you, we'll need margins from you?'

'Yes, I understand that. See what the price for ten lots would be.'

'We'll phone you back.'

While I wait, I begin to consider the consequences. I can lose a lot of money if the price goes seriously wrong, and I have little or no money; but I've been mesmerised by Harry's story and I just can't resist it. I don't want to mention it to Herbert because I know he'll react badly to my doing something on my own. The phone rings.

'We can buy ten lots for you at 131.' I'm almost trembling with excitement as I say, 'Right, buy then.' I can't believe the ease and suddenness of it all. Am I being stupid? I sit in the office, unable to concentrate on anything.

* * *

218

The phone rings. It's Gus.

'I hope you have my cloth ready.'

'Not yet. The first pieces aren't due for another two weeks.'

'You said you could deliver this week!'

'I didn't. Yes, you asked me to deliver this week, but I said I couldn't.'

'You said that at first, then you said you could.' His voice is getting more strident.

'Look, Gus, you argued with me about delivery and I said I'd do my best.'

There is a long pause. Then, in a dramatically resigned voice, 'This is what I get for helping you. I should have known.' I'm tempted to say I'll try to improve delivery, but I know they'll be empty words. I say nothing, and there is a frightening silence. Suddenly he erupts.

'Do you realise what it means? I'll have to send my machinists home because they have no work. My customers will cancel their orders. This will cost you a lot of money!'

His onslaught blows away all my defences. I listen, powerless to fight back. It all sounds so logical. I haven't promised to deliver, but that doesn't seem to matter. Gus is so convinced I'm in the wrong that I can't fight it.

'I'll do my best. I'll try to bring delivery forward.'

'When?'

I've no idea but I have to say something.

'A week to ten days.'

'Right. Now don't let me down.'

I put the phone down, committed unnecessarily to an unachievable delivery time. How on earth did I manage it? I realise that it's purely his aggression that made me say it and put myself in an impossible position. I dread the conversation I'll be having a week from now.

But the following day, I come into the office more preoccupied with the price of wool than with manufacturing and delivery. It's important to discover how the market opens.

I ring the broker as soon as I can. 'What's the price this morning?' It's up fourpence. I've already made a profit of £800 – more money than I've ever had in my life.

'What's the price for another ten lots?'

'We'll phone back.'

That same morning I buy a further ten lots at 138 pence.

The excitement of gambling in futures makes the ordinary business of running the mill seem dull. I'm unable to concentrate on anything else and I sit scribbling figures and calculating how much profit I might be able to make. Then, my secretary Mary announces, 'You have a visitor.' The visitor is right behind her.

To my surprise, it's Herbert's accountant, Sydney. He relaxes in the leather chair, and I ask Mary to bring us coffee. As soon as we're alone, he leans forward conspiratorially.

'I wanted to come and tell you what I've done. When I first met you, I was working for other people like Herbert, saving them tax. That's a good way to make a living, but not to get seriously rich. I began to wonder how I could profit from my knowledge for my own benefit. I answered an advert in the *Financial Times* from a private company, and I've ended up buying the shell of a public company with huge tax losses. What I've decided to do is approach profitable private companies whose owners are being taxed to the hilt, and buy the businesses by offering share capital and a seat on the board in exchange for the equity of the company. It's such a good deal for them that I've already acquired eight companies, and the profitability of the group just keeps going up. The tax losses mean we have no problem with tax, and because the company's assets are growing, the shares are increasingly valuable. I'm placing 30 per cent of the shares on the market, so I still retain 70 per cent. That 30 per cent will realise me a few millions, but the companies taking the shares will make far more.'

As I listen and look at Sydney, I realise he's wearing a suit noticeably smarter than last time I saw him. And he's got a gold Rolex on his wrist.

He gets to his point.

'Before you arrived here, this company wasn't worth buying, but it's different now you've taken over. To cut a long story short, I've offered Herbert a price for all his business interests and he's accepted.'

How do I react to this? I'm flattered that I'm the reason he's interested, but at the same time worried that too much will be expected of me. None the less, my ambition and natural enthusiasm quickly persuade me that any problems can be solved. Sydney anticipates the one problem that might not be so easy for me to sort out.

'Let me tell you something. I've known Herbert for years and you'll never get a penny from him.' Surprise – possibly shock – must have registered in my face. 'He's not made you a director, has he?'

He hasn't.

Sydney drives the message home. 'Join me, and you can have a seat on the board of the public company.'

I can hardly believe what he's proposing. It's such an exciting prospect that I momentarily feel dizzy. My instinctive reaction is to immediately say yes, thank you, but something warns me to be careful, and not seem too eager. I manage to look undecided, helped by Mary's return with a tray of coffee and biscuits. She senses the seriousness of the conversation and leaves quickly. Sydney assumes I need more persuasion.

'You must believe me, Herbert won't give you anything. I've known him a long time and he's a very astute man. You might imagine he's made you one of the family, but he's only done it so you'll work for next to nothing. I'm the only chance you'll have to make some real money for yourself.'

In truth, it had been dawning on me that Herbert was getting a great deal of work and commitment out of me without giving me anything in exchange. From the moment I started in the mill, I'd worked as if the business was mine. Whenever I hinted at becoming a director, he always managed to avoid the issue. His constant refrain when under pressure was, 'What are you worrying about? It'll all be yours one day.' It never sounded entirely convincing but it lulled me into feeling that my future was secure. I felt more perplexed than annoyed that he resisted making me a director of the company, because to everyone else I was a director. But without a doubt it's come as a shock that Herbert has sold the business over my head. He's suddenly forgotten his promises when it comes to looking after his own interests.

'I've told you the shares will go up,' Sydney persists. 'So I'm prepared to lend you £20,000 to buy shares in the company. Pay me back when you sell them.'

I'm overwhelmed by his trust and generosity, and begin to realise that the prospect of becoming a businessman is within my grasp. It's far removed from my dream of being a musician, but it's now more exciting. It seems as if Herbert, without realising or intending it, has given me a great opportunity. His decision to sell out is propelling me forward.

'Oh, by the way, I've also bought a business from a friend of yours. Gus has accepted my offer and he'll be on the board with you.'

So many things are going through my head that I can barely absorb everything I've heard. Such a short time ago, the world of business was alien to me. Now, here I am in my twenties, about to sit on the board of a publicly quoted company. What can I say?

'I just hope I can be as useful as you think.' Sydney looks at me with a sly grin.

'You'd better be as useful as I think or you'll be out.'

The meeting is effectively over. Within minutes of Sydney leaving the office, the wool broker rings.

'I thought I'd let you know that you can get around 145 pence for your wool lots at the moment.' I quickly calculate how much profit this would give me.

'Sell them for the best you can get.'

That weekend the Suez Crisis blows over, and on Monday the market opens at 139 pence. By the end of the day it's dropped to 131.

It's been a very narrow squeak.

When I get home that evening I can't wait to share the good news with Ruth. 'It's been an extraordinary day. Sydney's invited on to the board of a public company, and I've made £4,000 tax free.'

'I've never liked Sydney and I hope you're doing nothing illegal.'

I feel exasperated that Ruth is being so negative about the most exciting prospect I've ever had.

'Of course it's legal, and whether you like him or not doesn't change the fact that he's a clever man.'

'I just don't want to think you'd turn into the sort of person he is.'

'I've no intention of allowing anyone to change me from the person I am.'

There the conversation ends, but I feel a sense of disquiet about Ruth's attitude.

That evening, a small advert in the local paper attracts my attention. We've been looking around for a new house for months and haven't found anything suitable. Every house we've looked at has been turned down by Ruth. I've seen plenty I could happily live in but Ruth has vetoed every one, and I've begun to feel despondent. 'We'll never find anything you like,' I moan. But to my great surprise I'm proved wrong.

The advert which attracts my attention is simple and unostentatious. No photograph, just a few lines and a phone number: 'Country house in a wooded valley, idyllic situation, five bedrooms, trout stream, stables.' There is something appealing about the simplicity of the advert. I phone the number and speak to the owner, a Mrs Kershaw. I arrange for us to visit the house the same evening.

We find ourselves in a valley we've never seen before. We're immediately attracted by the quaint houses on the steep hillsides, and the stone setts of what we later discover were packhorse roads leading over the Pennines.

222

The village appeals to both of us. It hasn't yet attracted smart middle-class money and is still inhabited mainly by working-class families. Property is thus considerably cheaper than in the residential areas we've been looking at. Just past a small bridge, we recognise the house we've come to see, even without a photograph. It's a charming, Georgian-style building with a beautiful front garden directly on to the cobbled road we're driving along. We park the car and an elderly man appears. He has the keys and he leads us in. Within seconds, we feel sure it's our destiny to live here.

The following weekend is sunny and warm, and as the house is empty we can't resist walking round the garden. We sit on the private lawn to the rear of the house and look up into a great yew tree. We see birds flitting from branch to branch: chaffinches, wrens, great tits, blackbirds, a woodpecker – all in the space of twenty minutes or so. The idea of having a garden with such beautiful birds is thrilling. We negotiate with Mrs Kershaw and in a very short time the house is ours.

Ruth and I are now living together in our own home, big enough to accommodate our two grand pianos. My growing involvement in business has taken away the pain music created during our early years. There is no longer any sense of competition or conflict between us, and we even begin to play two-piano music together.

I remember Mam's dream of a green patch of land in the middle of urban squalour. Now I'm realising her dream in a way that she would find incomprehensible. I've seen little of Mam since our marriage, and I know that my life is moving in a way which makes the divide between us even deeper.

24

Member of the Board

I haven't seen Herbert for several weeks following his sell-out. I suspect he's too embarrassed to come to the mill and face all the people he has now turned his back on. He's gone for a continental holiday with Sophia to enjoy his success, while I enjoy the freedom and responsibility of running the company. But with that responsibility comes a growing awareness that I'm now answerable to people I hardly know, in a way that seems increasingly onerous. I'm worried that the trading results won't be good, and the prospect of explaining to the board why we're doing badly isn't a pleasant one. When it was Herbert's business, the trading results hardly seemed connected to me. Now it's mine, the trading results not only have much more serious repercussions, but are also a public rather than a private matter.

When Herbert sold out, I'm sure he had no idea that in the long run it might prove more beneficial to me than to him. I've been officially appointed managing director of the company and I'm on the board of the public company, which is already getting favourable coverage in the financial press.

There is a great deal of interest in shell companies which are being revived by the injection of new, dynamic companies. From having little or no value, they suddenly become asset rich. In the short term, the success of these companies is assured because of investor interest. There is generally a limited market in the shares, but once the financial press begins to tip the company as a good prospect, the interest of buyers ensures an increase in the share price. Not only that, but most of the shell companies start with tax losses, so an injection of profit-making companies has the double benefit of raising the profile of the company and making the former private companies more tax effective. Because there is no capital gains tax, everyone wants to make capital profits instead of revenue profits. It's the way people make the most money on the Stock Exchange. I watch my own investment in the company begin to grow in value.

It's a huge relief to escape Herbert's constant prying, but I know it's only a matter of time before he's back again.

One evening Ruth answers the phone. 'Daddy, how lovely to hear from you! Did you enjoy your holiday?'

I feel my heart sink. I can see the smile on Ruth's face and know from experience that she'll be hearing a litany of the lavish lifestyle they've enjoyed, the important people they've met and the high regard they all have for Herbert. I can't help but contrast her evident delight in hearing from her father with my own feeling of distaste and resentment. At the end of a long conversation, Ruth hands the phone to me.

I make a big effort to conceal my real feelings. 'Herbert, how good to hear from you. I hope you enjoyed your holiday.' But Herbert is not in a mood to reciprocate. It's immediately obvious that he's been brooding and simmering.

'Sydney tells me you've joined the board.'

In a flash I realise I should have told him. I kick myself for not breaking the news to him as soon as it happened. I quickly try to cover my tracks.

'I wasn't sure it was definite. That's why I didn't say anything.'

'You must have known for some time.'

'No, it's only just happened.'

'But he must have told you before you were appointed?'

'You were away and I wasn't sure where to get hold of you.'

'My secretary had all the details about where we were. I told you that before we left.'

'I should have thought of that.'

'He wanted me to join the board as well, you know. I turned him down.'

Neither Sydney nor Gus wanted him and I'm sure he knew that, but it's a measure of how much he's been hurt that he tells such a feeble lie. I suddenly feel so sorry for him that I want to make him feel better.

'I'm sure he was disappointed you refused.'

'I hope you realise what you're doing.'

There is a hint of menace. His voice is slurred, and I can almost smell the combination of whisky and cigar on his breath. I say nothing and let him make the running.

'It's not as simple as it seems. If you put a foot wrong, you can end up inside. I took cash out of the business, but it was my business. The taxman might have had a view on it though.' He's almost talking to himself. 'In a public company, every move is open to scrutiny. You'll have to forecast the result and God help you if you get it wrong. Sydney will expect good profits from you. By the way, I understand he's loaned you money to buy shares. The taxman could ask some awkward questions about that.'

I haven't the slightest idea what he's talking about but I feel mounting unease as I listen to him. I begin to wonder if he's actually jealous of the upturn in my fortunes. His unpleasantness doesn't encourage further conversation and after a short time he puts the phone down.

What he said about forecasting the result begins to bother me. Up to now, the financial result has seemed of little consequence. The major problem has always been paying the bills. From the moment I started working in the business, I discovered that every bill was paid late. All the yarn spinners ring on the twenty-sixth of the month, which is the day after the bill is due. They expect to be paid on the due date, and if the cheque doesn't arrive they're never slow in phoning to ask for their money. They all have to balance the need to sell yarn against the danger of dealing with a late-paying customer. They don't like it, but if they begin to trust you, they continue to supply yarn.

When I first started dealing with the spinners, I found it both embarrassing and uncomfortable explaining why they hadn't got their cheque. The reason was always simple – we hadn't got the money – but I couldn't say anything as obvious as that. To keep them happy I needed to convince them that they would have their cheque in the near future. As I became more experienced, I began to enjoy handling them. I never had any doubt that they'd all get paid; I had no feeling of guilt that I was keeping them waiting. In fact, I began to enjoy the feeling that I could build their confidence *and* keep them waiting. I never had any clear idea about whether our difficulties in paying suppliers had anything to do with whether or not we were making profits. In any case, the trading results were so late that they seemed irrelevant when we got them.

But now, the profit isn't simply relevant; it's extremely important. It begins to dawn on me that I'm in what could be a very difficult situation.

As soon as Herbert sold the business there was intense scrutiny of the books and the stock, and I realised then that Herbert had given orders to value everything in the warehouse at the maximum price so he could get the best possible deal. Previously, in order to minimise tax, he'd been doing the opposite – writing everything down to a very low level. As a result, this year's exceptional profit simply reflects the difference in stock valuation, not the actual trading profit. It now hits me that the price Sydney paid for the business was based on the assumption that the profits will continue to grow from this artificially high level. I begin to understand why I've been invited to join the board; Sydney assumes that my arrival, and nothing else, has produced the sudden leap in profits.

All of this goes through my brain in a flash. I realise that only Herbert knows the situation I'm in. Now I understand his warning. What can I say? Tell Sydney he's been duped? Tell him I'm not as good as he thinks I am? The loan to buy shares is more than I deserve, but I can't go back now.

My only hope is to make a genuine success of the business.

My brain warns me of the dangerous position I'm in, but in my heart I feel such optimism and determination that I can't imagine the consequence will be anything but success. It's clear I'll have to find a way of retaining Sydney's confidence while having a comparatively poor trading year. The excitement and pleasure of joining a public company is now overlaid with fear, and I can't share any of this with anyone. This is the price I'll have to pay for my opportunity. My predicament is not of my making, but it's one I must solve unaided if I'm going to succeed.

Is it worth it? Up to now, I've enjoyed a transparently open life without any hidden fears. If I carry on and say nothing, I'll become an accomplice unable to enjoy a clear conscience. The age of innocence has quickly given way to the age of experience. It had seemed too good to be true, and it was.

'I'm off to London to my first board meeting next week.'

The thought of spending more time in London is enticing, and it's clear Ruth isn't going to be negative about it.

'I'll be quite happy with my music.'

I think back to the dark days when I tried to inspire her with my piano playing and my composition, naively believing she'd be happy to live in my shadow. I now have a career which throws no shadow and I've left the world of music to her. My happiness seems to depend on my committing myself to longer and longer days in the mill.

The following morning, a letter arrives from Sydney.

I am delighted to confirm my invitation to you to join the board. You are there in your position as Managing Director of what is now a subsidiary company. The date has been fixed for the 26th June.

A bedroom will be reserved in your name at the Berkeley Hotel for the evening of the 25th June and we will be eating dinner in a private dining-room there.

I look forward to seeing you.

Yours ever,

Sydney

Only a few minutes later, Gus rings.

'Have you got the letter confirming the board meeting?'

'Yes, I've just read it.'

'You're a big businessman already, aren't you?' Gus gets as close as he can to teasing me, realising, I'm sure, that I'm overwhelmed by it all.

'Perhaps we should travel to London together,' he adds.

I'm flattered that he's treating me as a colleague, because he's well aware of the difference in our financial situations and experience.

'Oh, and I'm expecting my cloth next week. Don't let me down again. I told Sydney I was having problems.'

I can't believe he can be so treacherous, especially when the problem is always his unreasonable pressure, not my inability to deliver. I suddenly realise how careful I need to be. After confirming the timing of our train journey, I put the phone down.

I walk into the weaving shed. It's noisy, but I love the sense of activity. I go into the inspection room, where all the finished cloth is stored. Harold is looking at the cloth with the cloth inspector.

'I understand your father-in-law sold the business.'

I'm taken aback that the news has leaked out earlier than I'd planned. All the mill will know now, and I wonder what they think will happen to them.

'I'm joining the board of the holding company.'

Harold looks surprised and pleased. 'You'll be able to watch out for us.'

I realise how vulnerable they all feel. They don't know whether the new owner has bought it to run it, or close it down.

'I can tell you that I'm joining the board to protect the interests of this company. It's my job to make a success of it, and I need you to help me do it.'

I see the relief on Harold's face. I know the whole mill will soon get the message.

I've had a growing desire to buy a sports car, and on the spur of the moment one afternoon I buy an MG TD. It's cream with red leather. I can't resist touching the beautiful shining chrome and the leather. As I climb into it, the thought of Stephen and his uncompromising rejection of this world momentarily spoils my pleasure. The MG seems to symbolise my fall from grace. A short time ago it would have been unthinkable in every sense. It's hard to believe how much has changed so quickly. I'm now inside a world that is closed to everyone I know, yet it has all seemed so simple.

I get into the car. It's a sunny afternoon and the top is down. I start the engine and drive off. I've never felt anything quite like it. Abandoning a career as a pianist seems a small price to pay.

When I next see Gus, we're both on the London train. He looks even sharper than usual. His briefcase is brand new, perhaps a sign that his appointment to the board means as much to him as it does to me. And we're travelling first class.

'Sydney tells me you're making good profits. I must be paying you too much.'

I squirm inwardly as I think of the truth.

'You're certainly not paying too much. Not enough, in fact.' I say it as a joke, even though it's true. I just hope he isn't going to delve any deeper into the state of my company's profits. Fortunately he doesn't.

'I'm going to do some shopping in Bond Street while I'm here, so you may be catching an earlier train back than me. I never pay the price they ask. They accept bids, you know. I've developed a technique. I offer a ridiculously low price, they have a think about it, then lower the original price.' So I'm not his only victim, I think. 'I bid a price below that, and they refuse to go any lower. I start to walk out of the shop. As I get to the door, they'll ask me to come back and we carry on negotiating. It's when they make no attempt to call me back that I know I've got the best possible price.'

I can't imagine having the nerve to do it.

'I've bought quite a few diamond rings that way.'

I've always associated diamond rings with women, but his comment diverts my eye to his immaculately manicured hands. I notice for the first time a diamond ring.

As we begin to near London, I find it harder to concentrate on what Gus is saying. There is an excitement about this strange new world that is beginning to grip me.

It's extraordinary to think that my first formal meeting of any kind is the board of a public company, and I'm a director of it. As I walk into the boardroom, I feel nervous and out of my depth. Sydney is surrounded by a group of important-looking, smartly-dressed men and barely acknowledges me. Gus immediately joins them, shaking hands and murmuring routine pleasantries. I gaze on as an outsider for a few minutes.

'Are you a new board member?' I look round and see a smiling, handsome face. 'I'm James Parsons. Are you the one with the mill?' He almost sniggers, as if the idea is preposterous, but his casual suit and engaging friendliness are greatly reassuring.

'I hope there's no trouble at t'mill,' he laughs in a mock-northern accent. 'Come and meet the others.'

He takes me over to the group. Sydney introduces me in an offhand way which ensures that I'm left with only a vague idea of everybody's name. There are manufacturers of dressing-gowns, buttons, rainwear, dresses and radios. The dressing-gown man is the most intimidating. He's smoking a Herbert-sized cigar and can barely conceal his indifference when I'm introduced to him. I feel like the poor relation.

All the men here have sold their businesses to Sydney for large sums of money, and are now directors of the company which owns the businesses. The conversation before I arrived has clearly been about their respective holidays, no doubt paid for with Sydney's money.

'Well anyway, I *strongly* recommend the Palace Hotel in St Moritz.' I'm not even sure which country St Moritz is in.

But with everyone now present, the pleasantries are cut short and we all sit round the board table so the meeting can begin. Every place at the table has an expensive-looking blotter with sharpened pencils. Large bottles of mineral water surrounded by glasses are set in the middle, perfectly symmetrical and gleaming in the light from the window.

'Welcome to the board, for those who are joining us.'

I notice that James is sitting next to Sydney, and I soon discover he is there as an assistant to Sydney, not as a board member. This explains his earlier manner, and instantly makes me feel like a child whose new best classmate turns out to be from another school.

Sydney continues briskly, 'We have a relatively light agenda, because I thought it important that we have time to get to know each other. There are also other acquisitions in the pipeline, so in a sense this isn't yet a fully formed board. Our success depends primarily on our profitability – er, *your* profitability, I should say.' He beams in a slightly cynical way. 'But before we start the formal meeting, I thought you might be interested to see these figures.'

He hands out sheets listing every company he has acquired. Alongside each name is a predicted profit figure. I'm terrified when I see the profit he expects from my company. It's impossible. The total profit for the group is enormous.

Gus screws up his eyes and examines the sheet of paper intently, as if greatly worried by it. He's the first to speak. 'I don't want you to be too optimistic about next week's profit in my company. If we have unseasonal weather it can play havoc, because if the retailers don't sell their summer stock they've no money to buy winter stock.'

The dressing-gown man is the next to speak. 'Could I just mention that I'm still owed £250,000?' His face is impassive and stern. Sydney reacts with sudden aggression. 'I don't think this is an appropriate moment to bring that up.' He's obviously upset that such an unpleasant issue should mar the first meeting. He explains to the rest of us, 'We reached an agreement about the price, but before it was completed Mr Flowers changed his mind and wanted an additional £250,000.'

Mr Flowers shows not a flicker of emotion. Everyone shuffles uneasily, unsure what to do next.

It's Gus who speaks. 'I'm sure we all want to settle this matter amicably.'

Mr Flowers blows out a large cloud of Havana smoke and still shows no sign of wanting to engage in any debate. He just sits passively, staring into space.

'Perhaps we could compromise?' Gus may be thinking of trying his Bond Street shopping technique, but Mr Flowers remains unmoved and shows no interest in improving relationships with Sydney or Gus or anybody.

'I think we should move on to the agenda and not spend any more time on this.' Sydney doesn't look up as he speaks, and I realise that it's likely Mr Flowers will win.

The rest of the agenda is tame compared to the bloodshed of the opening bout with Mr Flowers, and it isn't long before a sense of euphoria begins to overcome the unpleasantness. After all, what can be more pleasant than speculating on a rosy future of unending profit? Somehow,

Sydney's hypothetical figures take on a life of their own. Even my highly fictional profit begins to feel achievable. Perhaps reality will be transformed by the power of Sydney's optimism?

I begin to dread the compulsory inquisition which accompanies the figures at the monthly board meeting, but I also begin to get on the inside of them in a way that allows me to anticipate disaster.

Dressing-Gowns' company is one of the impending disasters. I'm always fascinated by the relationship between stock and profit, and I can't help but notice that although his profit is rising, his stock is also rising significantly. Every month reveals the same pattern.

The impassive face with its omnipresent cigar shows no sign of concern when a question is raised about the increase in stock.

'We've had to buy most of the cloth for next season's range, and we have some major orders held up.'

'Why did you have to buy the cloth early?' Sydney asks incredulously.

'Because I got a special offer and I wanted to take advantage of the price.'

'Are the orders going to be taken up?'

'Of course.' His manner is so intimidating that I wouldn't be surprised if his customers were afraid of him.

Sydney clearly resents the extra money Dressing-Gowns has bullied him into paying for his company, but for that very reason it's hardly in Sydney's interest to rock the boat. His own success depends on the success of the individual companies he has collected. Without them he is nothing, and the choice has been his, so he has no one else to blame.

The board members seem easily reassured by the explanation about the stock levels. I conceal my own disquiet for obvious reasons. It's likely I'll have to face a similar interrogation, and I feel far from sure how I can answer any questions.

25

Business as Usual

If I'm ever going to get out of the hole I'm in, I need to make more profit urgently. There's no way I can charge my existing customers more, because they can so easily buy elsewhere. The only possible way I can make more profit is to sell more cloth.

So many of our costs stay the same, regardless of how much we produce, that it's obvious we'll be more profitable if we sell more. I calculate what the costs would be if we put on a night shift. Playing with the figures on paper becomes an obsession. I can see that our profits would be transformed if we could sell everything we produce, but it isn't so simple. To sell more I need to find new customers, which probably means reducing prices to attract them. I calculate the trading profits using different production figures and different profit margins to see what happens. It's exciting to be able to leave behind the depressing world of reality and project myself into this dream world of possibilities.

It becomes clear that the only customers who could buy in the quantities I need are the customers I've been afraid to approach so far: the multiple clothiers. There are several of them, and their large stores dominate the high streets in every town and city. I had bought my tails from one of them when I was nineteen, and Gerald had borrowed them from me when he played the Beethoven Fourth Piano Concerto with the Royal Liverpool Philharmonic Orchestra. Every time I look at them hanging in the wardrobe, I think, 'They've played the Beethoven Fourth.'

I've always been afraid to approach the multiples because I fear a rebuff, and I'm not wrong. I try several times to fix an appointment with the buyer of one of the biggest names, but every time I speak to his secretary she's evasive and won't commit herself. 'Mr Longhurst is very busy at the moment and he likes to make his own appointments.'

'Could you tell me when to try?'

'Well, he has meetings all day today and tomorrow.'

I come to the conclusion that her purpose is to make it so difficult that I'll give up trying; but I persist, and finally, after several months, I get an appointment with Mr Longhurst.

I park my car outside the enormous factory, which I have passed many times but never entered. I feel intimidated by the scale of it and follow the signs to reception with trepidation. When I get there I see four men sitting waiting. The receptionist asks me to become the fifth. After what seems an interminable time she announces, 'Mr Longhurst will see you now.' I follow her directions to his office, deeply apprehensive.

As I walk in, I look around a huge room, panelled in light wood with a formal seating area around a table on one side and a more informal group of comfortable leather chairs on the other. Mr Longhurst is sitting at his large desk in the centre of the room, resolutely refusing to lift his head to acknowledge my arrival. As I stand awkwardly waiting for him to say something, I notice several trophies, which I connect with framed golfing photos. It's obvious that Mr Longhurst is a keen golfer. As I've never had any interest in playing the game, I know straight away that he and I won't be on the same wavelength.

I can smell cigar smoke, which has impregnated all the fabric in the room. Mr Longhurst exudes the same characteristics of good living as Herbert: the smell, and a complexion suggesting a combination of sun and whisky.

Eventually, when he decides he's kept me waiting long enough to convey the message that I'm of no importance, he looks up.

'What can I do for you?' He speaks brusquely, as if he isn't interested in the answer and has no time to waste.

I begin nervously, 'We're worsted manufacturers.' Before I can say any more he cuts me off.

'Your mills were taken over by a large group several years ago. After a year or so the mills were closed and the production was moved, wasn't it?'

'Er, yes.'

He looks at me with distaste. The implication behind his question is clear: we're fourth division, the shell left behind when the heart of the business was transplanted.

'We've already placed our spring orders and it's too early for autumn.'

'I just wanted to introduce myself. If you would give us a chance in the future, I'd be very grateful.'

'I'm sure you would. Anyway, if you'll excuse me.'

He puts his head down again. I withdraw from the office, feeling humiliated.

It's the first time I've tried to sell to someone who doesn't own the business, and I suddenly realise the great difference between my usual customers and Mr Longhurst. People like Gus have a vested interest in looking for new suppliers and lowering their costs. Mr Longhurst has no such interest; his suppliers are golfing companions who probably entertain him lavishly, and the prospect of changing suppliers only threatens a very comfortable lifestyle. My hope of finding big buyers quickly begins to fade, and it becomes increasingly obvious that I'll find no swift way out of the trap I'm in.

I hate the idea, but I begin to realise that if I'm going to survive, I have to value the stock in the same way Herbert had done when he sold out. But a few months later, when I begin to work on the valuation, my naive belief that this will solve the problem proves to be wide of the mark. Even when I value it high, the profit shows a steep drop compared to last year's figures. It has become a nightmare from which it seems I can't wake.

What makes it worse is that the auditors are showing increasing interest in our stock calculations. It isn't that they suspect anything; it's just that less and less is taken on trust and more and more figures are subject to scrutiny and analysis. When I started in the business, the value of the stock was simply whatever figure Herbert gave the auditors. No detailed stock sheets were offered, no checks were made. Of course, tax was then so high that few sane private company managers would create a fictitious profit in the books; they'd be far more likely to understate the value of their stock in order to reduce profitability.

But times change. One morning, the auditors arrive unannounced at the office. Joe comes up to let me know.

'There are two fellas from the accountants here to see you. You know who I mean, don't you? One's got a spotty face and the other's a sly-looking little bugger.' The description doesn't make me feel any better, but I know exactly who they are. I go to meet them and bring them back to the office.

'Do you want coffee or tea?'

'No thanks, we need to get back. They're asking questions about the stock values in London and we'd like to take the sheets back with us.'

'What sort of questions?' My heart is racing.

'Well, they don't think the value can be right because the gross profit has dropped so much. Have you altered the selling price of the cloth?'

'Not really.' I fudge the answer because I'm not sure whether 'yes' or 'no' is better in the circumstances. They're worried that I've *under*valued the stock! If only they knew. I struggle to conceal my rising panic. The stock sheets are a shambles anyway, and the thought of them being subject to intense scrutiny is horrifying. I'm desperate to win time to make them look more credible.

'I need to go and find them, because they've been in few different places. Just leave it with me and I'll send them down to you.'

'No, we'll wait.' They both settle in their chairs.

'Honestly, it would be better if you left it with me.'

'We need to take the figures with us now.'

There is no hope of an adjournment. No way out. I leave them and go into one of the mill offices, where my rudimentary stock figures are filed. I know before I pull them out and look at them that it's unthinkable to hand them over. I sit down, sweating with fright, wondering what on earth I can do. This is the first major crisis I've faced, and I begin to wonder whether I'll survive it. I need something concrete, but I know I can't give them any stock sheets without starting an investigation that could lead to my humiliation and worse. What would Harry think of me? He wants to support me, but not if I suddenly seem like someone who could lose his money. And Gus's growing admiration will quickly evaporate if he finds out I'm not the smart businessman he thinks I am.

The weight of it all crushes me. It isn't simply Herbert's overvaluation, but the amateurish way I've dealt with it. It's a moment of truth that can destroy me. I continue to sit, nervously drumming the table. In the midst of my agony I reflect on what it must be like to have the clear conscience of a successful composer, famous and wealthy without the need of auditors' approvals.

The phone rings. 'The auditors are asking if you can hurry, they need to leave.'

'I won't be long.' I weigh up my options. The unvarnished truth? Out of the question. Can't find the stock sheets? At best it might buy me some time, but I'd still have to create them in a form that satisfies them and doesn't leave me vulnerable to serious questions about the method of costing individual items. No, the stock sheets are too close to fiction to have any credibility, now or in the future. Then – a flash of inspiration.

I rejoin the auditors, empty handed.

'Look, this is really stupid, but there's been a major disaster. When we finished the stock take, Mary asked me what to do with all the sheets and I said I wouldn't need them. I've just discovered that she threw them all out. Back-up sheets, all my own calculations and summaries, the lot.'

This is my only safe way out. The stock sheets and the evidence supporting them no longer exist, and because it's months after the stock take they can never be recreated. I'm certain Mary wouldn't know which sheets I'm talking about, and that if I say she's binned them, she'll assume she has.

The auditors look horror-stricken. I continue to drive home my newly discovered advantage.

'If I'd been told the sheets would be needed, of course I'd have kept them. As it is, no one has mentioned them till today. I had no idea you'd want them, and no stock sheets have ever been kept in any previous years.'

The ground has been cut from under their feet and there is nothing they can say.

'It's our fault. We should have said something before.'

And they're gone, crestfallen and contrite.

I'm off the hook, but for how long? The results can't improve in the short term, and any scrutiny of the figures will reveal the over-pricing.

That evening I feel a sense of relief as I return home to Ruth and to music. I ask, 'What sort of a day have you had?'

'I'm enjoying learning a new Schubert sonata. I've arranged a lesson with Gordon.'

Schubert's music seems so serene. It's a long way from the world of commerce and unclear consciences.

I realise I can't share with Ruth the one thing troubling me: a sense of guilt.

'Do you mind if I play the piano?'

I pick up a volume of Bach's *Well-Tempered Klavier* and turn to the first Prelude and Fugue. Many people have commented that C Major is the purest of all the keys. I begin to play the music better than I've ever played it. The arpeggios have a simplicity and beauty which move me as I play them. I repeat the Prelude, determined to play the notes even more evenly. The music has a cleansing effect, but more than anything it gives a secure moral underpinning to my life. I'm working in a corrupt world, but my music means I can never be corrupted. A piano is all I need to keep at bay the seedy, shady world of dressing-gowns and raincoats, and reaffirm the world I believe in.

Yet if I'd continued as a musician, I might well have jeopardised that world. I would probably have compromised and taken some soul-depleting job for no better reason than needing money. As it is, my original ambition to be a pianist and composer is still intact and untainted. The business world I'm discovering might be corrupt, but it's better than any other option. When I play the piano, it doesn't make me feel remorseful about turning my back on the world of Chopin and Liszt; on the contrary, it restores a sense of deeper purpose in my life. Beneath everything, I'm still an artist with a mission.

The board meetings in London, at first so exciting, are progressively less comfortable. The share price, which rose meteorically in the beginning, now looks a great deal less secure. Many of the board members still have substantial holdings of the shares, and it's becoming clear that they're locked in as the share price drops.

In the early days, soon after Sydney had acquired the carcass of the company, the hype surrounding every announcement had created such demand for the shares that almost none were available. There were also no hard, sorry facts to depress expectations. It was all a glorious, but imagined, future.

Sydney's method of buying companies was to pay for them by issuing new shares in his company. He would add cash only very reluctantly. Because the shares are speculative, and all the owners of the companies are astute enough to know the risk of accepting shares instead of cash, he has invariably had to pay significantly more than the companies are actually worth. The result is that the asset value of the shell company is gradually weakening as more and more shares are issued. Moreover, the most desirable companies from Sydney's point of view are the most resistant to accepting all shares. They know they have other options they can pursue. The result is increasing numbers of shares and a growing bank overdraft. Everything depends on generating profits. Sydney's figures on the back of an envelope can prove anything, but the figures in audited accounts are different. As both the hype and the demand for shares fades away, more and more people are anxious to sell their shares.

We gather around the board table for a normal monthly meeting. We've all had the board papers for a week, but a slip of paper which has just been tabled is proving to be of considerably more interest. It's the share price of the company over a six-month period, ending with the current month. It shows a significant decline. It's of no direct interest to me, as I sold the few shares I bought with Sydney's money as soon as I could in order to repay the loan. Fortunately for me, this was when the shares were near the highest price they ever achieved. This wasn't clever judgement on my part, just a puritan instinct to repay my debt. It's a very different story for everyone else.

Sydney is only too well aware that a glut of shares without demand will cause a collapse in the share price. The shares are his currency – the only mechanism that will allow him to continue to expand. His safeguard – or so he thinks – is that he has undertakings from all the owners of the companies he's bought that they won't attempt to sell any shares for at least twelve months.

In the early days this seemed to be a blessing because the share price rose sharply; but as it starts to fall, discontent surfaces as the board directors calculate the day-by-day decline in their personal wealth.

As I look around the table I see a lot of grim, unhappy faces. Heading them, with an expression of frightening discontent, is Dressing-Gowns. He twirls the slip of paper in the air.

'Where does this fit into the agenda?' Sydney is quick to answer.

'I put it on the table because it seems that despite the agreements we have, some board members are placing blocks of shares on the market.'

Dressing-Gowns is impassive. 'Speaking for myself, I can only say I have no knowledge of who is doing it. It's certainly not me. But I should point out, Chairman, that in my case the agreement not to sell for a period was a gentleman's agreement. Presumably that's the same for everyone else.'

Sydney retorts, angry now, 'I'd have thought a gentleman's agreement was enough, but obviously not.'

Gus says, 'Surely you'll know who it is when the share transfers come through?' To me, this clearly implies that he is completely innocent.

'Not if they're sold in the names of nominees.'

I'm learning more and more.

Someone else speaks up.

'I don't think the share price is a matter a company should be directly involving itself in.' His comment suggests a moral issue. I'm fascinated; it's all new to me. Sydney looks fiercely in his direction. 'That may be the theory, but the fact remains that a collapsing share price could lead to a collapsing company. We're going to have to create a fund and buy shares until the market stabilises. Now, how many of you are going to join me?'

There is an awkward silence, then Gus comes to the rescue. 'I'm sure we'll all join in.' As he obviously hasn't sold any shares, he wants to see his shareholding going up in value, not down.

Just then Sydney's secretary comes into the room quietly, almost stealthily, and whispers to him.

'Gentlemen, please excuse me for a moment.' He leaves the room and in no time the back-stabbing starts. Even Gus joins in.

'This isn't a good situation. Artificially rigging the share price is a criminal act.'

'I think he's overstretched himself.'

'Power's going to his head. He assumes he can just dictate to us.'

I make my own moderately critical comment. 'Is what he's suggesting legal or illegal?'

'It's definitely illegal.'

'Then we should tell him we won't do it.' I feel ashamed to be encouraging dissent, particularly as I'm not affected by the drop in the share price and Sydney knows I have no capital sum to contribute.

Soon Sydney doesn't have a friend in the room. A small inner voice tells me that this is cheap behaviour, but it's so easy to join in a chorus of discontent.

The only one who doesn't join in is Dressing-Gowns. He remains aloof, obviously quite satisfied that he can find his own answer to the problem.

Sydney returns. 'That was a phone call to let me know that a specially big parcel of shares has just gone on to the market.'

'That's probably a family trust of mine.' Dressing-Gowns owns up without a trace of embarrassment. 'When I vested my shares in the trust I agreed not to sell for a period. But I don't control the trust. It's controlled by independent trustees, and they've obviously decided their first duty is to the trust. With the share price going down they must have decided to reduce their holding. There's nothing I can do.'

He pulls out his Romeo and Juliet, slices the end off with his gold cigar cutter, and proceeds to light it for several seconds with a match.

There is yet more awkward silence. Everyone realises that nothing can be done and reproval is pointless. Cigar smoke fills the room and Dressing-Gowns looks imperturbably content.

The rest of the meeting is a formality and Sydney isn't anxious to prolong it. The awkwardness of the rest of the board is in marked contrast to the barely concealed triumph of Dressing-Gowns. He'll be returning home with a clear conscience, having brazenly told the truth, and with a bank balance enhanced by the sale of his shares at a price that will never be repeated.

I now know what it is to be a ruthless businessman. I also know I'll never be one.

As Gus and I sit on the train going north, the conversation replays the day's events. Gus is astute, and I know from experience he can be treacherous, but he realises he doesn't have the strength of Dressing-Gowns. He is clearly disturbed by the whole affair.

'Do you realise how much I've lost over the past week?' He looks at me as if I'm in some way responsible. The lack of any appropriate response provokes him to repeat the question with even more fury.

I know it's not intended to be answered. These are facts Gus would never disclose. 'You don't understand, do you?' He speaks the words with real contempt, and I feel them. His pathetic self-centredness, his obsession with money, suddenly unleashes in me a viciousness I can't control.

'I do understand. You've lost money and now you're squealing.'

I didn't choose the words consciously; they just emerged, but I've hurt him in a way which immobilises him. The rest of the journey home sees Gus descend into subdued self-pity. As for me, I feel victorious. Insulting him has taken all my reserve of courage, but having done it, I feel much stronger in my relationship with him. I've gained the upper hand for the first time in my life.

Very late that night, the phone rings. I pick it up apprehensively.

'You bloody rat.' The words are slurred. Whoever it is is drunk. 'I thought at least you might be loyal.' My heart sinks as I realise it's Sydney.

But how on earth...? He knows too much about what was said in the board room during his absence. It suddenly hits me that he must have had listening equipment concealed there, and recorded our conversation. I feel deeply ashamed. How I wish Sydney had heard me speaking courageously in his defence. He continues to heap coals of fire on my head, but the heavy drinking is having its effect and he soon puts down the phone.

I desperately try to recall just what I said in the meeting. Was it even worse than I remembered? Did I make a particularly treacherous remark? Sydney knows only too well that my personal success is due in no small way to his generosity. I can picture him listening to the tape, hoping I'd repay him by standing up for him. I could tell he felt more let down than angered by my behaviour. He'd believed I was loyal, and now he knows otherwise. I am mortified.

26

A Man of the World

Over the following weeks I'm still unable to produce a profit in line with Sydney's expectation, and the thought of having to justify the bad results is never far away. I wrestle with the problem day and night, and eventually the only possible solution emerges. If I can't improve the profit in the short term, and I can't face having to report bad results, I have to remove the need to report the results. The only way to do that is to own the company.

At first it seems ridiculous, but the more I think about it, the more I begin to realise that it might be possible. Buying the company hadn't been Sydney's most brilliant idea in the first place. In fact, I discover it was more Herbert's idea than Sydney's. I know from experience Herbert's formidable ability to pressurise, and in their initial relationship Herbert had been very much the dominant figure.

Over the few years I've been involved, things have changed dramatically. Sydney's expectations and ambitions have grown, and there are probably many things he did in the early days that he wouldn't do again if he had the option. Buying the mill from Herbert is probably top of that list. Most of the other board members look down their noses at what is increasingly standing out as a business of little consequence, with no apparent relevance to anything else in the group.

The thought of having a business of my own is now rarely out of my mind. The constant pressure of being scrutinised, knowing that the business is on shaky foundations, the high profit expectation, all contrast in my mind with what the position would be if it was my own business.

It would be a return to something akin to the innocent happiness of business with Herbert. Herbert still phones from time to time, and on one occasion I'm foolish enough to casually mention my interest in starting my own business.

'You haven't enough experience to do that yet.'

'But you started your own business when you were younger than me.'

'Things were different then.'

It never occurs to him that I'm planning a management buyout of his former company. I have, of course, kept quiet about my profits from futures and shares, but he'd be more jealous if he knew that Harry W is prepared to back me. The combination of these factors allows me to be more ambitious than Herbert would have imagined possible. I know I have to keep my plan to myself, or he'll try to take it all away from me. For the moment, I decide to say absolutely nothing more until the deal is done.

While the poor performance of the company is making me less and less popular with Sydney, it's also making a takeover deal more possible. Although the trading result is invariably a disappointment, it doesn't diminish my excitement at the prospect of owning the company. I imagine that once it's mine, all problems will be solved. My happiness about the future is more attributable to naivety than anything else. It's the consequence of my ability to dream. Tomorrow *must* be better than today.

One day, the moment seems right to talk to Sydney. The irrelevance of the company I run is becoming increasingly embarrassing for him. The deal with Herbert has perhaps always been Sydney's way of paying off a debt of gratitude. When they first met, Sydney was young and starting out on his career; Herbert was a seemingly wealthy and successful businessman. Herbert gave Sydney a leg up. But Sydney's inexperience led him to overrate Herbert. Now that the balance of power has shifted, he sees Herbert for what he is – a minor figure in the business world.

'How is Herbert?'

'He's abroad quite a bit because of his bronchitis.'

'He's a crafty old devil, he's probably abroad because of the cheap booze.'

'He always wants to know what you're up to.'

'I hope you don't tell him.'

As the warmth grows, my moment arrives. Or I think it does.

'There's something I've been meaning to chat to you about. It's obvious to me that the company no longer fits in with the development of the group.' Sydney looks quizzical and I feel the temperature drop. Maybe this is going to be more difficult than I expected. 'I've been wondering whether it wouldn't be better for both of us if I took the company over.'

I realise as I say it that I've done too little preparation. The idea suddenly sounds presumptuous, even to me. He's used to confident, experienced businessmen, and I don't fall into that category. He's taken aback by the emergence of someone he didn't know existed. I'm the green youth he's adopted as a kind of apprentice, and he'll never believe I can be anything else. But for me, there's now no way back.

'I think I could raise enough money to pay a good price in excess of the asset value.'

I don't realise when I say it that I'm offering more than the company is worth. It's actually worth less than the asset value, and even then no one would want to buy it. It's a poor building in a poor location with clapped out old machinery, and the only person in the world who wants to buy it is me. That's because I'm naive and inexperienced, but also because I've grown to love the business. In any case, I'm convinced it's the right way forward for me. I don't for one moment think I have any option. To me, it's the only way I can join the world of business. It's a moment of opportunity I can't afford to let slip.

'Are you sure?' He almost sneers. There is nothing of the father figure about him now.

'I've found a wealthy spinner to back me.' He's genuinely astonished.

'Well, well, little Herbert.' He's speaking almost to himself. I take it as acknowledgement that I've made progress since he made me an apprentice. 'You'd better find a solicitor and we'll take it from there.'

I feel a real sense of deflation. In my innocence I imagined it would all happen immediately. The reality, of course, is that it will be a slow, laborious process. My heart begins to sink. I leave his office, not with a sense of achievement but wondering whether it will ever happen. What I don't know at the time is that he is already under enormous pressure from the bank, and far more concerned about his own future than mine.

As it happens, the solicitor I know best is a great friend of Sydney's. The following day I go to his office in Bradford. Roger is patient but unbelievably formal. He listens to my plans with transparent scepticism.

'Where will you get the money from?'

'I think I can raise about twenty thousand in cash, which I hope will be enough for a deposit. The rest of the purchase price I'd like to pay off over, say, two years.'

'Sydney will need to keep a charge on the business until everything is paid.'

'Of course, I understand that.'

'But where will the rest of the money come from?'

This stops me in my tracks. I'd imagined that owning the business would give me access to the money it generated. If I'd known more, what I'm planning would have seemed impossible. I'm unbelievably ignorant about money matters. When I explain to Roger what seems to me simple and obvious – that the company will pay off the balance of the debt with the credit created by Harry W – he looks shocked.

'You do realise it's illegal for a company to buy its own shares, don't you?'

I didn't.

'It's against Section 54 of the Companies Act. Having said that, it's not a criminal offence and the punishment is a moderate fine.'

With that sentence I feel it's settled. As Gus once said, when a team is winning ten-nil five minutes from time, they play like gentlemen. When I'm struggling to get even close to the goal, a minor infringement of the rules seems a small price to pay.

For the first time in my life I'm thinking and behaving like an entrepreneur. It's exhilarating.

'I'll prepare the agreement and send you a draft.'

'How long will that be?' I'm so anxious to do it.

'I'll get it to you at the beginning of next week.'

The draft comes. I barely have the patience to read more than the essentials of the deal. All the rest is jargon which seems to me to be irrelevant. I go to see Roger again, when he once more spells out his advice that infringing Section 54 is undesirable and if he were me he wouldn't do it.

'If you have no more amendments, I'll get the agreement engrossed. If you sign it, I'll take the agreement with me next Friday, when I'm meeting Sydney in London.'

Friday comes and goes, and I'm in a state of agitated suspense, wondering what has happened. I'm too nervous to ring and ask; I just wait. On the Sunday, Roger rings.

'I had a terrible time with Sydney. The bank is replacing him with a so-called company doctor. There were so many documents I'd taken for him to sign, but he's afraid to do anything now in case it's construed the wrong way.'

I feel my spirits plummet.

'The bank has really turned on him and he's feeling very let down.'

The conversation seems set to go on forever without touching on the only thing I want to know.

'What about the agreement?' I eventually ask, hardly able to bear listening to the answer.

'I don't know how, but I managed to get him to sign it.'

I nearly yell with joy. I've managed to get my foot on the first rung of the ladder.

'Send me the cheque for £20,000 and we'll be able to exchange agreements.' I put the phone down, hardly able to believe it's happened.

I go to the mill that night, just to look at it and experience the feeling of being a mill owner. No one to satisfy now but me. I wander round the weaving shed, looking at the silent looms and the cloth on the rollers, smelling the oil and wool, and in that silence contemplating my future. This is it. I'm now beginning my new career as the *owner* of a worsted weaving mill.

Ruth understands well enough, but she doesn't share the feeling of excitement that possesses me. That evening, I try to describe what it means to me to make the transition from employee to employer.

'When Dad came home and said he'd been sacked, even though I was only four or five, I could sense the terrifying powerlessness of his position. I think I knew from that moment that I needed the security of being in control. It's nothing to do with money or having power over other people, it's simply having personal responsibility for my own life and career.'

'I find it difficult to understand what's so exciting about working in a mill.'

'To me it's a kind of romance. It's a sort of dream world where I can discover who I really am.'

'I just hope you don't forget who you are.'

As I lie in bed that night, too excited to sleep and imagining, over and over, the probable course of my new life, the phone rings. It's Herbert, and as usual, he's drunk.

'Sydney tells me you're buying the mill.'

'I mentioned the possibility to you.'

'I thought we'd agreed to do it together.'

'No, I don't think so.'

I can tell he's angry and wounded, and it's probably more to do with losing the power to manipulate me than anything else. He loves to play with people's lives, and mine has been particularly useful to him. Now I've broken free and he doesn't like it.

'You can't do it without me. You haven't the experience.'

'Probably not, but I'll try. If I do succeed, it'll be very largely thanks to the lessons I've learned from you.'

It's easy to be magnanimous, albeit ambiguously. I have the whip hand for the first time, and I'm not letting go. Herbert knows he's been outwitted.

With a mounting workload that often takes me away from the mill, I start to feel the need for an assistant. There's only so much one person can do, and only so many hours in the day. No one at the mill is suitable – they're all too valuable in their present jobs, and in any case I can't think of any who would be comfortable or happy in the sort of role I have in mind. One day, I call in by chance at the Manchester office of one of our suppliers. The manager is a friendly and astute woman who soon latches on to the fact that I'm running myself into the ground. She tells me about one of their newer employees, a young man called Ronald. 'He's as bright as a button, keen as mustard and he can turn his hand to anything. I've never known anyone like him. I'd love to keep him but the work we do just isn't challenging enough, even I can see that. We won't be able to hold him for long so you can have him now with my blessing, if the two of you hit it off.'

She introduces me to Ronald and we have lunch in a corner of the works canteen. He's short and stocky, and clearly has enormous intellectual energy. He also has a better grasp of the textile industry than many people who have been in it far longer than him. I describe my business and its problems and he instantly comes at me with all the right questions, some of which I can't answer. And that, I tell him, is why I need someone like him to work for me. Is he interested?

He is. He wants to start immediately. And the thing that sways it for me – he doesn't ask how much I'll pay him. Not a word. Like me, he's driven much more by enthusiasm than materialism. I'm convinced I've found the perfect right-hand man. I offer him the job, he accepts, we shake hands.

I can't possibly appreciate it at the time, but that simple transaction will have enormous consequences for both of us.

Ronald settles into his new life in Yorkshire with a confidence and commitment which impresses me immediately. All the practical issues, like finding somewhere to live, he fixes effortlessly. Any job I find tedious and boring, he takes off my hands. He knows instinctively how to make himself indispensable. Without discussing it, in no time at all we've settled into complementary roles: I'm the salesman, he's the backroom boy. The tedium of stocktaking is no longer my worry; I concentrate on all the things I like doing most. I find myself spending more time looking for new customers so we can expand production, which Ronald takes care of. We replace the old looms with second-hand newer machinery, and soon our turnover is increasing. After all the anxiety of struggling to meet Sydney's profit expectations, it's a relief to be making a profit for its own sake. Ironically, within a year of my taking over the business, turnover is significantly higher than Sydney's seemingly impossible targets. Automatic looms and a clear division between sales and production contribute to its growth. Confidence has progressively replaced the fear that ruled in the days when I was a managing director.

News of our growing success spreads. One day I'm rung by Angus, the senior partner in a firm of chartered accountants.

'Can I come to see you? I have a proposition I think you'll like.' The voice is cultivated Scots, the professional confidence obvious. I don't know him but I have no doubt I'll like whatever it is he's going to propose.

Two days later, he arrives promptly at the mill. 'I won't beat about the bush, I have a long-standing client whose family business has been steadily losing money for the past few years. The young generation aren't up to it. All they understand is how to spend money. It's been a very successful company in the past, but without radical change it'll come to a bad end. It still has very substantial assets. There's a weaving mill and a healthy order book, but it's losing money. From what I've heard, I think you could turn it round.'

It sounds an exciting prospect, but we're already using all the bank overdraft we can get. In fact, we're struggling to pay our way at times. He can read my hesitancy and with unerring instinct adds, 'Don't worry, you'll be able to finance it. I think I can persuade them to take fifty pence in the pound.'

I'm amazed. The deal means that our balance sheet will immediately be half a million pounds better off.

'Oh, and you'll find it has tax losses of several hundred thousand pounds, which will come in useful.'

I'm even more amazed. Of course I have to stop the losses, but I'm confident that will be simple. Old-established companies all have the same problem: they can't break free from tradition. Their overheads are all geared to the past and they never understand that if you want a future, you have to jettison the past. Their managers can't cut overheads

251

because they simply can't imagine how the business will run if they don't spend the budget they've planned. Every suggestion that costs can be significantly reduced becomes a futile debate. I know that the only way to stop losses is not to debate overhead items but to cut them mindlessly – almost stupidly. The old management will reason endlessly, and nothing will happen because reason always comes to the aid of tradition.

I discover that the company is well respected. More important, its fabrics are designed for the export market, which I barely know.

I meet two young men from the family that owns the business. They're charming, polite and public school educated. They understand very quickly that the consequence of selling the business to me is that any hope of continued employment depends on me. They've spent most of their time overseas, selling fabrics through agents. It's obvious that they regard travelling abroad as a very enjoyable part of the job. They find it easy to justify endless trips on the grounds of keeping in touch with markets, looking after customers and supporting agents. Suddenly all this will be coming to an end, because I insist on budgeting the cost of the trips in relation to the actual business being generated. No one has ever done this before.

Neither of them has any great shareholding in the company, so the consequence of its losing money isn't serious for them. Their greatest interest is to justify and cling on to their present working lifestyle. I decide to hold on to whichever of the two I think the better, until I have more experience. In any case, I want to maintain confidence in the overseas markets. There will doubtless be a lot of rumours circulating about the impending changes. The older of the two is reputed to be the better salesman. I take him to one side.

'Are you willing to consider working for me?'

'It depends on the terms, and what you're planning.'

I immediately decide I don't want him. I want an unqualified, resounding yes. The younger man is less experienced but has more of the qualities I'm looking for, so I settle on him.

By putting the two companies together, we more than double the turnover; but more importantly, the asset value of the company increases substantially. I've negotiated a two-year period to pay for the shares in the new company, and the increase in asset value makes the payment to Sydney for the purchase of the original company a very simple affair.

It's inevitable that my working partnership with Ronald becomes crucial to the whole business. I'm delighted to find that I can trust him and his judgement absolutely. I rapidly realise that my best interests are served by feeding his ambition and not holding it back. His ability to take responsibility for all the production leaves me free to begin travelling overseas and developing the export business.

Only a short time before, it seems, I was an impecunious music student, and now I own a business valued at nearly a million pounds – a huge amount in the 1960s. But I couldn't sell it for anything like that, and if I don't succeed in steering it through countless treacherous difficulties it can become valueless very quickly. Everything depends on how much confidence the bank and my creditors have in my ability to manage it. This is the key to success in business. This is the thing most people can't understand. There is no money in the bank, just a large bank overdraft. But if you can manage the bank overdraft without exceeding the agreed limits, you can get anything you need. Fundamentally, what it all depends on is my having confidence in myself. If I have confidence, everyone else has confidence.

My experience of the world expands dramatically. Our export markets are in Hong Kong, Singapore, Bangkok, and the Middle East – Kuwait, Saudi Arabia, Lebanon, Iran and Iraq. I spend as little as possible on the air tickets, but once I'm in the country I stay in the best hotels available.

The freedom and power I experience are intoxicating, and I often reflect on how lucky I am to have left behind the humdrum existence of most of my former musician colleagues.

My acute pleasure in beautiful things is stimulated time after time. For example, I've met so many Greek customers in England that I decide to pay them a visit. As I'm driven from Athens airport by my agent, I suddenly see the Acropolis on the skyline. My eyes fill with tears; I can't believe it. That evening, I beg my agent to leave me to my own devices. I walk from the Hotel Grande Bretagne in Constitution Square, up to the Acropolis. It's surrounded by fencing, but floodlit, and I wander round and round in a state of ecstasy. Sacrificing my career as a musician and becoming a businessman has been very worthwhile, if only for this evening.

The success of our first acquisition gives me an appetite for more. The urge to grow isn't part of a thought-out strategic plan, it's quite simply ambition. I find a public company in the same business as us, and after doing a search of the share register I realise that it's broadly held and not controlled by the board. It's much bigger than my company, but I decide that if it's available, I want it.

Every time I bump into Gus I can tell that he's full of admiration for my progress. I'm not as astute as him and know I've never had as tightly controlled a business as his, yet I have some qualities which are driving me further than him. He's so afraid of losing what he's made that it constrains his progress. I on the other hand have retained the same naivety that launched me into business – the naivety that allows me to pick up the phone and speak to the managing director of the public company without any elaborate ritual.

'Would you be interested to meet and talk? I have a successful private company and we're always looking for opportunities to expand.'

'By all means, let's meet; there's no harm in that.'

It's as welcoming a reaction as I can ever have wanted.

I know from the share register that he has very few shares and I discover that he is an exceptionally cautious man, more intent on doing the right thing than running the business. As a result, the profit record is dismal and the shares have been lifeless for several years. No one wants them.

When I meet him it gets worse. He's older than I expected, and I soon discover that he has little drive and a very limited knowledge of the textile trade. I go to met him with Ronald, who listens while I do most of the talking.

The mills, near Leeds, house both spinning and weaving. The favourable reaction to our overture is enough to carry the idea on to the next stage. We never seriously question whether it's the right thing to do. The whole project has emerged from nowhere, and now that there seems to be a tide taking us along, we neither resist nor question it.

We meet our bank manager, who has proved to be a great supporter, and seek his advice. Most bank managers would be sceptical at the idea of our taking over a much larger public company. This one simply gives us the information we need. He names the senior partner of a firm of solicitors in Huddersfield.

'He'll be able to help you, I'm sure.'

So we meet him, and he too is carried along by our enthusiasm and energy.

'I suggest we ask N M Rothschild to act on our behalf.'

It's a name I know well – there are few in business who don't know it – and it's extraordinary that I'll be employing them. I never question how it can happen, or where the money will come from. It seems as if all the professionals worry about that. But the centre of the whole thing is purely the confidence we have that we know what we're doing.

Meeting follows meeting, culminating in our grand meeting in Rothschild's with every professional from both our side and the public company we're taking over. The enhanced balance sheet resulting from our first takeover gives us vital credibility. The key to the negotiation is our rising turnover and profit over the past five years. By contrast, the public company's record over the same period is stagnant, with profits now barely above break-even. Nevertheless, the company has assets of over £1,000,000, not to mention mills and machinery which currently stand at a very low figure.

The meeting drags on for the whole day, with Rothschild's and their opposition in constant conspiratorial discussion. Eventually we're approached by the senior Rothschild's man.

'We've got you the best deal we can, and I think it's fair. They have an existing share capital of £375,000 and they're prepared to issue £625,000 in shares for the purchase of your company. That will give the company issues share capital of £1,000,000, of which you'll have 62 per cent and the existing shareholders 37 per cent.'

'Could I have a few moments to discuss it with Ronald?'

We both withdraw to a small private office.

'What do you think?' I ask, knowing it's a better offer than I expected. Ronald is never quick to decide, but I respect his more considered reaction.

'I think you should accept,' he says after a few minutes.

'If I do, I propose handing ten per cent of the shares to you.'

I've been thinking of making some kind of transfer to him for some time. It's the way our relationship has developed: he never asks for anything, but I instinctively sense when it's right to give something. He has proved his worth beyond any doubt, and I know his commitment to me is absolute. His reaction indicates that the share offer is both unexpected and deeply appreciated.

We rejoin the meeting and a timetable is agreed for the work which will lead to the public company meeting, when the shareholders can vote for or against the proposed deal. I feel a little deflated when I realise that the agreement is still subject to the view of the shareholders. It's obvious when I think about it, but any celebration in advance of the shareholders' meeting will be premature. As it's such a good deal for me, I can't help worrying that some of the shareholders might think it's a bad deal for them. There won't be any reduction in the shares they hold, but after the deal their ownership of the company will plummet from 100 per cent to a paltry 37. The solicitor acting on behalf of the public company looks in my direction.

'By the way, we haven't discussed the future management. As majority shareholders you can obviously decide whatever you want once the deal's done. Could I suggest that when the deal is announced, the present chairman steps down and you become managing director? I think this would reassure the shareholders.'

I agree; it seems a small concern. We've already met the chairman, a partner in the very old established firm of solicitors who act for the public company. I subsequently discover that he knows little about law and even less about business.

After the meeting is over, Ronald and I return north, savouring the prospect of a new career in a public company. I'm 36 years old; Ronald is in his late twenties. We have the world at our feet, and a future of endless possibilities.

27

A Dedicated Follower of Fashion

It is increasingly difficult to keep all the looms busy in our three weaving mills. There is a growing feeling of desperation every time we book an order large enough to reduce the profit margin to a minimum. Our costing system isn't accurate enough to work to fine limits, so that, without realising it, we often sell at no profit and sometimes even at a small loss. When you need orders badly, it's easy to be optimistic about your costs and difficult to be realistic. The roles of salesman and managing director fit uneasily together. The prudence a managing director must have is eroded by the enthusiasm of the salesman intent on getting orders.

It's only in retrospect that we discover the folly of our ways, because it can be a year or more before the management accounts reveal the financial consequences of any decision. The fact that our bank overdraft has been increasing steadily isn't in itself an indicator that we're not trading profitably. Our ambition to modernise means we've spent more and more money on machinery, and, in the absence of up-to-date accounts, it's easy to believe that the increasing overdraft simply reflects an expanding business.

The problem is that we had barely enough money to run the business even before we reversed into the public company. Because the public company had a larger bank overdraft facility, we decided to merge our bank account with theirs. This was done with some misgivings because our own bank had been great supporters from the beginning and had seen our business grow successfully. Now, we're increasingly unable to pay our creditors when the money is due, so our creditors are always pressing us for payment. Every time we receive a cheque, we scrutinise the list of monies we owe and decide who we'll pay, which is just about enough to keep our creditors happy. Unfortunately, the bank is less and less happy. No bank likes to see an overdraft moving only upwards. The ideal is one that swings regularly from debit to credit. Our overdraft is locked solidly at the limit. This means that every time interest charges fall due and the bank debits our account, our overdraft exceeds the agreed limit.

We continue in this perilous state for several months, but eventually it becomes impossible to work at the agreed overdraft limit, and, after discussions with our bank manager, he suggests a meeting with the local director.

It's our first visit to head office, and we're invited to have lunch. The director is a large man with a florid complexion, and the instant we walk into his office I feel a total absence of the kind of sympathetic and understanding response I experienced in my first bank. He makes it very plain that in principle he is against increasing the overdraft, and indeed wants it reduced.

'We're not here to provide you with working capital. You should get that from your shareholders. We're here to give you short-term finance. I've been looking at the figures over the past year, and it's obvious that you need more working capital. In any case, your trading results are well overdue and there's nothing we can do without seeing those. So far as I can see, the amount we're lending you at the moment is greater than we should allow. I think we're going to require you to reduce the overdraft by at least a quarter, with a view to reducing to a half in a year's time.'

As he speaks I feel a growing sense of panic. We have no hope of reducing our overdraft; indeed, it seems impossible to think of continuing without increasing it. We leave his office dispirited and uncertain about the future, no longer sensing that we have a bank that is either confident in us or supportive.

Unfortunately, within a few weeks of the meeting, I get a catastrophic phone call from our bank manager. 'I'm afraid your overdraft is now £100,000 over the agreed limit.'

'But that can't be! Can I look into the situation and phone you back?' As I say it my heart is pounding. Utter disaster looms. Inevitably, he's right. Our accountant has made a serious error in the cash book and issued more cheques than we can cover. In fact, when I look at the cash book as it really is, I realise we've exceeded the overdraft by far more than £100,000. I ring the manager as soon as I have the facts.

'You're right. We've made a serious mistake and I've got to tell you that, at the moment, there could be cheques worth an additional £50,000 to be presented. However, I have promises of more than that being paid in within the next day. We'll work desperately hard to ensure that we get the overdraft within the limit within the next three or four days.'

Under the circumstances, the manager is remarkably understanding, but the local director isn't. I'm summoned to a meeting with him the following morning at nine o'clock. He doesn't waste any time on pleasantries when we walk in. There is no smile on his face and he's clearly in a belligerent mood.

'We're going to take a charge on the business. It's the only way for you and for us.' He knows he has full control of the situation, so he dispenses with the formality of treating us as if our opinion matters.

Ever since I started in business, Herbert always said, 'Whatever you do, don't give a charge to the bank.' I never fully understood the significance of his warning, but now I do. The feeling of powerlessness overwhelms me. If the local director had been someone more sympathetic and positive, it might have been different; but as it is, Herbert's advice hits home. As we sit uncomfortably in the office, I feel a growing sense of anger against this arrogant man.

'I've already given the details to our solicitor, and the documents are being prepared for signature.'

There seems little else to say, and I leave his office incensed and dejected. As soon as we're outside, I erupt.

'I'd sooner close the whole thing down than be at the mercy of that detestable man.'

It would be the end of everything we've created. As expected, Ronald interprets what I've said as an outburst of emotion, not a rational comment.

'There may be other ways of dealing with it. I'd already anticipated something like this, so I've been talking to our old bank. To them, everything depends on an improving trading profit, and I'm confident I can organise production so we can make much more profit without increasing our prices.' This is more like it. Thanks to Ronald, there is suddenly a ray of hope.

Within a few days of our unpleasant meeting with the director, a large envelope arrives from the bank. We open it and see the legal documents which have been prepared for our signatures and the company seal. A formal letter is enclosed with the date when we should deliver the completed documents to the bank. Fortunately, the talks with our original bank have progressed so well that it's a date I begin to look forward to.

We're ushered into the bank director's office with little politeness. No coffee is offered, no niceties exchanged. We've brought the documents with us, all unsigned. We put them on the desk. The director picks them up and pushes them back to us.

'They need signing.' He's clearly annoyed.

'I don't think so,' I reply.

Ronald pulls an envelope out of his inside jacket pocket and passes it to the director, who opens it with a puzzled look. As he takes out the contents and reads them, the blood ebbs from his face. One particular slip of paper is a cheque from our old bank, for the full amount of the overdraft. He's totally flabbergasted. It's a wonderful moment.

'Look, I'm sure we could discuss this. We weren't really serious about the charge,' he splutters, attempting to get back on to dry land.

'Another day, perhaps.' It's a gloriously superior, throwaway comment that closes the meeting and finishes with him and his bank forever. As we leave, we scoop up the legal documents we brought with us. When we get back to the office, we place them all in a drawer for posterity.

'Lest we forget,' says Ronald, in a mock-solemn voice.

From that turning point, everything changes for the better. In particular, there is a bloodless revolution going on that is destined to lift our status and profits beyond anything we've previously achieved.

Our agent in London is Rex, a young man who is always cheerful but isn't bringing in much business. One day I get a phone call from him.

'I think it would be worth your while coming to London for the day. I'd like to introduce you to some new customers. There's a lot of potential business here but we need new designs.'

I groan inwardly. Every time salesmen fail to get orders, they complain that they don't have the right designs. We're continuously producing new designs, but the differences between them are subtle. The whole of the men's trade is dominated by designs which are variations on the same theme. There are hundreds of navy stripes, all similar but all different. They have one thing in common: they're all increasingly complicated in a drive to satisfy buyers' jaded appetites. Buyers are constantly looking for something new, but they don't want to stray too far from the designs they've been buying for over 20 years.

I agree to go to London, with no awareness that the meeting will revolutionise my business and my life.

Rex meets me at King Cross and drives me to the King's Road. The moment I get out of the car, I sense it's a new world. Everyone looks different from the people I see in the north. The King's Road area in

1970 is alive with attractive young men and women. The shops are bustling; the air vibrates with dynamism and innovation. We park in Flood Street and walk into the side entrance of a men's shop. I've only glanced into the shop, but I've already seen a quality of look and presentation in complete contrast to the traditional men's retailers I'm used to supplying.

We climb to the first floor, converted into a corridor of offices. It's informal chaos from end to end. Every room is packed with goods and people. We stand where we can, watching and waiting. As one particularly energetic and bustling young man walks out of an office past us, Rex tries to stop him.

'Jeff, can I –' He doesn't get any further: Jeff turns and barks, 'Just wait.' He's in a rush and we're totally unimportant. In that moment, I recognise someone with the rare kind of confidence that comes from knowing you're one step ahead of the rest of the human race.

His confidence doesn't come across as arrogance, but rather impatience. He's busy and knows what he's doing; the fact that we're there waiting tells him we don't know what we're doing. He passes us a few minutes later, again without stopping. I'm fascinated by the power he exudes. He reminds me of Gus, but a much stronger Gus. His eyes are intense and remind me of the film actor Robert Newton.

Rex is getting nervous that he's wasting my time.

'Should we call back later?' He looks at me.

'No, we'll wait.' I know instinctively that Jeff is doing us a favour seeing us, and that if we leave he'll write us off.

After about half an hour he curtly beckons us to follow him into a small but unconventionally furnished office. A TV is showing a W.C. Fields film. He looks at it as we walk in and I see him smile for the first time.

'Great, eh?' Before I have a chance to respond, he's on to the next subject.

'Look, I've no time to waste, what do you want?'

'We're worsted cloth manufacturers and I understand from Rex you're buying a lot of cloth.'

Rex pulls out his bag of samples and pushes them towards Jeff. He takes one derisory glance.

'Have you looked in the windows of my shops?'

I suddenly feel stupid. I've been in such a rush to see him that I've failed to do the obvious.

'Don't answer that question. If you'd looked, you wouldn't waste my time showing me your patterns.'

The more he talks, the more I think he's the key to our future. He can so clearly see what I can't. I realise instantly that I need to know what he knows.

'Any patterns you want me to make, I can do it.'

He smiles contemptuously. 'Why should I tell you what to do?'

'Give me a chance and I'll show you what I can do.'

'Look at you. You look like a middle-aged cloth manufacturer.' He speaks so scathingly but honestly that it's impossible to take offence. He's utterly right. A revolution in clothing is changing the world and I'm still dressing as if nothing is happening. He pulls a jacket off a clothes rack.

'Put that on.'

I do. Then more jackets, suits, shirts, ties. Each ensemble is adjusted painstakingly by Jeff.

'You look twenty years younger.'

It's astonishing: I feel twenty years younger.

'You might have a chance of giving me what I want right now. You must have old pattern books from the 1940s. Bring them.'

Everything he does and says is at top speed. We're with him only minutes, but it's enough for him to teach me a huge amount. As he leaves us, his final comment is 'Keep the clothes.' It's another order I find impossible to disobey.

I soon discover that I've experienced Jeff's habitual style. He always begins by being destructive and mercilessly honest. When people react defensively, it's the end of the relationship as far as Jeff is concerned. If he senses that he's shocked people into seeing what is so obvious to him, the relationship might move up a level.

In my case, my instant recognition that he is right, my pleasure in being helped to change, give him a answer to his own question. He has decided to tell me what to do.

'When do you think you'll come back with the pattern books?'

'The day after tomorrow.' It needs to be that soon. I know that something exciting is about to happen to me and the business.

We walk back into the King's Road through Jeff's shop. All I've known so far is the traditional multiple clothier's shop; typically, a middle-aged man with a bald head and paunch and a tape measure round his neck greets you and measures you for a suit. It's an unexciting experience. The resulting suit is never a delight and often a disappointment. It should fit perfectly but rarely does. That's how I bought my first suit. As I look round Jeff's shop, I'm astonished by its style: the natural wood, the design and layout, the *young* feeling. The shop assistants look smarter

262

than any I've ever seen in the north: they're walking adverts for the clothes they sell. And every suit is made to be worn instantly. No more measurement, no more disappointments. If it doesn't look right in the mirror you needn't buy it, and if you want a particular style, quality or colour, you needn't wait.

It's a new world, and it's clearly creating enormous demand. Young men are coming in and buying the clothes as I look around. How can I have been so blind? It's obvious that the new look has created an exclusive club, and the way you dress signals that you're either in or out of it. Today, I'm clearly out of it. Tomorrow, through Jeff, I'm determined to be in it. Everywhere I look, the division becomes sharper.

I return north a changed man. I feel an excitement about textiles I've never experienced before. It's not simply the opportunity to sell to the new fashion trade, it's the opportunity to spend unlimited time in London, in the most exciting environment I've ever known. Everyone looks more glamorous and attractive, and for the first time in my life I become aware that fashion can make you feel more confident.

The idea at first seems demeaning. My life has been built on the principle that your value relates to what you are, not what you look like. A great composer, through spirituality and inspiration, transcends any physical manifestation and makes the concept of fashion seem trivial. And yet now, in a single day, I've learned that fashion is far from trivial and superficial. Later that evening, I try to convey something of my experience to Ruth. I tell her that only a few years ago Jeff was a sales assistant in a men's clothiers'. He now has 16 shops in the West End selling 3,000 suits a week, all made from the kind of worsted suiting we produce. I tell her the traditional multiple clothiers are washed up; Jeff has tapped into an enormous unsatisfied demand. He's made it a young man's world overnight. Ruth isn't impressed.

'It sounds like a superficial world to me. Why attach so much importance to clothes?'

'It's a way for people to assert their identity and distinguish themselves from people they don't want to be lumped together with.'

'Well, don't expect me to take any interest in fashion. I can't bear the thought of all those shallow people taking themselves seriously.'

I find it hard to share her view. I've been touched by my glimpse of this arguably superficial world in a way that has made it irresistible. I'm changing in a way I can't control.

Ruth symbolises everything I admire. She has enormous integrity, nobility and fastidiousness. Her understanding of music, her love of

263

it, her modesty, her purity all make her the exceptional woman I fell in love with. But the change which begins as a consequence of my contact with the world of fashion alerts me to something that's missing. Ruth's contempt for any concern with appearance means that I've never known what it is to be attractive. Ruth isn't vulnerable to attractive men; she positively dislikes them. I shared that view until I put on the clothes in Jeff's office. I tasted in that moment the intoxicating feeling of being someone else, possibly less admirable but definitely more human and more attractive. It dawns on me that however worthy and high-minded, the eschewing of appearance has a lot to do with a lack of self-confidence.

Two days later, Rex and I are back in the King's Road. We're carrying some very large old pattern books. I'm wearing one of the suits Jeff gave me.

Every shop and café has verve and style, and there's a swagger and confidence about everyone I see. In Jeff's clothes, but also in myself, I feel younger and more alive than I've ever felt in my life.

We're ushered into Jeff's office but it's already full. We stand at the back, waiting our turn.

'What do you want in this window? You can have the pinstripe navy suit, the window-pane, or the pick and pick.'

The man he's talking to pauses too long.

'Jeff, if only I could have a navy...'

Jeff strikes like a cobra, his voice full of contempt. 'Shall I start again? You can have...'

'Okay Jeff, I'll have the navy pinstripe.'

As he ploughs through this session with his shop managers, I watch, fascinated. It's a virtuoso display of Jeff's control and understanding of his business and his power to expose and crush every irrelevance and every mindless remark.

The accountant enters with some papers. He's smiling, looks excited, goes over to Jeff with the papers open. Jeff condescends to glance at them. 'Good, eh?' He then immediately ignores the accountant and carries on talking to the shop managers.

I've never seen anyone treat accountants so dismissively. He's only too aware that the profit he's making doesn't need confirming by an accountant. It's evident, I later discover, from the growing cash balance. Jeff is awash with money.

Eventually we have some semblance of privacy, perhaps to discuss business.

'I'm giving every employee a copy of *Jonathon Livingstone Seagull* this week.' He points to a pile of books in the corner of the office. There must be more than a hundred of them. 'Have you read it?' I admit that I haven't. He throws me a copy. 'You're a musician, aren't you?' I'm astonished he knows; Rex must have mentioned it.

'We've got someone in the shop who wants to play the guitar.'

'Really?' I struggle to sound interested.

'You'll talk to him if he comes round, won't you?'

'Of course.'

It seems as if I'll never get any orders. Jeff looks at me and reads my mind.

'Don't worry, I'm going to give you some orders.' He says it like a parent humouring a child fretting for some promised treat.

He continues to hold court with the managers, and demonstrates an amazing knowledge of exactly what is in every shop window. The cloth, the style, the colour are all referred to as he analyses what they should do. He treats them mercilessly and exposes their weaknesses with cruel skill.

His favourite game is to ask them a question only he can answer. No one can come up with anything like the right answer to one question. After hearing several desperate attempts, he finally says, with mounting exasperation, 'The answer is that there is no answer. *Do you understand?*' Their public humiliation is complete.

In mid-flow the phone rings and he answers it. After listening for thirty seconds or so he snaps, 'Mind your own business,' and puts the phone down. The shop managers are finally dismissed and only the accountant remains, apart from Rex and me.

'What was all that about, Jeff?' the accountant asks.

'One of our competitors rang to say someone had offered him a load of our suits, which he assumed had been knocked off. He asked me what he should do and I told him.'

'But you told him ... Jeff, it might have been a good idea to...'

Jeff cuts him off. 'Just keep the score, eh? I'll do the rest.' There is no arguing with him. The accountant shrinks out of the office and Jeff picks up one of the pattern books I've brought with me.

'I'll have a thousand yards of this, this, this...'

The orders come rattling out so fast I can't write them down quickly enough. He loses patience with my inability to keep up.

'Do you want orders or not?'

'Of course I do, but…'

'Just pay attention.' He repeats his order and I scribble furiously.

'When do you want delivery?'

'Four weeks.'

'That's difficult but I'll do my best.'

'Your best may be no good.'

'Jeff, it will be.'

Once I've got the details, I can't leave quickly enough. I want to get back to the mill. I know Ronald is having a desperate struggle to keep the looms going. We're making orders knowing we'll have to hold the finished cloth for delivery instructions. That means stock is going up and money is ever tighter. I've now got some orders which are deliver-as-ready. The price I quote is above the bottom price and Jeff adds as I'm leaving, 'I'll pay you by return.' This is the greatest incentive of all.

I stop at the nearest phone box to tell Ronald the good news. 'I've enough orders to keep us going for a week or two but the most exciting thing is that these designs will give us a new reputation. He's the king of the fashion trade.'

I'm convinced we're on the brink of the greatest advance we've ever made. That evening I return home to Ruth, still elated by the day's events.

'For the first time in my business life I've met someone creative. He behaves like an artist, isn't obsessed by money and his personality is magic. I'm sure I'm on the inside of something that will revolutionise my business.'

'How can he be successful in business if he doesn't care about money?'

'If you're doing something that catches the tide of public approval you can do everything else badly and still succeed. Most people only succeed when they skimp and scrape and cut corners. What he's doing is so uniquely and powerfully successful that he can get away with being inefficient in all the small things.'

'Well, I hope he stays successful.' There's an edge of cynicism in her voice. She can never allow herself to be swayed by someone she doesn't even know. I've begun to accept that the survival of our relationship depends on keeping more and more of my activities and feelings private. It seems that our happiness can't extend to excitement as well.

Later that evening, I go to the piano and begin to compose music for the first time in a decade. I still have a plentiful supply of manuscript paper, bought when I still had hope that I could fill it with wonderful sounds. As I begin to write, I start to feel that I've discovered my own sound, my own voice, my own language. This is new – the glorious freedom of expressing me, of not being yoked to another composer. It seems that my musical life is far from over.

Our growing business with Jeff proves to be the foundation of our success in textiles. Fashion is dominating the textile world, and we're right at the heart of it. One day I get an unexpected phone call; it's the secretary who works for Mr Longhurst, the buyer for the multiple who treated me like dirt in the pre-Jeff days.

'Would you like an appointment to show Mr Longhurst this season's range?'

'I'm going abroad tomorrow for a week but I can see him sometime after that.'

'Would there be any chance of coming this afternoon?'

I can't resist the opportunity of going to see him under such different circumstances.

His greeting is much more effusive than on my first visit.

'I understand you supply a lot of cloth to this whizz-kid in London. Are these the kinds of pattern he buys?'

I though this would be behind it. The revolution is hurting the establishment. Mr Longhurst looks through the cloth patterns with great interest.

'Leave these patterns with me and I'll give you an order.'

'Sorry, can't do that.'

'What do you mean?'

After a lifetime in the business he's used to everyone doing exactly what he wants.

'I can't leave the patterns without an order.'

'But I've told you I'll give you an order.' His face is red with indignation.

'I'm delighted you like the patterns, but I can only leave them if you give me a contract for 20,000 yards.'

I know that if I leave the patterns without a commitment, he'll give them to his golfing buddies to copy. He might give me a thousand yards, or even five thousand, but I'm not taking any chances.

'In all my experience I've never come across such an attitude.'

He paces round his office, unsure what to do. I know I have what he wants and feel I have the upper hand. He leaves the office to show a colleague the patterns. He soon comes back.

'All right, we'll give you 20,000 yards. We'll probably want it in one pattern but we'll specify it in the next week.'

I feel triumphant. The price I've quoted is high and the idea of weaving so much in one pattern is even better. This is all thanks to Jeff.

Gradually we gain more and more new customers, all anxious to share the success Jeff is having. Jeff doesn't seem to mind. He knows I'm selling to his competitors but he has a total disregard for conventional business practice.

I ring up to speak to him one day and Sheila, once a cleaner but now promoted, answers.

'No, Jeff's not coming in today. He says the weather's so beautiful he's staying in the garden.' I listen to this audacious truth in astonishment. A business trip, a meeting, a dental appointment is the normal excuse – but self-indulgence is unheard of as a valid reason for not coming to work.

One day, I go in to see him with new patterns, but I also have a recording of my new piano sonata.

'Jeff, I've written this sonata and it's dedicated to you.'

I catch him off his guard and am touched to see tears come to his eyes. He hastily regains his composure and gives me a book by Krishnamurti as a reciprocal gesture.

'Read this.' It puts him in control again. 'Come on, we're going somewhere.'

We climb into his Rolls Royce Corniche and drive to Kensington High Street. The 'somewhere' is a charmingly decrepit bookshop with an ornate glass porch. I've never been in such an eccentric bookshop. Jeff immediately takes charge.

'Get us some coffee, we want to buy some gear.'

The shop owner obliges, clearly used to people like Jeff.

Within minutes, Jeff has amassed a great stack of books, all early editions: James Joyce, Ezra Pound, Henry Miller... He continues to pile them on. I hunt out a beautifully illustrated early edition of Blake's *Songs of Innocence*. Here I am, far away from Stephen and Manchester, but still clinging to the sources which have influenced me most. Perhaps it's in this shop, in this moment, that I feel the first stirrings of my belief in the linkage of art and enterprise.

Jeff looks at my Blake with interest. I want it and can't resist the impulse.

'Do have it.' It's an unnecessary gesture. He's on the point of adding it to his growing pile, but I stop him.

'No, I insist on buying this.' Jeff shrugs in acquiescence. I pay for the Blake. The prices of Jeff's pile are totted up.

'That comes to £496.'

'Round it off,' Jeff orders.

The bookshop owner looks carefully at the books.

'All right, £490.'

'Not down, *up*,' Jeff snaps. He hands over ten fifty-pound notes. The man is as bemused as me. I think of Gus and his horse-trading in Bond Street. How cheap it all seems. For a mere ten pounds, Jeff has expressed his uniqueness. What a bargain! It's a minor stroke of genius that elevates him above Gus, Dressing-Gowns, and every other small-minded businessman.

My life in business has never been so exciting. It's no longer separated from my inner world of music and the arts, but through Jeff is increasingly connected with it. The excitement of life in London and the fashion world all serve to give me a greater feeling of purpose as an artist. By coincidence, the day after my visit to the bookshop I get an unexpected phone call from Gerald.

'I don't know whether you remember a long time ago Mrs Gainsborough mentioning the possibility of playing at the French Embassy?'

'Yes, I remember it.'

'Well, she's been on the phone to say she wants to organise it for a date two months off. Would you be able to do it? I assume you're still playing?'

'Of course.' I don't hesitate. Business has given me a lifestyle and power that satisfies me, but I realise that being a musician serves a deeper purpose. Gerald's invitation satisfies something money can't buy.

'How about Beethoven Opus 96, the Mozart B Flat – the big one of the two – and the Shostakovich sonata?'

'That sounds wonderful.'

That evening I sit at the piano and work as I've never worked for years. My fingers feel as if the absence has done them good. I tackle the technical problems with more zest than I've ever known. I'm still a pianist; perhaps I can be an even better pianist. The thought of having a prestige concert in London is so thrilling that I can barely contain my excitement. It seems as if my career in business is no longer an obstacle to my developing career as a musician.

*   *   *

269

I can hardly wait for Gerald to arrive for our rehearsal a week later. I've been practising hard and am confident I know the piano parts. I've been to the odd concert when Gerald was playing, but I'm conscious that my growing financial success has made relations between us more difficult. My more affluent lifestyle seems to impel him to make self-deprecatory comments.

To me it seems so unnecessary, but I realise how sensitive he is about every detail of my life. The quality of my clothes, shoes, furniture, paintings, cars, are all commented on favourably but with awkwardness. I can tell he feels a need to apologise for himself in some way. A lot has happened since our Leyton Hall days. I ask if he's seen any of our college friends recently.

'Not really.'

I'm surprised. I can hardly believe you can be a professional musician and not bump into people who were fellow students. I'd assumed there would be so much we could talk about, but it doesn't seem so. He takes his violin out of its case and begins to tune up. It's the Stradivarius he bought years before.

'By the way, I'm selling a half interest in the violin to the Orchestral Concerts Society. The money will be useful and I'll still have the use of the violin. What do you think?'

'It's never a good idea to exchange an appreciating asset for money that's likely to disappear quickly. But if you need the money, there may be no alternative.'

It's embarrassing to be asked for an opinion after a decision has been made, but my reply seems to satisfy him.

Ruth comes into the room just as we're about to start playing.

'Gerald, would you like a cup of tea?'

'No, I'm all right, thank you.'

'It's no trouble if you'd like one.'

'No, really, thank you anyway.'

'I'm just going to have one myself. Are you sure you won't have one?'

'All right then.'

'Why didn't you say you wanted one in the first place?' She's teasing, but her relentless determination to get her own way shows even in her warm-hearted hospitality.

When we start to play, I'm surprised to hear that Gerald is a little bit out of practice. I feel distinctly more confident when I hear him fluff something. Once more I ask myself: do we all need someone else to fail in order to give us the confidence to succeed? None the less, it's wonderful to be playing great music with someone else again.

I'm conscious that Ruth will be able to hear. Her own dream of being a pianist has been abandoned long ago. My renewed ambition to play no longer conflicts with hers, but my growing involvement in the fashion industry is creating a deep divide between us.

After we've finished rehearsing, I feel that Gerald has really responded to my enthusiasm. It's easy for me because I haven't struggled to make a living as a musician during the intervening years.

'You don't realise how lucky you are.'

He could be reading my mind. Abandoning music for such a long period hasn't just given me renewed enthusiasm. It's given me an enthusiasm greater than anything I had before. Could it be that I can still achieve my dream of playing the piano?

28

London Swings

As I stride along the platform at King's Cross towards the exit barrier, the booming noise of the tannoy and the clatter of trolleys and footsteps resonate under the vast, glazed canopy. Every time I visit Jeff I feel as though my life as an artist is growing and my life as a businessman receding. Glancing at my fellow male passengers, it's impossible not to feel a sense of smug superiority at the contrast between the dowdiness of most of them and the reassuring recognition in the eyes of the few peacocks who have joined me in this new exclusive club of fashion.

As I walk to Rex's car with my heavy case of samples, I reflect on the difference between my first visit to London as a young and very green member of a public company, and now, when I'm a mill owner supplying some of the country's – no, the world's – most successful fashion shops. It's not simply the fact that I own the business, it's also the headiness of dealing with people whom I think of as kindred spirits.

We settle into the car and Rex drives to the King's Road and Jeff. We arrive a little early for our appointment and go to our usual coffee shop in the same block as Jeff's headquarters. It's a place I always enjoy spending time in. The clientele are so fashionably dressed that it's a prime source of new fashion ideas. I look around, trying not to stare but yearning to be a part of this world. Although my clothes say I am, I don't have the instinctive confidence of the insider. I'm an outsider masquerading as one of them. And when I sit among them, I'm very conscious of my outside-ness. The coffee shop is bustling and the coffee tastes completely different from any I've ever had in the north.

'You see the woman on the table over there?' Rex whispers. She's wearing the most exotic dress I've ever seen. The material is a beautiful, subdued red and greenish check and the pattern never repeats. I can't help but stare, fascinated by the sheer impossibility of weaving a cloth that doesn't repeat. 'She's Noelle. You've probably heard of her shops.'

273

I've actually seen the shops and been impressed by the stunning interior design. She looks as glamorous as her shops. It seems too good an opportunity to miss. On impulse I cross to her table.

'Forgive me intruding, but I just wanted to tell you how much I admire your shops.'

Noelle is surprisingly appreciative. 'Are you in the textile trade?

'Yes, I've got a mill in Yorkshire and I'm selling a lot of cloth to the men's fashion trade.'

'Will you be showing in Paris?'

'Er, I think so.'

'If you are, I'll come and see you there.'

I've never thought of it seriously but yes, this is the next step. I've heard of the fashion shows in Paris, Frankfurt and Milan, but haven't thought of showing there. Suddenly, because of this chance meeting, it seems the obvious thing to do. Her positive response to my out-of-the-blue approach confirms in my mind that I'll do it almost before I've thought of it. I'm elated by the success of defying my instincts, which said, 'She won't want to talk to you.' I return to Rex flushed with triumph and excitement. He looks at his watch and says, 'Time to go'. As we leave, I smile and nod a discreet farewell to Noelle. I start to feel that maybe I'm not such an outsider after all.

Jeff isn't in, but we're ushered into his office, where we sit and wait. Clothes and books surround us, covering every horizontal surface. A few minutes later, Jeff appears. 'Have you met my astrologer?'

This is a surprise. 'No.'

'I'll get him to do your horoscope.'

We're here to sell cloth, but that always seems the least important thing to Jeff. He shouts into the phone: 'Andy, get hold of Stars and ask him to come to my office.' He looks at me. 'We've got a company astrologer. You're interested in the future, aren't you?'

'Yes.'

'Well, you'll know what it is soon.'

And he disappears again. This is Jeff's uncompromising, radical attitude to business. It certainly makes an impression.

A nervous young man enters the office.

'Jeff wants me to do your horoscopes.' He looks at Rex, who demurs.

'Not me, him.' Perhaps fortunately, Rex never seems to resent the fact that in Jeff's eyes he is of no consequence at all. Stars sits at Jeff's desk with a pen and paper. 'I'll do your chart. What's your date of birth?'

I tell him.

'What time of day were you born?'

'I've no idea.'

'It won't be so accurate if there's no time of birth.' He looks critically at me, as if annoyed that I don't know such a vital piece of information. 'Jeff says you're a musician.' I feel a frisson of pride that I've been elevated above being a businessman.

'I'm a composer and pianist.'

'What are you doing here?'

'I supply Jeff with cloth.'

'Ah.' He says it as though I've suddenly disappointed him. Or maybe presented him with a challenge he isn't ready for.

'I'll let you know when I work it all out, but I've a lot to do at the moment. I'll be a week or two.' He leaves the room, quite possibly anxious to get away before Jeff returns, which he does almost immediately.

'Have you got your future?'

I hate to disappoint him.

'He says a week or so.'

'Oh.' He flashes annoyance and looks at me as if I'm responsible. 'Where are the patterns I asked for?' I open my bag. At breakneck speed he rummages through what I've brought. 'A thousand yards of this, this, this...' I scribble down the pattern numbers. As selling cloth goes, it's the most exhilarating experience possible.

'Would you like to come to a fashion show?' The question implies that I'd be stupid not to, and anyway it's a privilege to be asked.

'I wasn't going to stay overnight,' I say hesitantly, knowing it's a feeble thing to say. Jeff adopts his customary don't-mess-me-about attitude.

'Do you want to or not?'

'Yes,' I say, not sure whether I actually will stay.

'Where do you stay?'

'I'm not sure, probably Brown's.' I always have a problem choosing a hotel. The Ritz, Savoy and Claridge's are too grand and make me feel uneasy. Brown's was the hotel an in-law said he always stayed in.

'You don't want to stay there. Stay at Blake's.'

I've not heard of it but I jump at the chance of trying it; it must be good if Jeff approves it.

'Here's the number, use my phone.' Immediately, he dashes out again. I ring Blake's, and to my relief they have a room. I establish with Jeff that I'm to be at his office at five, and we'll go together to the Royal College of Art, the fashion show venue.

In the meantime I go on to see a few new customers. It's obvious they're in awe of Jeff, and as his favoured supplier I'm treated with a respect I've never enjoyed before.

I check in at Blake's at about four. The building isn't impressive but the interior is different from any other hotel I've known. Most are like mausoleums; Blake's is vibrant and seductive. More than that, everyone in the hotel looks young and part of the new style now dominating London life. I recognise one of the guests: the current Formula One world champion. Jeff clearly knows the right places.

When I get to my room I phone Ronald first.

'I've got a pile of orders from Jeff, and some other new customers.'

'What price did you quote?'

'I didn't talk prices.'

'It's fortunate we bought a lot of wool at what now looks like the bottom. At today's wool price we'd need to charge a lot more.'

'Perhaps we should buy some now and average the price?'

'I'm doing that, but it still means increasing the selling price.'

Every time I raise the question of price with Jeff, it causes a furore. I've come to realise that the success of his business isn't just style but price too. Jeff is aware that disturbing the delicate balance between customer demand and the price of our cloth could imperil the promising business we have.

'I'll see what I can do. Oh, by the way, Jeff's invited me to go with him to a fashion show so I won't be back at the mill until sometime tomorrow afternoon.'

'Don't worry about it, you concentrate on getting the orders.'

I replace the receiver and dial again.

'I'm sorry darling, but I need to stay the night in London. I'll be back tomorrow.'

'What's so urgent?'

'Jeff invited me to go with him to a fashion show and I thought it might be important.'

'Do you have to do everything he says? Thank goodness I don't have to be there. By the way, Gerald wants to speak to you. I told him you'd be home tonight but I suppose you can ring him from there.'

'No problem. Are you all right?'

'I'm fine. I'll see you tomorrow.' The way she says it makes me uneasy. I'm moving further and further away from Ruth, and I know she has no interest in changing.

Rex drives me back to Jeff's and we go into his office. Jeff glares when he sees Rex. 'What are you doing here?'

Rex smiles good-naturedly. 'I'm just dropping him off.'

'Well, what are you waiting for?' His ruthlessness in cutting out everything and everyone he doesn't consider necessary operates in all aspects of his life. After we've arranged our next meeting in London, Rex simply disappears.

'Come on,' says Jeff, as if I've been keeping him waiting.

We leave his office and walk down Flood Street to his parked Rolls Royce. As we drive, I'm conscious of heads turning.

'We'll park away from the college. You don't mind a bit of a walk, do you? A year ago I always tried to park right next to it so they'd all see my car. I don't care now.'

As we approach the college on foot I realise we're passing the Albert Hall. This massive, circular brick edifice has never been more than a name to me. I stop to look at posters advertising the Proms. I particularly want to know which pianists are playing. Arturo Michaelangeli, Solomon, Moura Lympany... and *Stephen Smith*. The surprise is so great that I almost shout out loud. *Stephen is playing at the Proms!* My heart races and I feel almost unbearably jealous. Not only is he playing, but he's playing *his own piano concerto!*

So, this is the consequence of abandoning my dreams. No material success can rival an achievement I would have sold my soul for. I've been weak in abandoning my career as a pianist. Stephen's ruthless tenacity is the quality an artist needs; a focus which makes every other consideration seem trivial. Regret, envy and self-loathing flood into my mind in the few moments we spend looking at the programmes.

'Why aren't you playing?'

Jeff's simple question implies that he can see no reason why I shouldn't be playing if I want to. If only he knew the commitment and work required to achieve this level of playing!

As we walk on, my spirits slowly revive and I push the thought of Stephen as far away as I can. And then I remember.

'I'm going to be playing in London at the French Embassy. Would you like to come?' Jeff's reply is non-committal, but at least I've restored a little bit of self-esteem. In my eyes the disparity between the two events is ridiculously large, but to Jeff I'm sure it's negligible.

Final thoughts of Stephen are dispelled on entering the Royal College of Arts. The glamour, noise and excitement are overwhelming. For a start, the place is packed with gorgeous women, not all of them models. The air seems saturated in perfume. Jeff takes it all in his stride, stopping every few seconds to speak to people he knows as we head for our reserved seats. I'm pleased that I'm able to recognise several designers, even if only the well-known ones. I take it as more evidence that I'm becoming an insider in the fashion world.

There is an explosion of lights and the catwalk becomes the centre of a maelstrom of noise and colour. Pop music booms out at an astonishing volume. The show combines menswear and womenswear, and Jeff periodically exchanges approving nods with friends nearby. He gives me a running commentary. Being with him grants me a status I wouldn't otherwise have, and I enjoy it enormously.

After the show there's a reception in a large room covered in student artwork. Trays of champagne and canapés do the rounds, and I soon have a glass in my hand. Jeff has disappeared and I wander round looking at the pictures. I notice a stunning woman, also alone and also looking at the pictures. I'm sure I've seen her before, but can't place her.

She's wearing a beautiful yellow suit. Jacket and skirt are both long and straight, and the fabric has a subtle mix of colours which create an overall impression of depth and luxury. Her face is beautiful but in an unusual way, with large round sparkling eyes. Perhaps more than anything, her hair dominates – luxuriously thick, and the shiniest black. A Queen Nefertiti hairstyle. She catches my eye, which is only too ready to be caught, and to my delight walks over to me. I can hardly believe my luck that this goddess is approaching. Luckily, she speaks while I'm still searching for something to say.

'Are you in the fashion business?'

'I'm a cloth supplier. I have a mill in Yorkshire.'

'I'd love to see it.'

'That's easily arranged.'

'What brought you here?'

'I came with someone I supply.'

'Who?'

I point Jeff out while he's briefly visible.

'Jeff?' A fleeting hint of incredulity is swiftly replaced by something close to admiration. 'I know him, of course! I teach at the college so I stayed on to see the show. Are you going back to Yorkshire tonight?'

'No, I'm staying over.'

'Where?'

'Blake's.'

'I live very near. If you like, I can drop you there. By the way, my name's Arabella – I'm a painter.'

The penny drops.

278

'I thought I recognised you – I've certainly heard of you.'

'Are you interested in painting?'

'Very much. I'm interested in all the arts. I started life as a pianist, then stumbled into being a cloth manufacturer.'

'What an interesting career. You've not stopped playing, I hope?'

'No, I'm playing at the French Embassy next month.'

'You're not! I'm a friend of the ambassador – he's a lovely man.'

More champagne is offered, but Arabella whispers, 'It's revolting stuff. Cheap and nasty, isn't it?' Her comment is suddenly disconcerting. I'm still so used to taking everything at face value that I haven't yet learned to question anything in an environment like this.

I'm drawn towards her; I want to benefit from her obvious experience of a more sophisticated world. We're suddenly interrupted by one of Arabella's friends.

'I've been looking for you everywhere, there's someone I want you to meet.'

Arabella turns to me.

'I'll see you later, don't go without me.'

She walks away and I resume looking at the pictures, but without quite the same concentration as before.

Eventually, Jeff comes over.

'I'm leaving now, are you coming or are you fixed up?' As he leaves, I begin to wonder if Arabella will bother returning. The room is so full of people that I've lost sight of her. I wander round, trying to look at ease with myself. After my first lucky strike with Arabella, no one else approaches me. Everyone is locked in conversation. This is going backwards: I start to feel like the only outsider. Just as I'm giving up hope, and to my far too obvious relief, Arabella returns.

'I'm ready to go, are you?'

We walk to her car, and I can't help feeling as though we're a couple. This is madness, I reason. Where's my loyalty to Ruth? We walk past the Albert Hall and I feel a momentary stab of pain as I think about Stephen again.

But life in London has never been so enticing. It's a beautiful evening, but then to me evenings in London always seem beautiful. As we walk, she gently slips her arm through mine.

We find her sleek black Mercedes 300SL sports car in a narrow side street. As she drives the powerful car, swiftly and confidently, I wonder where this is leading me. Initially, it's to Blake's.

'I've arranged to take a few friends to Morton's for supper. Do come if you'd like to.'

'Er, yes. I'd like to, but are you sure it's all right?' My working-class insecurity doesn't loosen its grip so easily.

'If you're free to come, come. We're meeting there about ten – you know where it is don't you?'

I know it's in Berkeley Square, so I manage a 'yes'. In an instant she's gone, and I walk into Blake's far more elated and confident than when I left it only hours earlier. Once in my room I decide I must speak to Gerald and Ruth.

First Ruth. As soon as I hear her voice on the phone, I'm stricken with emotion. She's such a loyal friend – difficult, demanding, uncompromising, tireless in pursuing her own ends perhaps, but strong and faithful. She would never descend to my present level of behaviour. She isn't vulnerable to romantic impulses. She isn't vulnerable to emotions. Her overriding philosophy is not 'Do I want it?' but 'Is it right?' The result is a paragon of virtue and integrity, but not someone easy to live with.

'Darling, I hope everything's okay.' My concern is genuine, but in the circumstances hypocritical. The main thread to her happiness at the moment is me.

'I've had a good day practising. I'm going to Gordon tomorrow for lessons. I'm taking the Schubert B Flat Posthumous.' She's buoyant. I feel hugely relieved that her focus is music and not me.

'That's wonderful. I look forward to hearing it when I get back.'

'Oh, I'm not ready to play it yet.'

Her lack of confidence is ever-present. What would happen to her confidence if she knew what I was doing?

'I'm sure Gordon will be impressed, your playing is definitely improving.'

'I'm not so sure.'

'You know it is.'

However much reassurance I offer, it only provokes the opposite reaction. It's so frustrating loving someone who is deeply insecure. Nothing that can be said helps. It's as if reassurance provokes a determination to prove me wrong.

'You've no idea, have you? You've so much confidence that you can't understand what it's like to be me.'

'You often call my playing untidy,' I remind her.

'Yes, but that doesn't affect your confidence.'

It's a delicate balance between a quest for perfection and determination to move forward. I've always been aware that an obsession with perfection can condemn you to run on the same spot forever. If I'm honest, I think

280

that's the problem with Ruth. To make progress, you need to climb higher and higher and overcome problems at the lower level by getting above them. Ruth doesn't seem to have the nerve to climb. She wants to perfect everything before going on, and she never achieves it.

Our conversation peters out. Fortunately, she raises no awkward questions about what I might be doing.

I ring Gerald.

'Is our next rehearsal still all right with you?'

'Fine by me. By the way, have you seen that Stephen's Proms piano concerto next week is being broadcast live?'

I try to sound blasé. 'I know he's playing it but didn't know it was being broadcast.'

'I'll record it for you, if you like. You might be too busy to listen.'

'Thank you.'

I lie on my bed, looking at the ceiling as I used to do in Haydock Street. What a difference there has been since then. I spent those years of daydreaming imagining myself as a pianist. Now I'm besotted with the world of business and fashion, and piano playing has lost the hold it had over me. The world I want is the one with Arabella in it. I suddenly realise that I'm vulnerable to emotions which could shake my life to its foundations. I feel ashamed of myself, but only temporarily. Other feelings make a sense of shame irrelevant.

The passage of Wagner's love music which has always stood above the rest in inducing ecstasy is not *Tristan and Isolde*, or the love duet between Brunnhilde and Siegfried, but the moment when Gunther welcomes Siegfried and Gertrude as the holy pair. Siegfried has been affected by the same love potion Shakespeare uses in *A Midsummer Night's Dream*. It induces infidelity without guilt: innocent infidelity. At this moment the sung obbligato to the orchestral music twists the complex threads of passion, yearning, sadness, ecstasy and nostalgia to exquisite effect. It's music to make the unthinkable thinkable.

It's perhaps also Wagner's way of dealing emotionally with a situation similar to the one which is progressively engulfing me. I know nothing about Arabella, and yet in just a couple of hours I'm infatuated. I've discovered a need I never knew I had. My relationship with Ruth has been both deeply satisfying and deeply frustrating, but it's never stirred the feelings I'm experiencing now.

I indulge in the luxury of an early-evening bath. Ostensibly I'm preparing myself for the night ahead, but in truth I'm preparing myself for something much more profound – the end, not of my love and respect for Ruth, but of my marriage to her. Lying cocooned in warm water in a silent bathroom, it's easy to imagine that Arabella doesn't exist. I could stay wallowing here beyond the appointed time and in effect she would become a figment of my imagination. But it wouldn't change anything.

29

The Only Failure is to Give up Trying

Our diversification into fashion has resulted in more creative excitement than I've ever experienced in business. Many of our customers are magnetic personalities more intent on creating beautiful clothes than making money. It's exhilarating to deal with the world's top fashion designers. Their success depends on developing a strongly identifiable image or brand.

Unfortunately, our fabric is anonymous and all our customers can switch suppliers without anyone else knowing. Although we're charging higher prices, our costs are rising and we become less profitable. The smaller quantities which are inevitable in high fashion cost a great deal more to produce. But however much we charge, it's never enough to maintain a decent profit margin. Ever-increasing prices lead inevitably to falling sales, and it isn't long before we're struggling to keep the machinery going. It's increasingly obvious to Ronald and me that we need to find a way of reducing our production capacity if we're going to stay in business. I decide to concentrate all our production in one weaving mill and close down the other two.

It's hard to do it. Our dreams of expanding prosperity have been shared by many people, and now we have to convince them that retreating is a way of advancing. But we can hardly convince the loyal workforce, who are redundant.

It's the first time since we were in business together that we find ourselves in retreat. Yet, just when the problems of survival are at their most acute, I get an unexpected letter from a London solicitor.

Sirs,

We have some clients who have been endeavouring to sell the mills adjacent to yours. They have now found a purchaser but it seems from our searches that your company, when it sold the mills in the 1930s, imposed a condition that the buildings could only be used for textiles. As you can imagine, there is no possibility of fulfilling this condition under present market conditions.

We are therefore asking for a release from the condition.

Yours, etc. etc.

The implication is that there could be a value to the release, but it can't be much. I wonder what they're asking for the mills. I realise I've been driving past the For Sale sign for over a year and have never given it a thought. I've got too many problems running our own mill to pay much attention to what might be happening next door. I phone the agent and discover that the mills are for sale for a paltry £20,000.

Ronald is quite clear about what he wants to do. 'I met a man recently who works for a property developer. I think you'd like him. He seems to know what he's doing and I got the impression the company he's working for is very successful. He's ambitious as he's quite young. I'll ring him. He might be prepared to come and talk to us.'

He is – the very next morning. Simon arrives looking alert and smart, and I can see immediately why he's made a good impression on Ronald. Fortunately he works only in commercial property, not residential. I ask, 'Is it new build or converting old buildings?' Simon starts giving us a crash course in commercial property development.

'It's a mixture of both. Often when we buy a site there are some buildings worth retaining, but a lot need demolishing. Once we've decided which we're keeping, we look at the need for access and car parking for those buildings. Any land surplus to that can then be developed.'

'How do you finance the new buildings?'

'If we can get a lease for the development from a blue chip company, then we have no difficulty selling the investment to a pension fund. Because they have something that's linked to inflation, they'll accept a very low rate of return on the initial investment. That means we make a reasonable capital profit on the development. It may cost a million to do the development, but once we have an assured tenant, what we sell on is the income, not the building. The tenant is responsible for keeping the building in good condition and the income is guaranteed because the company is first-class. If we can negotiate a yield of four per cent, we'd sell if for £200,000. There are lots of expenses to deduct but you're still left with a reasonable profit. It all comes down to finding the right location, putting up the right building at the right cost, and finding the right tenant.'

'But presumably when you start you need to persuade a bank that what you're proposing to build, you can let?'

Even as I raise the question, I recognise the stumbling-block in the way of every would-be developer. Everything works beautifully on paper, but the bank knows from experience that theory and practice can be light-years apart.

We walk with Simon round the site of the buildings next door. 'Would you do a scheme for these buildings for us? We'll pay you.'

'I'd be delighted.' He takes out his pen and begins to make notes. 'I'll phone you as soon as it's ready.'

He leaves and we sit together in the office, pondering what he's said. Property development might be difficult, but it seems more attractive than the textile business. If retailers buy the wrong cloth, make the wrong models or choose the wrong colours and the garments don't sell in the shops, we suffer. The vagaries of fashion, the capriciousness of buyers, the fact that customers make all the decisions but don't always take responsibility, make textiles a dangerous business. At least in property we'd be making all the decisions.

Ronald has no doubts. 'This is the business for me.' He's elated by the prospect he sees ahead. As events will prove, he has a natural and quite remarkable affinity for property.

It takes Simon only hours to draw up plans for the site. The following day we meet him again. He points to his drawings as he speaks.

'I think it could work well. I suggest retaining this single-storey shed, which is about 20,000 square feet. It needs very little doing to it and we could probably let it for four pounds a square foot without difficulty. Demolish the buildings here and here to create good car parking. The rest of the buildings aren't worth keeping. If we demolish them, we can build four 5,000-square feet units. They'd cost £150,000 each and the income would be £20,000. We needn't go at risk, they could be built after they'd been let.'

Simon is already talking as if he's one of us. 'The cost would be £600,000, plus whatever you pay for the site. The potential income is £40,000 for the building we're keeping, and £80,000 for the units once they're built and let.'

I quickly calculate that the income of £120,000 is a 20 per cent return on the £600,000. We think we can get the site for £15,000 but keep this to ourselves. If it's as good as this, why on earth have we been wasting our time in textiles? Every year in textiles is a voyage into the unknown. Whatever you've done in the previous year is history. You start again with a clean sheet. In property, you start every year building on the rental income retained from the previous year.

It helps that Simon is clearly very interested in the idea of joining us.

Once we're on our own again, Ronald and I discuss the prospect of starting a business in property. We decide that I'll handle our disengagement from textiles, while Ronald concentrates on developing the property business. It seems the best way to handle the transition.

It's a big, bold move. The culture of an established business can give a false sense of security. We're struggling to make a profit and pay our way, yet for everyone in an old established business there is always a reluctance to change course.

The more I think about it, the more I'm convinced of the need to abandon textiles. If we stay in textiles we'll go down. Customers are too powerful; they have increasing choice and our competition is the next supplier who goes in five per cent cheaper. We only have our designs, and those are open to being copied. The days of a great weaving industry are numbered. I'd sooner dispose of our textile assets in an orderly way than wait until the bank puts us into liquidation. We'll probably show a large loss because we'll never get the prices we need if it's known that we're closing down. But it won't matter, because we'll reduce the bank overdraft to next to nothing. The only people who will be concerned are the minority shareholders, because they have no idea whether we can make a success of property. But I'm sure they'll benefit in the long run, and what they think in the short term isn't particularly important because we own most of the shares.

The share price of our company has slumped from 25 pence when we took over the company to around five pence now, but there are still assets per share of around 75 pence. It occurs to me that we could buy the balance of the company for about £60,000. So that day, we discreetly buy another ten per cent of the company, which raises our holding to over 70 per cent. We're nearly a private company again.

Ronald rings the solicitor for the next door mill the same afternoon. 'We won't release you from the agreement, but we will make an offer of £15,000 for the property.' It doesn't go down well but they have no alternative. The property is derelict and without our release they can't sell it at all. We could have been more ruthless under the circumstances, but we're happy to go ahead at £15,000.

Within six months we've converted the property, let it, and have a rental income of slightly more than the £120,000 we'd anticipated. Simon is managing director of our new property company. The interest on the development is costing about £90,000 so, on balance, the net profit is small. The site and the units are not of a high enough quality to attract a blue chip tenant – we knew this when we started – but our success in transforming a derelict collection of buildings into a small industrial estate confirms the rightness of pursuing this alternative to textiles.

We discuss our next move very carefully. Simon's experience is invaluable.

'If we want to sell our investment on, we must develop in a location favoured by the pension funds. They're very inflexible, and however attractive a site is, if it's outside their preferred areas, that's it. Once they decide a particular area is good for them, then all the available land in it inevitably becomes dearer than in less-favoured areas. If we want venture capital from the banks, we have to put a case to them that leaves no room for doubt.'

We're on a learning curve, and it proves to be a steep one. We go on to develop a variety of buildings on several sites. Banks never have a problem lending money if you can convince them they can have it back. We get our development finance by persuading them that we'll find good tenants and sell the investment on. But without a first-class tenant, there's no way we can repay the money. That's the tightrope we walk.

Sometimes we gamble recklessly. In one case we borrow over £1 million to build a shed of 100,000 square feet without any tenant. As the months pass, the tension rises and the bank becomes increasingly anxious. It's an enormous relief to us and to the bank when, in the nick of time, we find a tenant and sell the development to a pension fund. We ought to have made £500,000 profit on the sale, but the bank interest charges and other expenses cut that in half.

On the textiles side, our finance problems are by comparison marginal. We might need more money because deliveries are held up or we're not being paid, but the sums we need aren't significant. In property, when things go wrong we can be short of millions. We calculate when we'll sell each investment on, and however cautious and prudent we think we are, we're usually wrong. But the irony is that if we'd been able to see the future and predict more accurately, we probably wouldn't have got the finance. The confident optimism which assumes that the future will be better than the reality is the quality that wins us friends, customers and bank loans.

Our property developments begin to spread geographically. Aberdeen becomes a hotspot. Because of the offshore oil industry, more and more companies needing warehouses and offices are attracted there, or expand their existing operations. Aberdeen becomes a weekly visit. It's only a short step to deciding we need a company plane – or rather, Ronald deciding we need a plane.

'I think we should seriously consider buying a Cessna. I've already met a pilot and co-pilot who are convinced they could find enough customers to keep the plane busy when we don't need it.'

'But how does it work financially?'

'The finance cost of the plane and the pilots' wages can just about be covered, but the flexibility of being able to fly whenever we like would be an enormous business advantage.'

I understand him well enough to know that disagreeing or being negative will be an emotional bloodbath. This has become the pattern of our discussions. Unless I respond positively to his ideas, he takes it as an affront.

'How would we market the use of the plane?'

'The pilots have all the connections. I don't think there'd be a problem.'

'It's not in their interest to see problems if they want to carry on flying the plane.'

'I've met them and I'm confident they could do it.'

It's obvious that Ronald is determined to fly in a private plane.

'How much does it actually cost to fly?'

'With eight passengers it's cheaper than flying scheduled.'

I don't need to be Einstein to work out that with one passenger it will be a lot dearer than flying scheduled. But I haven't the heart to carry on being negative. Ronald is progressively building a highly successful property company, and I find it hard to quibble.

Because we're using more and more finance for property, Ronald has developed a relationship with a merchant bank. My agreement to manage our strategic withdrawal from textiles means that I'm not involved in many of the new property developments and discussions.

I gradually become aware that we have very different ideas of the direction we should be going in. Between us we have most of the share capital. My dream is to acquire all the shares, become a private company and, over whatever time is needed, reduce our liabilities to a level at which we no longer need bank finance. In material terms, I can't imagine wanting more than I have. The conventional role of business tycoon is wholly repugnant to me. That's one of the secret concerns I have about the plane: will it be Ronald's first step towards that role?

I can tell there's something on his mind. Finally I make him spell it out.

'I've had quite a few conversations with our merchant bank about our finance requirements. As you know, they've been loaning us more and more against our developments and they've occasionally needed a strong stomach when our timing has slipped. But they've always stood by us, and I think they've got full confidence in us.'

This overture is already making me uneasy. 'Just for the record,' I point out, 'they've got full confidence in *you*. I've had very little involvement with them. I'd much prefer to eliminate the need for bank finance. I want to be independent of the conventional finance and business world, not a permanent fixture in it.'

Ronald presses on. 'What you've just said sharpens the issue. The bank are advising that we broaden the shareholder base and make an issue of shares, which they would underwrite. They suggest we issue half a million pounds' worth of shares.'

I'm horrified.

'That means our shareholding would fall from 70 to around 50 per cent.'

'Yes.'

I can't believe it.

'Why should we do that? It goes against the grain of everything I thought we wanted to achieve together. You just want to join the tycoon club.'

After so many years of comradeship, it's painful to realise that we're growing apart. I've never met anyone with more persuasiveness, astuteness, loyalty; but beneath it all, Ronald is deeply insecure. That insecurity is demanding the building of castles in the air. His friends in the merchant bank are massaging his ego with increasingly large loans. His personal strategy is no longer being shaped by what he wants for himself, but by the demands of his ego. As the dominant shareholder, my view is important; but the development of our property interest is in Ronald's hands, and there's no doubt that his efforts have elevated us above the problems caused by the decline of the textile industry.

There is now a deep division between us, and I have to make my position clear.

'I'm totally opposed to what you're suggesting. I want to find a way of going back to being a private company. If you don't agree, perhaps we should go our separate ways.'

'What you think and want matters to me.' Ronald seems suddenly penitent, and I wonder whether it's been too extreme to think of parting company.

For a while, we co-exist in a kind of stalemate. Our withdrawal from textiles is going smoothly, but I now need a way of handing on what remains. I decide that the best way out is to find an established textile company willing to absorb our business into theirs. I find one in Huddersfield. We continue to use one of our trading names and gradually transfer production to Huddersfield. The mill buildings we vacate are progressively redeveloped into buildings we can let. Our workforce shrinks slowly and the loss of jobs is never reported as a calamity by the local press. It's only a matter of months before we have no machinery and no workforce. It should be possible to continue trading profitably, but the same old vagaries of the industry mean that there is always more stress than profit.

One day soon after we're finally finished with textiles, I get a phone call.

'I believe you're an up-and-coming property company, and I have a deal I want to put to you.'

I arrange a date and we look forward with mild interest to what he has to say. We know from experience that there are plenty of people rushing around trying to involve companies like ours in deals. They're usually articulate but penniless, and we don't expect our visitor to be any different. The fact that he's coming to us indicates that he has no money and has so far failed in whatever he's trying to do. It's hardly promising, but you never know.

He's a small, seedy-looking man with shifty eyes and no charm.

'I'm looking for someone who can raise a few million pounds quickly. I have a contact with a large pension fund, and because of that contact the deal I'm talking about isn't available to anyone else. Don't try to go behind my back. It won't work and I can make you regret it. Let me explain what this deal is. There's a parcel of about 800 houses, all occupied by American servicemen. The rents are collected from the occupants but underwritten by the US Air Force, so there's no risk. The only risk is that the tenancy agreements come to an end in a year, with no guarantee they'll be renewed.'

'Presumably the houses are saleable?'

'Yes, but it would take time to sell 800 houses. What I've negotiated is a single premium insurance policy guaranteeing the income for a three-year period, during which time I'm sure enough houses could be sold to cover the bank borrowing.'

'So, what are the costs and what's the income?'

'The houses are for sale for £4 million. I want a million and the insurance policy is a million, making a total of £6 million. The income is £1.2 million gross at the moment.'

It sounds too good to be true. A 20 per cent return is enough to cover the bank interest, and a year will determine whether there is a new lease. If there isn't and we have to sell the houses, 800 houses of good quality, averaging £8,000 a house, is a bargain even in the depressed market of the 1970s. But the prices are low because demand is low, and it's clearly considered high risk by the people who have already turned it down.

Our visitor continues, 'I know it's a dream deal, but I've had bad experiences with so many timewasters that time has run out. The pension fund has decided that unless a signed contract is in their hands by the end of the month, they'll keep the property.'

He leaves us to think about it. As the more experienced borrower since we've moved into property, Ronald's opinion is the important one.

'There's no doubt it's worth doing, but is any bank brave enough to lend us six million, that's the question. We're already borrowing heavily and our existing banks may think we're overstretching ourselves. Simply asking for six million could be enough to unnerve them. I think it's better to try new lenders. We'd have to disclose it to our existing lenders if we went ahead, but with someone else prepared to take the risk secured only on the property we propose to buy, it would be more palatable.'

We set up the first meeting with one of the leading banks through a friend of ours. We've never used them before but the local director is young and reputedly dynamic, so it seems promising. We present the case for the loan very carefully. There are two possible developments. If the Americans don't renew the lease, then we need to sell enough houses in the three years covered by the insurance policy to repay the bank loan. It's difficult to prove that this is achievable, but we argue strongly that we can do it. On the other hand, if the lease is renewed, we should get sufficient rental income to repay the interest and capital over the period of the lease. There are inevitable risks, but we argue that they're minor and that the value of the property is significantly higher than the price we'll be paying. We believe we can revalue the properties and add around £10 million to our balance sheet values. This will make borrowing for new projects easier – something we don't mention to the new bank director, but it influences the way we sell the idea to him. We leave his office in high spirits, convinced he'll say yes.

The following morning he says no.

Ronald pushes over the desk a four-page letter. I'm shocked but don't have the patience to read it.

'Where do we go from here?' I begin to think the deal is slipping away.

'The real question is, can we get the finance in place before the deadline?'

'No, surely the real question is, do we sign the contract before we have the finance in place?'

'Not if we want to be secure.'

'But yes if we believe this deal could put us on the map in the property world.'

'If we sign the contract and don't get the finance in place, it could mean the end of everything.'

That's a frightening prospect.

The deadline approaches and the go-between rings.

'Are you ready to sign?'

'We think we can do it.'

'I hope you're not timewasters like the rest.'

We discuss and agonise in the few days that follow. All our energy and effort is absorbed in the daunting task of raising the money we need. However, it becomes clear that we can't get the money in place before the deadline for signing the contract. This, then, is the crucial issue: should we sign or not?

For some reason this particular deal becomes an obsession for me. Maybe it's premonition, but I sense it will be a major turning-point in my life. Ronald also wants to do the deal but is very concerned that it could be disastrous if we don't have the finance in place first.

We think and talk of nothing else, and on the last day before the deadline we're turned down by yet another bank. Like the others, they want a new lease in place first – the one thing they can't have. It's useless to protest that there's nothing serious to worry about: we'll either have a new lease within months, or sell the houses.

The same day, we get a very different call.

'I represent a consortium and I understand you're buying a parcel of houses from a pension fund. For private reasons we can't approach the fund ourselves but we're interested in buying the houses. Are you interested in selling?'

'What price have you got in mind?'

'We're prepared to give you a million over your purchase price.'

Could it be that our financing problems will be solved? 'Have you got the money to pay for the houses now?'

'No, but we'd give you a promissory note.'

A promissory note will enable us to claim in court for the money without any kind of counter claim; it's an acceptance that the money is owed without question.

'When will you have the money?'

'At the moment it's in Vienna and we need to process it through an overseas intermediary. It'll probably end up as gold bars and be shipped to London.'

It all sounds highly convoluted, but possible. It indicates that other people share our belief that it's a good deal. But timing is absolutely crucial.

'When can we expect to have the money?'

'I guarantee you'll have it within a week.'

We know that to sign the contract we only need ten per cent of the money immediately; the rest will be due on the agreed completion date, three weeks after signing. It'll be tight, but we can scrape together the £600,000 we need to sign. For the rest, we still have a few possibilities in the pipeline. An overseas bank is still interested, and another finance house is considering it. Looking at it optimistically, we can get the money as a straightforward loan, then sell immediately and make a million pounds. But we still agonise: nothing is yet certain.

We meet up with someone we've got to know in Rothschild's. We outline the deal to him.

'Would Rothschild's be prepared to lend us the money?'

'It sounds a good deal and they'd certainly consider it, but it would take a week to get a decision.'

'The question is, shall we sign? The deal is off if we don't, and a week is too long.'

He looks thoughtfully at his notes.

'I'd sign.'

It's what I want to hear, but Ronald is still uncertain.

We leave Rothschild's and walk slowly along the road.

'Surely he wouldn't say sign unless he thought he could get us the money?'

That sways it. With a mixture of excitement and trepidation, we agree that Ronald will sign the deal the following day.

I'm away in London that day, feeling elated as I think about the houses and the deal. We're moving into a higher division. I ring Ronald.

'Have you signed?'

'Yes.' But his gloomy tone tells me he's not remotely excited. 'I heard from the overseas bank this morning. They turned us down.' His words transform my elation into a cold, damp feeling of impending disaster.

'But we've still a few irons in the fire – like the consortium who want to buy the houses.'

'We have,' he says in a flat voice. He's clearly far from reassured.

The man from the consortium comes to see us.

'Everything's under control. Here's the promissory note; the money will be here in five days.' I look at the note for the agreed amount of £7 million. It isn't money, but it's close.

Yet there's a feeling of anxiety, and it's growing by the day. I lose my appetite; meal times come and go, and I have little inclination to eat. Ronald, on the other hand, seems to solace himself by eating for both of us. Our main hope is now the sale to the consortium. We get regular reports on the whereabouts of their – that is, our – money.

'There's been a hitch because of a problem bartering some wheat in Russia. The harvest has been poor, so the original deal has been impossible – but don't worry, we're now able to trade in steel bars.'

'When can you pay us the money?'

'It's going to be a few days longer than I thought – but don't worry, it'll be there.'

A couple of days later, another update. 'The steel bars have had to be routed through Poland and there's a problem with the railway. They've temporarily lost the consignment.'

The next day: 'Thank goodness, they've found the consignment. The wagons had been put into sidings by mistake. It's all on the move again.'

And the next: 'The consignment has been received and the money is being transferred now to our account in Zurich. But the Zurich bank can't convert the currency because of regulations, so they're proposing to pay in gold bullion.'

'When do we get the money?'

'It'll definitely be here in ten days.'

My heart sinks. I begin to wonder if the consortium is a fiction and we're dealing with a lunatic. I've virtually stopped eating. I look at my family, who have lived protected from the stress of my business career for so long. Will it all end in disaster? Will I destroy their lives as well as my own?

Ruth could never adapt to living as I'd once lived in Haydock Street. She isn't extravagant, but she is inflexible. I try to talk to her about what might happen if we're overtaken by disaster, but it's a waste of time.

294

The rapid loss of weight seems to change my sleep pattern. I sleep too lightly, continually worrying about the future and what my family will do, escaping from my worries into a strange, fictional world, and on occasion hallucinating. But by dawn my brain is crystal clear and I can't wait to dress and face whatever good or bad fortune the day might bring. It's comforting to be with Ronald, talking about our problems and what the outcome might be. He never slows his efforts to get the money. Cash-flows are despatched in the most unlikely directions, all requiring optimism and a great deal of work. Sometimes instinct tells me he's wasting his time with obvious no-hopers; but I say nothing, for fear of taking away his energy.

The man from the consortium rings.

'The gold bullion is now on the move. There was a delay because of bureaucracy, and I'm afraid it now has to be routed through the Eastern Bloc.'

'When do we get our payment?'

'It'll be about ten days before the gold is in the UK. It should then be only a few more days before we're able to pay you.'

I put the phone down. The consortium is history. The date they're now proposing, even if they stick to it, is after completion. Either we'll have found the money or we'll be facing catastrophe, and if we find the money we certainly won't want to sell to the consortium.

I prepare myself for the worst. I can no longer sleep, but increasingly the piano provides solace. I begin to compose, striving to express the complex emotions I'm experiencing. Whatever happens, I have to find a way forward. Perhaps I'll resume my career as a musician.

Gerald and I have been booked for one of our infrequent but very welcome performances. The prospect of playing the Brahms B Flat Concerto with him becomes a kind of vindication. Perhaps I've made a mess of my career in business, but music is a rock I can still cling to.

I've never played the Brahms B Flat at performance level. Many years ago I played through it on my own, but held back from making a wholehearted commitment to learn it. Now I've found that commitment. My material success, I discover, has given me the confidence to do what I've been afraid to do before. Every spare moment is filled with practising and preparing for the performance. Music helps me salvage my self-respect. This is what matters: if all else goes wrong, I have my piano and my composition.

The stress sours relations with Ronald. I was the one who persuaded him into signing, and now I'm depending on him to find the money. But that's the role he took for himself long before. That's why he's doing it, not me. None the less, the fact that he's taken on the responsibility in no way lessens my worry. If anything, it makes it worse.

The day for completion draws near and the agony piles up. I'm now so thin that my clothes are much too big for me. The concert with Gerald is just a week after completion. I hide the prospect of imminent disaster from everyone.

Our friend in Rothschild's rings us.

'I'm sorry, but they won't lend the money. Shall I come and explain the problems?'

'I don't think so, but thank you anyway.'

We look at each other.

'What a creep he is. He told us to sign, now he wants to explain in detail why he can't help.'

'We could take action against him on the grounds that he misled us.' As I say it, I know it's desperation talking.

Then, that afternoon, our own bank manager rings. We put the deal to him two weeks earlier and he passed it on to Head Office. He tells us they've agreed to loan us the money.

It's a triumph, but I don't feel triumphant. The torture of the past three weeks has been so great that it will be a long time before I'm rid of the fear that has been killing me. My appetite does not return overnight; my anxiety reduces only slowly.

We've been to the edge of the abyss and stared into it, and I know I'll never forget the feelings it generates. Only the thought of a childhood saying gives me the power to face anything like that again: the only failure is to give up trying.

30

The End of an Era

He's writing at a beautiful large rosewood desk which I'd bought on a trip to London. As soon as I saw it, I decided it would be perfect for Ronald. It was too grand for me to be comfortable behind it, but I knew he'd love it. It was expensive, and at that time we were short of money, so the decision to buy it wasn't straightforward. I looked at it for some time, pulling out the smooth-running drawers several times before I took the plunge and bought it. My decision was influenced by the significant discount offered because the desk was on display. It looked perfect in the shop, but once it arrived and Ronald saw it, it seemed to have a lot of scratches and marks and we ended up buying a replacement at the full retail price.

Ronald is immersed in a phone conversation and barely notices that I've come into the office. He pulls his pen out as he speaks and begins to write on the document in front of him. His pen is large, with a wide nib, and as I look at his writing I notice how much it's changed since I first met him. The script is ornate, florid, ostentatious. After a few moments he says, 'No, I couldn't agree to that.'

I sit in the chair opposite him and look at the pile of documents in front of me.

'I'll need to think about that.' He's always been good at negotiating. I listen to him with admiration. The conversation goes on and on. I begin to feel impatient. I pick up one of the documents and start to read; it's written in impenetrable legal jargon. Ronald wedges the phone between ear and shoulder, so he can write while talking and listening.

'What was that figure again?'

He crosses out and writes. The documents on his desk all relate to the American housing deal we've just done, and I begin to appreciate the complexity of it. The paperwork is voluminous and daunting, and I feel mentally at sea when I try to read it. When he finally puts the phone

297

down, I can't help but comment, 'It looks frightening to me.' Ronald shrugs nonchalantly.

'There's nothing to worry about, I can deal with it.'

'Shall we take a look at the houses?'

I still haven't seen them. It's been an enormous deal, yet I'm now so much on the fringe of the business that I've never been near the site. No one is to blame but me. It's a state of affairs I've allowed to develop. In the beginning it was convenient to leave everything to Ronald, but now I'm feeling irritated about being excluded from the deals he's managing. The houses are only two hours away, and I decide I'd like to visit them and meet the team who will collect the rents and manage the houses on our behalf.

Ronald of course has already seen them, before the completion of the purchase. This is the biggest deal we have ever done, but there is no shared excitement or pleasure in it. Ronald is becoming more distant, and his reply demonstrates it.

'Not just now, I'm too busy.'

'Surely you want to get to know the property managers?'

'Not at the moment.'

In the early days of our relationship we'd been very close. We were bonded by troubles and together we made what at first seemed insuperable obstacles miraculously small. The development of our property arm hasn't just divided the business; it's also divided us.

Although the textile business has reduced as we planned, my interest in the property side of the business hasn't developed. To me, it's simply a way of making money. The people I meet are not the kind of charismatic individuals I've been dealing with in fashion. Through fashion I rediscovered the creative energy I'd enjoyed in music. Not only that, but I had most of the glamour and excitement of textiles while Ronald remained the backroom boy. I changed my appearance, and in some ways became a different person. Ronald never fitted comfortably into the world of fashion. He had an appealing, touchingly self-deprecatory view of himself.

'If any woman looks at me twice, she's just making sure she doesn't fall over me.'

But appearance is irrelevant in the property business. Ronald has all the qualities needed for that, and he enjoys emerging from my shadow. It's increasingly obvious that he is reluctant to introduce me to the growing number of contacts he makes. We originally agreed to take separate roles in order to function efficiently, but he now seems to be creating a business for himself which excludes me. However, I'm still the majority shareholder and he needs my agreement to make any significant changes.

'I think it would be useful if you met Edward Woodhead. He's the man I deal with in our merchant bank. Do you remember I talked about increasing the share capital? Well, he's the person who proposed it, and I'd like you to hear what he has to say.'

All the alarm bells ring again, and I react immediately.

'I'm sure that from his standpoint there are plenty of good reasons why we should increase the share capital, but I remember our early days of being a private company, and that's what I want to return to.'

'I understand what you're saying, but we can't go forward in textiles, and I don't want to stand still.'

'Only five minutes ago we were facing a disaster, yet you want to push forward and take risks again?'

'I want to improve our capital base so we can finance more deals with less risk.'

'But all that does is increase the power of growing numbers of shareholders. That's too high a price. I want just you and me as shareholders.' But even as I say it, I'm aware that the idea of the two of us continuing to share the power and enjoyment we once had is a fading dream.

'You should still hear what Edward has to say.'

'Arrange a date and I'll listen, but remember it's for you, not me.'

As I return home I'm troubled. The conflicts between us are growing and the change in our relationship is disturbing me. I sit at the piano and begin to rehearse the music for the concert with Gerald, now only a couple of weeks away. It proves to be a panacea, and at the end of the practice session my concerns about Ronald have stopped nagging me.

Ronald has arranged a date for me to meet the merchant banker in London. By now he's a regular visitor to the bank, and on arrival we're treated like VIPs. When we sit in the office with Edward, the conversation begins in a way which unnerves me. He looks only at Ronald as he says, 'I'm proposing to increase the share capital by more than I mentioned at first.' It sounds to me as if everything is already agreed and arranged.

I feel an immediate sense of panic. I haven't realised that borrowing a lot of money is reducing the power we have to make decisions. It's naive of me, but in my book having the majority of the shares gives us control. I suddenly understand that borrowing so much money gives the bank power to intervene. The borrowings are all subject to repayment on demand. That's normal, and one lives with it knowing that summary repayment is very rarely demanded. But this is different. We're being persuaded to reduce our control by increasing the number of shares issued. Eventually I erupt.

'Just a minute, I'm here to discuss the proposal, not listen to details of implementing it.'

Edward looks shocked. Ronald has not been open with me and has obviously given the impression that my agreement is a formality. It's a shaky start to the meeting, and it doesn't improve.

'I didn't realise you weren't in the picture. I assumed you were up to speed.'

This isn't a discussion at all. The share increase is, in the bank's view, a fait accompli.

'I'm not yet convinced it's a good thing for the company.'

'I see.' He says it in a patronising way. As the meeting continues I become more and more unhappy. I don't like the bank, the way the business is developing, or my relationship with Ronald. He's getting too pompous, too self-important, too independent of me.

When we negotiated the deal for the American houses, we knew the lease would end within a year. We always anticipated that if it wasn't renewed, we'd sell the houses individually. But I assumed that the existing lease would be renewed. Ronald now explains what he has learned.

'It seems there's no way we can renew the existing lease for an extra ten years. The US government won't allow it. We have to meet a senior officer authorised to negotiate on their behalf.'

'That's not a problem, is it?'

'Not really, but it's an Air Force colonel based in Spain.'

'I don't think I need to come with you, you're perfectly capable of doing it on your own.' I say it to quell the feeling that I'm redundant. We're out of textiles, and the property business doesn't need me. Ronald takes command of every situation. I've been reluctant to believe he can manage without me, but it's now indisputable that he can.

I begin to wonder what I might do.

The following week Ronald flies to Madrid, to meet the Air Force colonel. He returns within twenty-four hours, and I've never seen him so excited.

'I've got a lease for ten years, direct with the American government.'

'What, no tenancy arrangement?'

'No, I've secured £2 million a year index-linked, plus another £250,000 a year for day-to-day management.'

It's an incredible deal.

'That isn't all. While I was in his office, he left to take a private phone call and out of curiosity I started to read the papers on his desk. One was a similar lease with a Spanish company. I was astonished to read that the Americans had agreed to pay their rent annually *in advance*. I managed to get that clause included in our own agreement.'

'You mean we get two million pounds in rent *now*?'

'Precisely.'

I'm overwhelmed by his success. The deal means we'll receive £4 million within a year, and we've only paid £6 million for the houses. I'm full of admiration. He continues, 'I can raise at least £15 million against the lease.'

'What do you want to do next?'

'I want to buy a building in London for £40 million. I can raise that against our assets including the lease, and I'm selling it on to Robert Miller for £45 million.'

'What?'

'Yes, I've met a fixer. He's got no capital but he has deals coming out of his ears and I think he can make us a lot of money.'

It's extraordinary that from being relatively small textile manufacturers, buying the American houses seems to have propelled us straight into the first division. It seems unbelievable that no one else wanted to buy the houses and most of the banks we went to turned the deal down.

More than anything, I begin to understand that the rapid growth in the business is giving me an opportunity to move on. The shares in our company are increasing in value as our reputation grows. I had always believed that Ronald and I were united in our ideas, but I now accept that he wants to be a tycoon. His growing ego and ambition are increasingly apparent in his lifestyle. The private jet, once an option, is now an essential part of both his business and private life. He feels too important to travel on public airlines.

And his changed lifestyle is resulting in a greatly changed attitude to me. He is no longer interested in having the kind of close conversation we once had, in which we can share the pleasure of success and waste time savouring it. Our conversations become infrequent. I almost have to bully him into talking to me about anything. His growing confidence has turned into an arrogance he never had before. His once appealing

301

personality is now slightly repellent. He's so sure of himself that I feel a growing sense of insecurity about the future, in which I sense I'll be playing only a walk-on role, if that.

Ronald returns from London and his meeting with Miller.

'I sold him the property for £45 million, but he insisted on a ten per cent retainer because he says the deal is being rushed. I told him, "Don't come back to tell me there's something wrong with the panelling in the boardroom. I can get the money I'm charging you for the building for the site alone."'

'What did the accountants and solicitors say?'

'They all said, "Don't trust him, he'll twist you in the end." But I told them, "Leave it to me, I can deal with Miller."'

Come completion date on the London property, Miller has a stack of reasons for not paying the ten per cent retainer, as Ronald's advisers had predicted. I wonder if Ronald has got it wrong, but he shows no sign of concern and is reluctant to discuss it. A week later he opens an envelope and shows me a cheque from Miller for £4,500,000. I'm astonished.

'How did you do it?'

'He didn't want to pay but I knew his Achilles' heel. I went to see him yesterday and said, "All my financial advisors told me not to trust you, they all said you're a crook. I said to them, 'I know Robert Miller and I trust him.' Now, Robert, it's up to you to prove who's right, me or them." He looked at me and said, "Ronald, you'll have the cheque for the balance tomorrow."'

Ronald's fixer begins to play an increasingly important role, constantly coming to Ronald with multi-million pound deals, all quick to execute and very profitable. I only ever see the fixer from a distance. I think Ronald realises he isn't the sort of person I'd like or respect. Despite his growing success, I think Ronald is still keen to have my good opinion of him, and while the fixer may be good for profits, Ronald suspects that my opinion of him might go down if I get to know the sort of people he's now dealing with.

The growing business demands frequent contact with the merchant bank, and Ronald's obvious success is reflected in the way they put out the red carpet for him. I can't believe he can swallow all the insincere compliments they heap on him. His integrity is slowly being eaten away by his obsession with becoming a big-shot. A string of lucrative deals, each greater than the last, results in success beyond our wildest dreams. The higher he climbs, the more nervous I am, and the more desperate to leave him to it.

Fortunately this becomes possible, because it seems Ronald can do no wrong. His growing independence and success leaves me free to leave the company. One day I meet him in his office to prepare him for my departure.

'It must be obvious to both of us that we're pointing in different directions. I think it's time I left you to it.'

'If that's what you want, you could easily sell your shareholding for a lot of money. Are you quite sure that's what you want to do?'

'As sure as I'll ever be.'

After a few meetings with the brokers to discuss placing my shares, I feel overjoyed at the prospect of having serious money in the bank for the first time in my life. It's a dramatic change from the catastrophe we'd been facing such a short time before.

Two weeks later, the morning post arrives as usual. One particular envelope stands out. I open it and look at the cheque, payable to me. It's the end of an era, and the beginning of a new one.

My dream of being a pianist is no longer enough on its own. I still love the piano, but my experience of business had added a new dimension to my life.

That's how I begin to work towards a fusion of art and enterprise – the concept of a practical Utopia.

Postscript

Towards a Practical Utopia

My eldest son Jeremy had been at school in Dartington in Devon from the age of eleven. I got to know Dartington well, and was impressed by what I saw. It wasn't a school isolated from the real world, but part of a community of artistic and commercial enterprise.

The Dartington experiment was begun in 1925 by a wealthy American, Dorothy Whitney-Straight, and her Yorkshire husband Leonard Elmhirst. Their purpose was to pioneer new ways of thinking about both education and enterprise, based on a belief that the creative arts are crucial to prosperity and happiness.

From the beginning, their idealism attracted artists and thinkers of the time. Wittgenstein and Tagore were closely involved with Dartington, as were the potter Bernard Leach and most of the Cornish painters of the 1930s. Barbara Hepworth and Henry Moore regularly visited and worked there, and Dartington commissioned Benjamin Britten's *The Rape of Lucretia*.

The dynamism and optimism of Dartington was in complete contrast to what I saw around me closer to home. In the late 1970s, when I was enjoying my greatest financial success, it seemed as if the north of England was in the grip of a terrifying, inexorable decline. The contrast couldn't have been greater between my own feeling of triumph and achievement and the general mood of apathy and depression as a consequence of growing unemployment. I began to see my change of career as an opportunity to demonstrate the life-affirming power of the creative arts. I decided it might be possible to create something like a Dartington in an urban environment.

My chance came in May 1983, when Jeremy and I bought the redundant and semi-derelict mills of Dean Clough in Halifax. Once the world's largest carpet factory, the former Crossley's Carpets consisted of sixteen huge, nineteenth-century mills on a single site stretching nearly a mile from end to end.

305

For generations the buildings had been a proud symbol of confidence and success, providing employment for some six thousand people. Now empty and forlorn, they were a testament to the greatness of the past but also a threat to the future. They literally stood in its way. After a year of standing unoccupied, no interest had been shown in redeveloping these vast and sturdy buildings.

I saw them as a magnificent opportunity to demonstrate to the community that the great negative can become the great positive. This was, after all, the central lesson of my own life. I also wanted to demonstrate that the future isn't something we inherit, but something we create. My own success in enterprise had given me the confidence to believe that every failure can be transformed into success. It was my passion to demonstrate that transformation publicly which led me to buy Dean Clough.

As there was no possibility of any public subsidy, the principle on which we started to develop the mills was that they would be both *practical* and *utopian*. They would be commercially successful, but they would also demonstrate the powerful consequence of combining enterprise, arts and education.

During my time in textiles I had always been fascinated by the idea of bringing art into commercial buildings. We were never without contemporary art on the office walls, but performances of live music and theatre, however attractive, were a pipe-dream. We were usually struggling financially, and the bank would have regarded any attempt to fund performing arts as fiscal insanity. Dean Clough now gave me a legitimate reason for doing what I'd always longed to do: bring poetry, painting and music into mill buildings.

This was the philosophical basis of my 'practical Utopia'. In such an unpromising environment it would be the most convincing evidence of the life-affirming potency of the creative arts.

And it has worked. It started working from the very beginning, as both business people and artists flocked to Dean Clough – initially curious, then intrigued, then enthused and committed. Over a quarter of a century on, it's the largest, most multi-faceted and most dynamic enterprise and arts centre in Britain.

It has worked for me too, in ways which I would never have thought possible even a few years earlier.

These are the interwined stories I intend to tell in a second book – the story of the Dean Clough 'practical Utopia' since 1983, and of the discovery of myself at the age of 53.

This, then, has been the story of my life before it began. Although I can't deny that some of my motivation has been the fascination of looking back over my first 53 years, my main motivation is to encourage others to look forward. I'm absolutely convinced that most people's lives can be transformed in a similar way to mine *if* they believe in themselves, and *if* they believe that they *do* have power and potential beyond their wildest imagination. If my story inspires someone to achieve something that they long felt – or were told – was impossible, this book will have done its job and I shall be delighted.